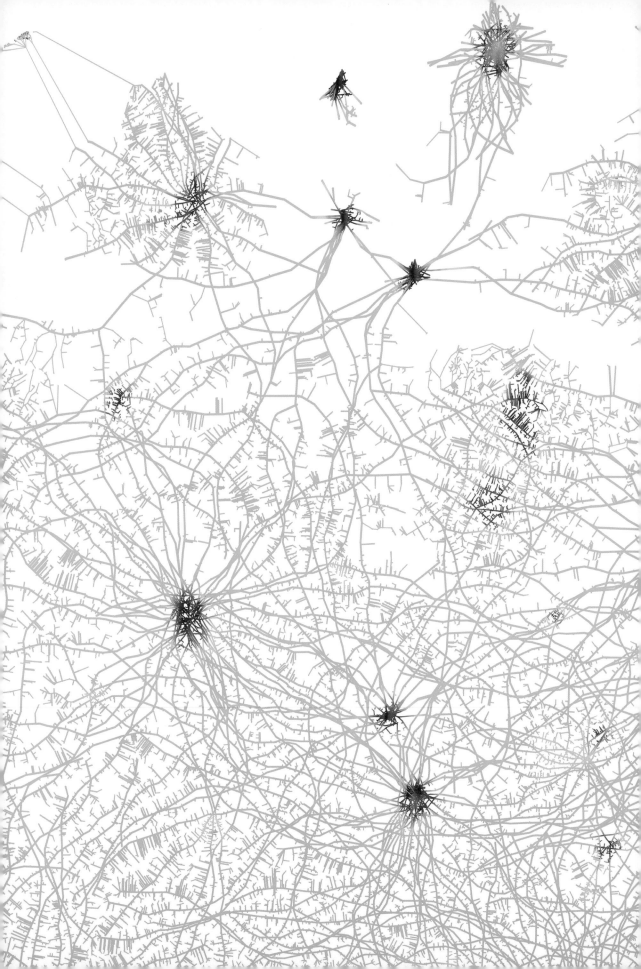

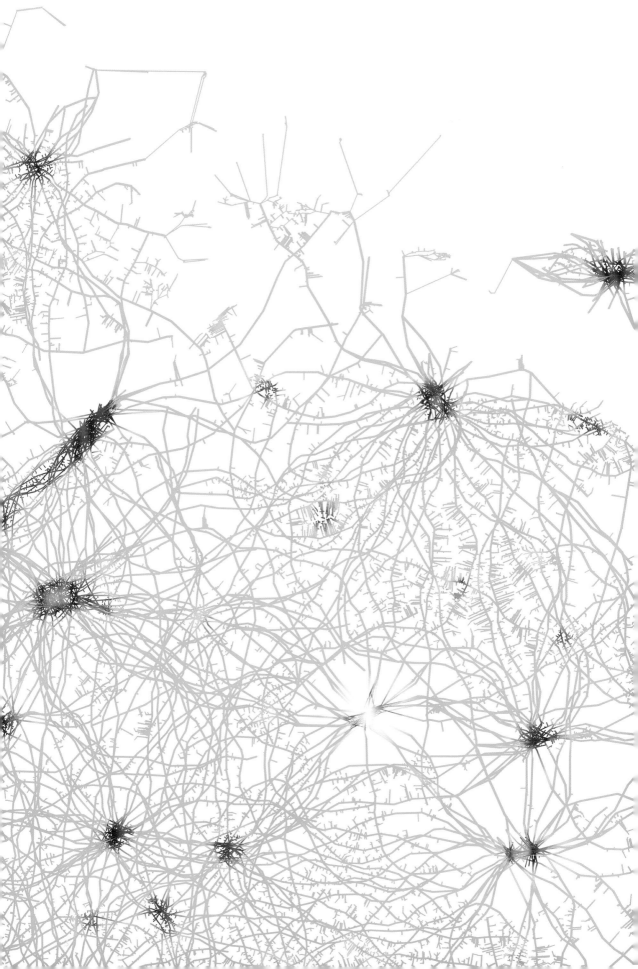

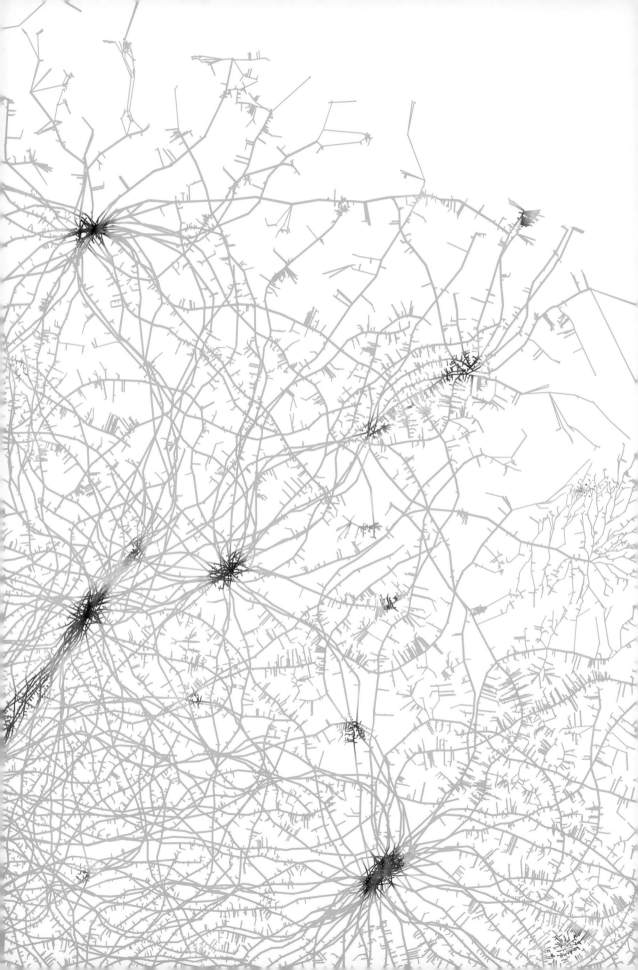

fdc5d7a97c1caf1f272a3b998b29e3be7b61d20f8ab4ce7c5294bed05a15081e

ライゾマティクス_マルティプレックス | rhizomatiks_multiplex

監修 | 東京都現代美術館

supervised by | Museum of Contemporary Art Tokyo

フィルムアート社

_ particles
2011

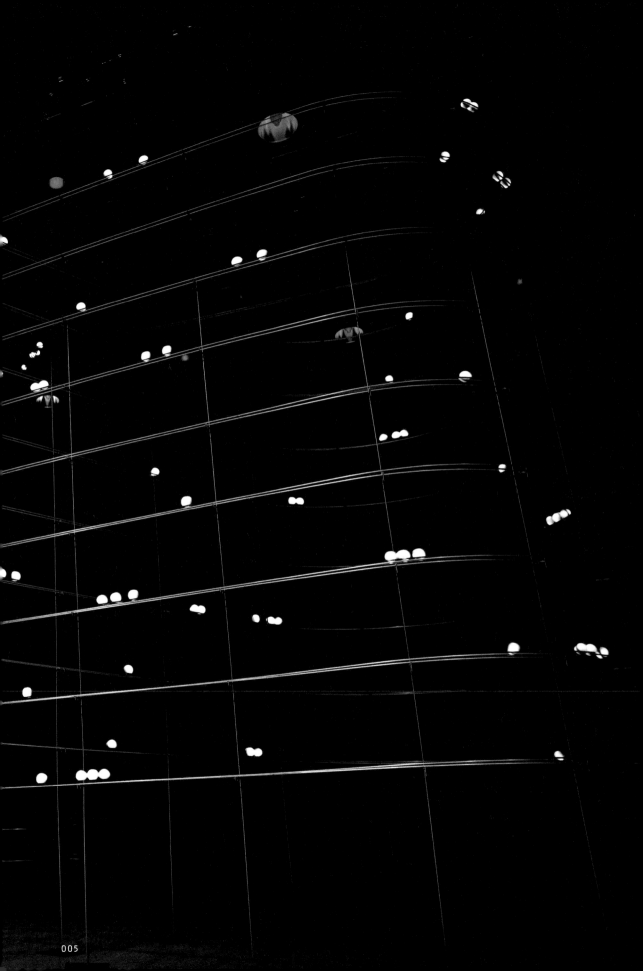

Rio 2016 Flag Handover Ceremony to Tokyo 2020
2016

4de628a6ad8d9a4617991867d6098418be12c3e721349794957e74461b6ffd1f

—

Perfume Imaginary Museum “Time Warp” @ P.O.P. (Perfume Online Present) Festival

2020

目次｜Contents

Images

凡例　本書中の解説文は、ライゾマティクス／森山朋絵（東京都現代美術館）の執筆／編集による。
各チャプターには作品タイトル、制作年、解説のみを掲載し、詳細なデータ／クレジット等については巻末にまとめて記載した。

Notes　The description / text of each work / item in this book are written / edited by Rhizomatiks / Tomoe Moriyama (MOT).
Each chapter contains only the title of the work, the year of production, and a description.
Detailed data / credits / photo credits are given at the end of the book.

083　CHAPTER 3

Visualization: post human body

dot. | shape | cube | ray | fly | right brain | shadow | 24 drones | border / border 2021 | border installation ver. | phosphere | LEXUS DESIGN EVENT 2019 | LEADING WITH LIGHT | discrete figures | S . P . A . C . E . | 結成10周年、メジャーデビュー5周年記念! Perfume LIVE＠東京ドーム「1 2 3 4 5 6 7 8 9 10 11」Lighting Balloon System Perfume LIVE＠TOKYODOME 1 2 3 4 5 6 7 8 9 10 11 (10th Anniversary as a Group/5th Anniversary on a Major Record Label!) Lighting Balloon System | 結成10周年、メジャーデビュー5周年記念! Perfume LIVE＠東京ドーム「1 2 3 4 5 6 7 8 9 10 11」Interactive Visuals Perfume LIVE＠TOKYODOME 1 2 3 4 5 6 7 8 9 10 11 (10th Anniversary as a Group/5th Anniversary on a Major Record Label!) Interactive Visuals | 結成10周年、メジャーデビュー5周年記念! Perfume LIVE＠東京ドーム「1 2 3 4 5 6 7 8 9 10 11」Balloon Explosion System Perfume LIVE＠TOKYODOME 1 2 3 4 5 6 7 8 9 10 11 (10th Anniversary as a Group/5th Anniversary on a Major Record Label!) Balloon Explosion System | 結成10周年、メジャーデビュー5周年記念! Perfume LIVE ＠東京ドーム「1 2 3 4 5 6 7 8 9 10 11」3D Scan Visuals Perfume LIVE＠TOKYODOME 1 2 3 4 5 6 7 8 9 10 11 (10th Anniversary as a Group/5th Anniversary on a Major Record Label!) 3D Scan Visuals | Perfume global site project #001 | Perfume 3rd Tour「JPN」"Spring of Life" | Physicalizing Data by Rhizomatiks Inspired by Perfume | Rhizomatiks inspired by Perfume | Perfume WORLD TOUR 2nd "Spending All My Time" Dynamic projection system | Perfume Cannes Lions International Festival of Creativity | Perfume 4th Tour in DOME「LEVEL3」"Spending all my time" | Perfume 4th Tour in DOME「LEVEL3」"Sleeping Beauty" | Perfume WORLD | Perfume 5th Tour 2014「ぐるんぐるん」"intro" Perfume 5th Tour 2014「Gurun Gurun」"intro" | Perfume 5th Tour 2014「ぐるんぐるん」"エレクトロ・ワールド" Perfume 5th Tour 2014「Gurun Gurun」"Electro World" | Perfume live "SXSW 2015" | 30周年記念特別番組 MUSIC STATION ウルトラFES 2016 Perfume "Spending all my time" Dynamic VR Display Music Station Ultra Fes 2016 Perfume "Spending all my time" Dynamic VR Display | 【docomo×Perfume】FUTURE-EXPERIMENT VOL. 01 距離をなくせ。[docomo×Perfume] FUTURE_EXPERIMENT VOL.01 Eliminate the Distance | Perfume×TECHNOLOGY presents Reframe | Reframe 2019 | 【docomo×Perfume】FUTURE-EXPERIMENT VOL. 04 その瞬間を共有せよ。[docomo×Perfume] FUTURE_EXPERIMENT VOL.04 Share that moment | Perfume Live at Coachella Valley Music and Arts Festival 2019 | Rhizomatiks inspired by Perfume 2020 | Perfume 8th Tour 2020 "P Cubed" in Dome | Perfume Imaginary Museum "Time Warp"＠P.O.P. (Perfume Online Present) Festival

Interview / Texts

Data / References / Lists / Credits

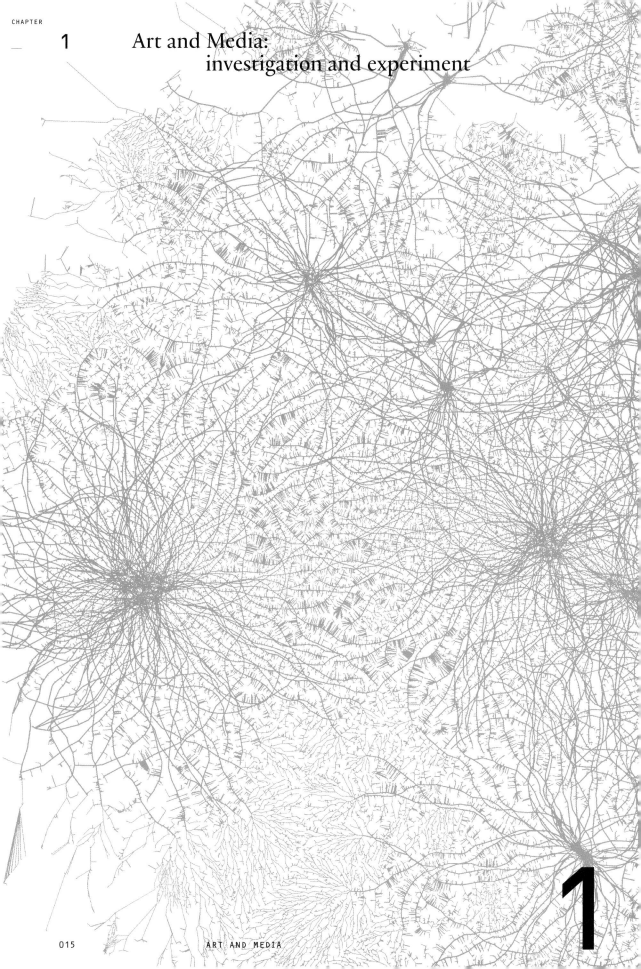

Art and Media:
investigation and experiment

Sonic Floor

2007

センサーとLED照明を内蔵した床、音響装置、ステッキ、センサーの値を用いて生成される
ウェブページからなる作品。ステッキを手に、その先端を床に接地させつつ歩き回ると、床に伝
わる凹凸の振動のデータから音と光が生成される。IoT時代における、現実世界のデータの
二次利用を予見した実証実験として制作した。

Installation consisting of a floor with built-in sensors and LED lighting, audio equipment,
canes, and a webpage generated in response to sensor input. As visitors walked around
the exhibit, their canes in contact with the uneven flooring tiles, the resulting vibration
data was used to generate light and sound. This exhibit was produced as a proof of
concept on the possible secondary uses of real world data in the coming IoT era.

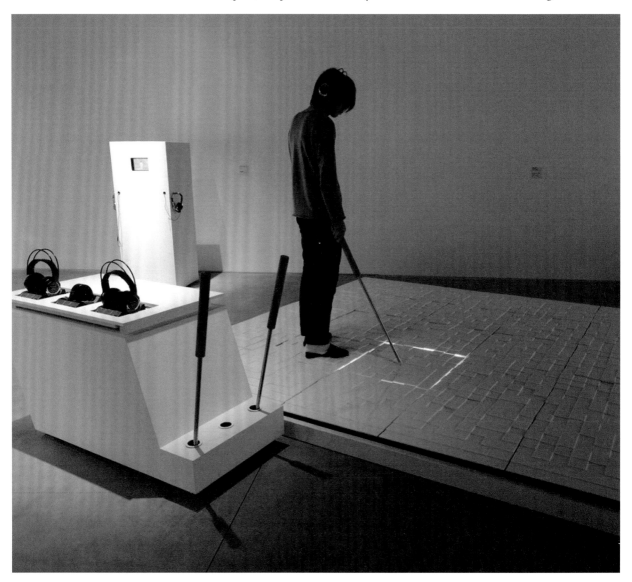

Proce55ing Life

2007　音と映像の再帰的なエフェクト処理のプロセスを体験できる作品。最初のマシンで音と映像を取り込み、シンプルなエフェクト処理を施して次のマシンに送信する。8台のマシンを通じて無限ループ処理を続けると、最終的には個々のエフェクトからは想像できないような複雑な音と映像が生成される。

Project allowing visitors to experience the limitless regenerative effects that can be layered on sampled sound and video. Video and audio captured by an initial device were processed and sent to a second computer. The process continued in an infinite loop across eight devices, resulting in the generation of incredibly complex sounds and images from the original simple effects.

Face visualizer, instrument, and copy

2008　筋電位センサー、電気刺激装置、ソフトウェアを用いて、自分の顔の表情を他人にコピーする
チャレンジを行い、その過程と結果をドキュメント映像およびパフォーマンスとして発表した。
制作過程では、表情から楽曲を、または楽曲から表情を生成するなど「顔」を入力／出力装
置として扱い、数多くの実験を行った。

Documentary film and performance utilizing myoelectric sensors, electrostimulators,
and software in an experiment to see whether someone's facial expressions could
truly be mimicked by others. The project involved numerous tests that explored the
human face as an input/output device, such as attempts to generate music from facial
expressions and vice versa.

61f8ed4b20c8287d723e717ba0042d264c81076c49437428a04bdb2968b38b19

electric stimulus to body + myoelectric sensor test

2010　自分の顔の動きを他人の顔にコピーするプロジェクト《electric stimulus to face》を進化させたプロジェクト。操作者の指に筋電位センサーの電極を装着してタッチセンサーとして使用し、指が対象者の体に触れると、指ごとに異なる音が鳴り、対象者の表情が変化する。

An evolved version of the *electric stimulus to face* project which copied one's facial movements onto the face of another. A myoelectric potential sensor electrode was attached to the operator's fingers and used as a touch sensor. When the operator's fingers touched the subject's body, different sounds were produced for each finger, and the subject's facial expression changed.

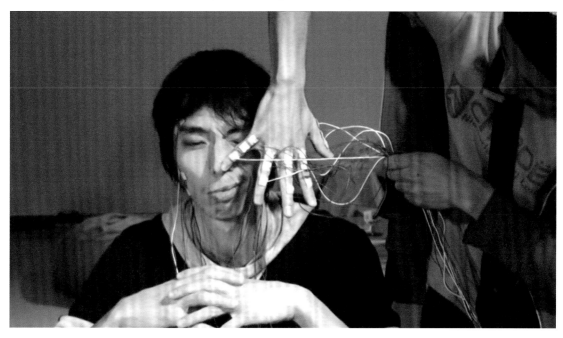

50a31a5616ecd7a041acedf44ff945182c72c1bbc6045fbc87fbe59a69718106

川口隆夫 "テーブルマインド" Takao Kawaguchi "TABLEMIND"

2011 肉眼では認知できないダンサーの身体の微細な動きを、筋電位センサーを用いて感知し、映像・音・振動に変換するという演出を行ったパフォーマンス作品。ダムタイプメンバー、川口隆夫によるダンスパフォーマンスとして2006年に初演され、2011年にはリメイク公演も開催された。

A performative dance piece utilizing an ultra-low-frequency-emitting acrylic oscillator coupled with an electromyographic (EMG) sensor fine-tuned to detect even the slightest movements of the dancer and convert these movements into video image, sound, and vibration.

619586b1809b201f4b81408c701e01a60041525773fe0890860783cfbde25b98

illion "MAHOROBA" ミュージックビデオ illion "MAHOROBA" Music Video

2013 《electric stimulus to face》の装置をミュージシャンillionに装着し、低周波刺激装置によって顔面の筋肉を動かした映像を撮影し、ポストプロダクションで一コマずつ電極と配線を消し、取り除く作業を行った。CGでは表現することが難しい、アナログとVFXの組み合わせによって初めて表現できる映像を制作した。

Film project in which the *electric stimulus to face* equipment was affixed to the musician illion. After filming footage of his low-frequency electrically-induced muscle paroxysms, vestiges of the equipment were removed frame-by-frame in post-production. The finished video combines analog and VFX to create the illusion that his face is being manipulated by an unseen force with a verisimilitude that would be difficult to replicate with CG alone.

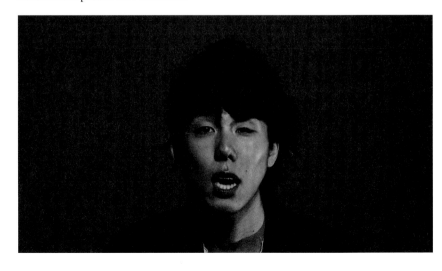

FaltyDL "Straight & Arrow" ミュージックビデオ
FaltyDL "Straight & Arrow" Music Video

2012 NYをベースに活動するFaltyDLとのコラボレーションプロジェクト。サウンドデータを電気信号として人体に流し、サウンドと体や指の動きをシンクロさせるシステム／デバイスを開発し、人体を使用したFaltyDLの楽曲のビジュアライゼーションを行った。

Collaboration with NY-based musician FaltyDL. Rhizomatiks developed a device that converted sound data to electrical signals which then coursed through the actors' bodies. This synchronization of sound and electricity causes the human body to twitch and dance, as if the participants themselves were part of an organic instrument in a corporeal visualization of FaltyDL's music.

c54ed0fa7dba846003090549e8945c178d473bf7ccbb7761840b9e4504528835

Command line wave

2008

マイクを内蔵したライトキューブと、光のパターンをコントロールするためのサウンドを使った、ライブパフォーマンス／インスタレーションからなる作品。FAXやモデムの通信時の音から着想し、可聴域の音を利用した独自の音響通信を設計した。光の制御自体をライブパフォーマンスとして成立させることを目指した。

Live performance and installation that used sound to control the lighting patterns of a light cube with a built-in microphone. Inspired by the sounds from the era of fax machines and modems, a unique form of acoustic communication was designed using sounds within the audible range. The project aimed to showcase the control of the cube's light itself as the focal point of a live performance.

d2c8df80502e7df3b30dc5a35277a84fed4fa366645399a5e790f363ed37891f

scoreLight

2009

描かれた線や近くにある三次元物体の輪郭を捉え、視覚情報を音情報に変換することで、人工的に共感覚を引き起こすインスタレーション作品。レーザースキャナーを改造した装置が感知器の役割を果たし、レコード盤の表面の溝から音を読み取る原理を応用して、描かれた線の輪郭から音を創り出す。

Installation designed to artificially simulate the experience of synesthesia, transforming visual input into audio. A modified laser scanner acted as a sensing device, creating sounds based on linear representations and the contours of nearby 3D objects, using a similar principle to how record players interpret sound from a record's grooves.

 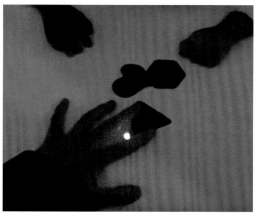

LED in my mouth

2009 顔の表情を拡張する実験をするために制作した、口に入れて利用する無線制御のLEDデバイス。皮膚や歯は光を透過するため、装着するだけの発光デバイスとは違う演出効果が得られる。YouTubeで実験作品を公開後、ラフォーレ原宿のグランバザールCM、ポスター、ラッピング広告等に採用され、広く認知された。

A wirelessly controlled wearable LED device created to experiment with the augmentation of facial expressions. The LED was used when inserted into the mouth. As both skin and teeth transmit light, it was possible to achieve a unique effect that transcended the range of the LED device itself. After a video of the experiment was posted on YouTube, the project was adopted as a large-scale ad campaign, and garnered widespread recognition.

The Way Sensing Go

2009 　身近な家電製品やおもちゃを改造してつくられた、「入力→処理→出力」の構造を持つ部品や映像の組み合わせによる連鎖反応の展開を楽しむ作品。ライゾマティクスに加え、事前に行なわれたワークショップの参加者によって各モジュールが制作された。多くの人のアイデアの連鎖によって、1つの作品となっている。

Project exploring the chain reactions created when remodeling familiar home appliances and toys, to highlight the recombination of components and images in a flow from input → processing → output. Each module was created by exhibiting artists and participants of a previous workshop, reassembled as a collaborative finished piece that was itself a chain reaction of ideas.

Pa++ern

2009　独自に開発した難解プログラミング言語を用いて刺繍のデザインを生成し、Tシャツを作る作品。一見難解な文字列はデザインを生成するソースコードであり、専用サイトでコードを入力すれば、誰でも刺繍パターンを生成することができる。Twitterからプログラムを投稿してパターンを生成する仕組みも提供した。

Project that made T-shirts using an industrial sewing machine and a unique esoteric programming language for designing embroidery patterns. The seemingly esoteric threads were in fact the source code for generating the design, and embroidery patterns could be generated by inputting the code on a dedicated website. Users were also able to post the program and generate their own patterns on Twitter.

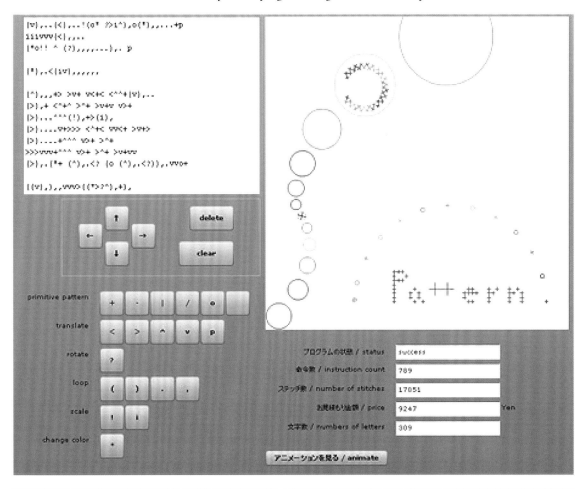

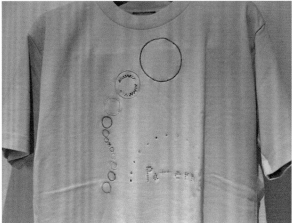

_ fade out

2010 蓄光塗料を塗ったスクリーンに紫外線レーザーを照射することによって、画像を描画する作品。蓄光塗料上の光が徐々に暗くなって行くことに着目し、画像の暗い部分から順番に照射し、グラデーションのある絵を描画する。即時的なインタラクションからの脱却を目指し、完成までの数分間足を止めてもらえる作品を制作した。

A filmed image was rendered on a phosphorescent screen by exposing the material to a UV laser beam. After exposure, the light gradual dissipated from the phosphorescent material. By first exposing the darkest areas of the image, then shifting the projection sequentially to areas of increasing brightness, it was ultimately possible to render a final gradated image. The project aimed to break free from immediate interaction, compelling viewers to pause for those few minutes until the complete image appeared.

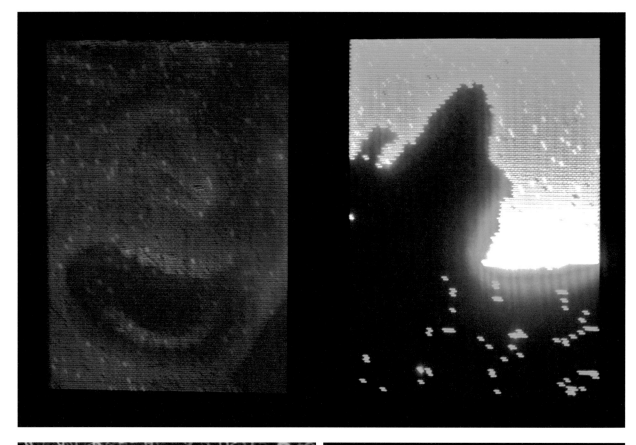

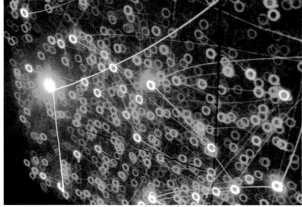

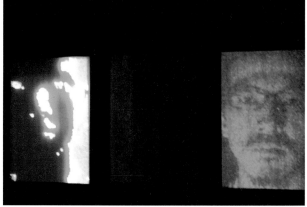

points

2010 おもちゃを改良したエアソフトガンの射撃で描写する作品。無秩序に乱射されるように見える
プラスティック製BB弾が、実際は緻密に計算された弾道を飛行し、紙に穴を空けて絵を描
く。通常の銃撃は暴力的かつ破壊的なものであるにもかかわらず、ここではそのプロセスは
生産的で、絵画を生成する行為となっている。

Modified airsoft guns render an image in bullets. While the percussive BB pellets
initially appear to strike the target at random, it soon becomes clear that they are
precisely outlining a predefined image. Whereas conventional gunfire represents a
violent, destructive force, this project remotivates the bullets for constructive means
to create artistic images.

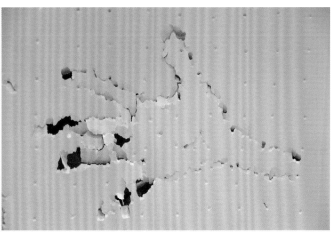

364f583eec28f26a61e8d762d50d41b8ba5da040b3fe55f6f4c0972ddd7106e2

particles

2011

LEDを内蔵した多数のボールが空中を浮遊し、幻影的な残像を作り出すイルミネーション・インスタレーション。8の字型のレールの上を、点滅する多数のボールが次々に通過し、LEDが多様なタイミングで発光して光の粒子が浮遊し、空中に多様な形態を描き出す。アルスエレクトロニカ準グランプリを受賞。

Large scale installation in which flickering light sources appear to float through the air, leaving behind an otherworldly afterimage. The indoor installation space is filled with a multistory rail structure shaped in an organic, spiraling configuration. A multitude of semitranslucent white balls outfitted with internal LEDs glide across the tracks. By freely adjusting the flicker rate to various timings, the orbs of light trace diverse patterns across the sky.

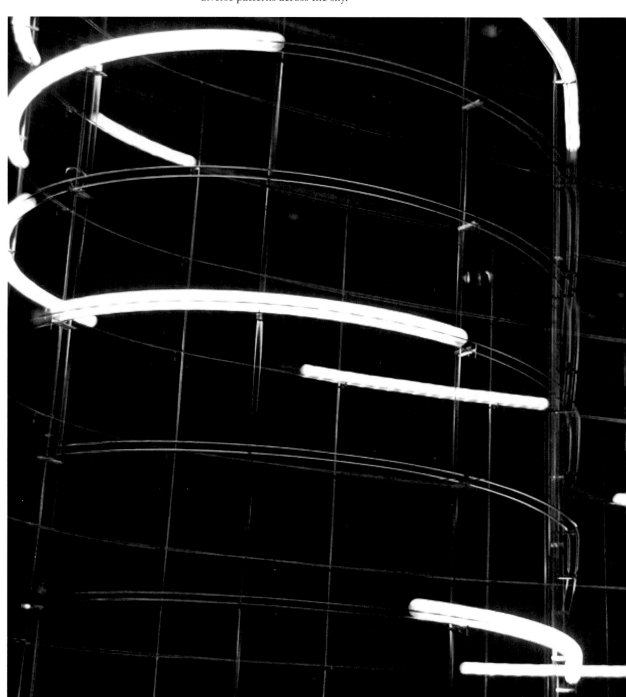

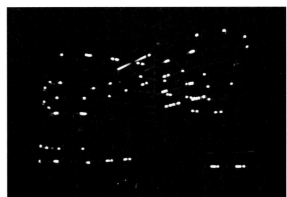

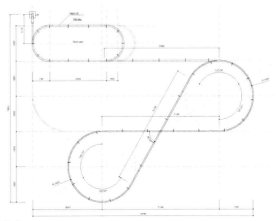

Particles Plan
scale = 1:50   unit=meter   28 March 2011

16 Forms

2011

ロボットアームとLED照明、回転盤に設置された16体の3Dプリントフィギュアによる作品。光源の位置と発光のタイミングをコントロールすることで、壁面にフィギュアの影がダイナミックに投影される。ダンスにおけるポーズやシルエットに着目した作品。

Project featuring a robotic arm, LED lighting and 16 three-dimensional printed figures. Silhouettes of the figures were dynamically projected by controlling the light source position and the timing of the emitted light.

＿ line

2012

2台の3Dカメラによって人体の全身の形状をスキャンし、人体の全方位3次元形状データを取得し、そのデータを解析して、全身の形状を1本の線でつないだデータとして完成させる。それをもとに、工業用ロボットが線材を曲げていくことで作り出される立体作品である。

A full body scan of the user's body was taken through the use of two 3D cameras, obtaining omnidirectional 3D data on the subject. This user data was then analyzed to create a single line representing their body's form, which the robotic arm reproduced by bending a wire rod in that shape.

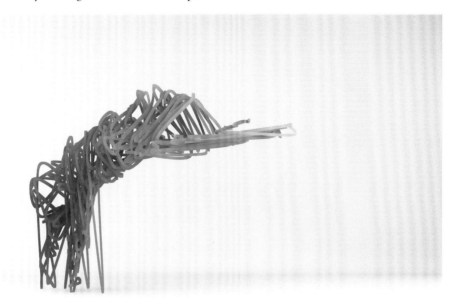

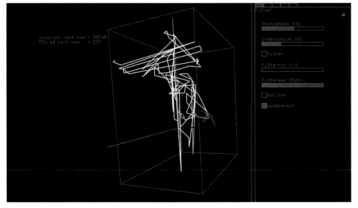

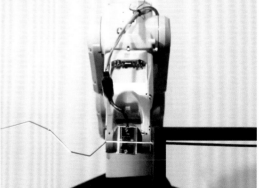

Your Cosmos

2015

人工知能ラップグループ Your Cosmos は、75000曲のヒップホップの歌詞とアルスエレクトロニカの30年分のカタログのテキストデータ、Twitter のトレンドを使用して韻を踏むシステムを開発し、アルスエレクトロニカにて合成音声ラップのパフォーマンスを行った。システムをアップデート後、東京公演も行った。

AI rap group, developed a rhyming system using 75,000 hip-hop lyrics, 30 years of Ars Electronica catalog text data, and Twitter trends, played synthetic speech engine performance there. The system was updated for an encore performance in Tokyo.

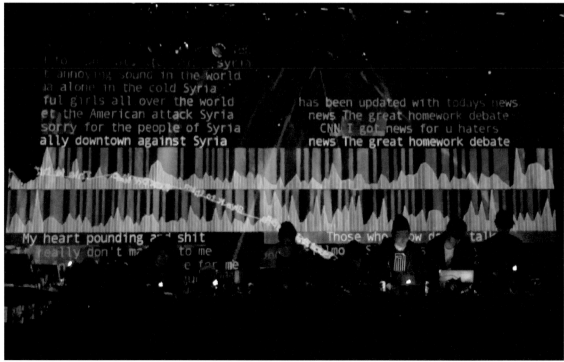

traders

2013 リアルタイムに取得した東証株式市場の市場データと、独自に開発した仮想的に自動取引を行うソフトウェアを使って、株式売買のデータをビジュアライズしたインスタレーション。将来的にAIが社会的な問題となることを予見し、2013年当時、人間とAIの競争が注目されていた株取引をテーマに作品を制作した。

Installation that visualized market data for the TSE stock market in real-time, as well as trading data from proprietary software developed to automatically perform virtual trades. Foreshadowing the advent of the AI era (and all the societal problems AI may entail), this topical project explored the conflict between human and AI traders, begin waged on the battleground of the stock exchange.

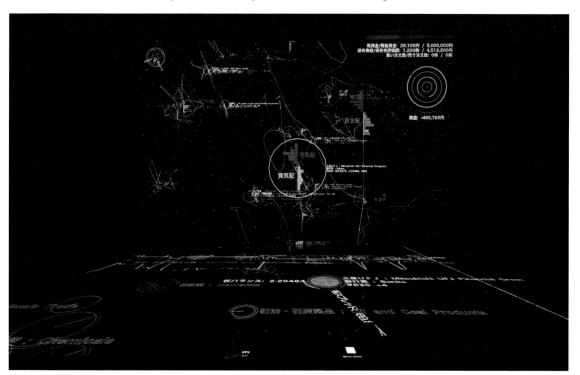

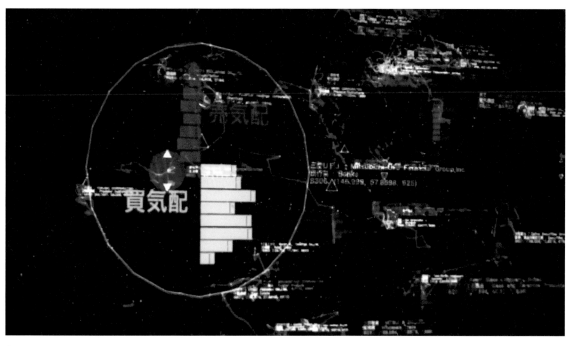

chains

2016

2013年の作品《traders》と同様の取り組みを、ビットコインで行ったインスタレーション。実際に自動取引を行うことが法的に難しかった東証株式市場での株取引とは異なり、自由かつオープンなビットコインのトランザクションの様子と自動取引の様子をビジュアライズした。

Installation that used Bitcoin to perform similar tasks as the 2013 work, *traders*. Unlike stock trading on the TSE, where regulations restrict automated trading, Bitcoin provided a more open platform for the visualization of automated trading.

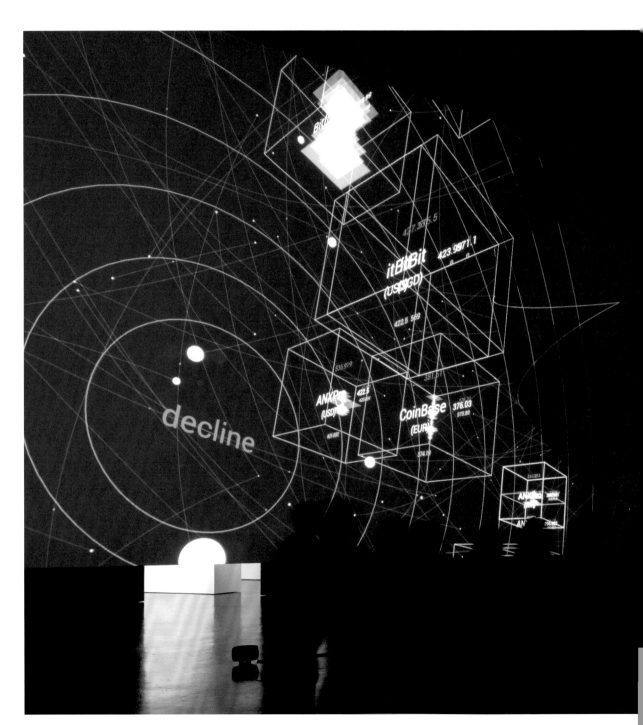

ART AND MEDIA

Deleted Reality

2016　フランスのパリ日本文化会館での企画展「トランスフィア(超域)」第1回で展示された。台の上に並ぶ多様な形のオブジェクトをスマートフォンのカメラで撮影すると、ローリングシャッター効果によって肉眼で知覚できない色が写る。存在しながら知覚できない事象・現象を、テクノロジーを介して再考させる作品。

Collaborative work between Daito Manabe and Motoi Ishibashi exhibited at "Transphere"#1 under the auspices of The Japan Cultural Institute in Paris. An array of multivariegated shapes aligned on a platform are illuminated by constant LED light that appears white to the naked eye. However, when visitors photograph the objects, the resulting images reveal that the light is in fact a rainbow of color unperceptible to human eyes.

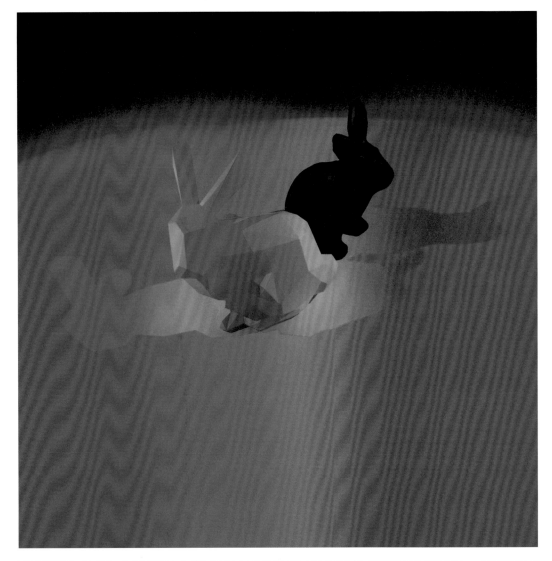

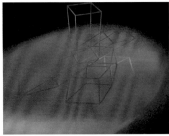

oscillation

2016

NSK(日本精工株式会社)100周年記念展「SENSE OF MOTION」で発表した作品。ボール
ねじを使ったNSK製品「モノキャリア」を向かい合わせに32台ずつ設置。鑑賞者が持つバト
ンの動きに連動して、モノキャリアにつながれたゴム紐がなめらかにスライドする。プリミティブ
な幾何学表現を、実世界で表現した。

Work presented at NSK Ltd.'s Centennial Anniversary Exhibition, "SENSE OF
MOTION." Visitors were given sensor-equipped batons, and 64 of NSK's ball-screw
products called the "Mono Carrier" were lined up in two opposing rows. When the
Mono Carrier devices sensed the batons, connective rubber bands slid smoothly in
response, expressing primitive geometries in the real world.

c4b88948783e375d5de886cf52f84f56877b6d0e277010d80b5e9a02921e5e52

dissonant imaginary

2018

京都大学／ATRの神谷之康研究室が開発したブレインデコーディング技術を用いて、音楽を聴いて頭の中に浮かぶイメージを予測し、映像に変換した作品。聴覚と視覚の相互作用、音と映像の関連性について着目し、脳活動データを用いて画像を再構成する様子を可視化させ、未来の音楽と映像の相互作用について考えた。

Project that sought to predict the mental image that comes to mind when listening to music, using brain decoding technology developed by the Yukiyasu Kamitani Laboratory at Kyoto University/ATR. By focusing on the interaction between hearing/vision and sound/video, the project envisioned future modes of reconstructing images from brainwaves, and speculated on the future of video and sound.

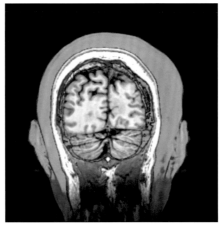

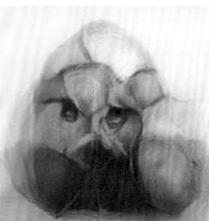

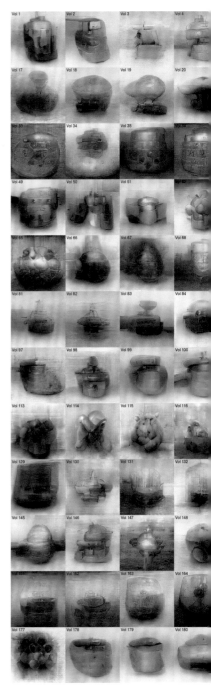

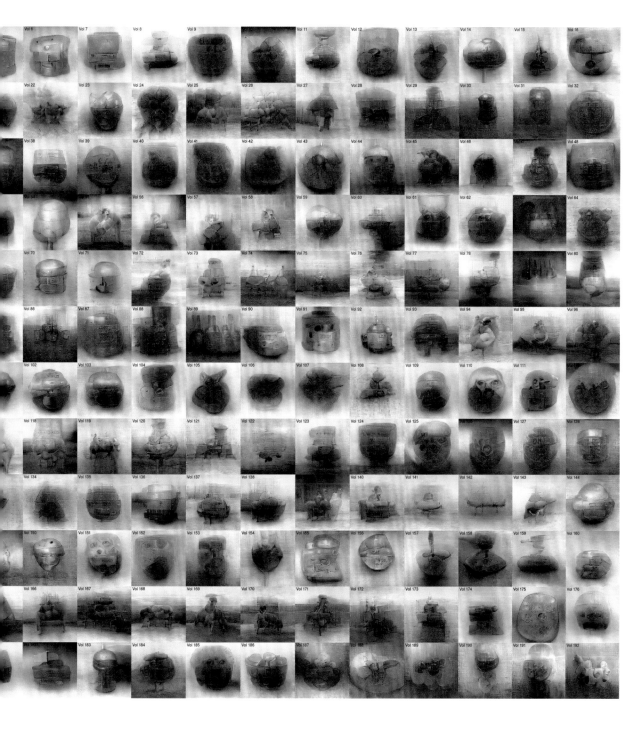

Cinema Analysis using IBM Watson™ Visual Recognition service

2015　人工知能技術を応用したコグニティブ（認知）システム、IBM Watson（ワトソン）による、俳優・本木雅弘出演映画の解析データのビジュアライズ。映像を1秒毎に解析し、室内／人がいるなど、画像のコンテクストを解析しメタデータを生成。そのメタデータを用いて類似映画のサーチ／ソート／可視化を行った。

Visualization of data from the films of actor Masaharu Motoki, powered by AI technology and the cognitive computing system IBM Watson. The system analyzed each second of film, generating metadata tags identifying the setting, presence of actors, etc. in each image. This metadata was then used to search, sort, and visualize similarities to other films.

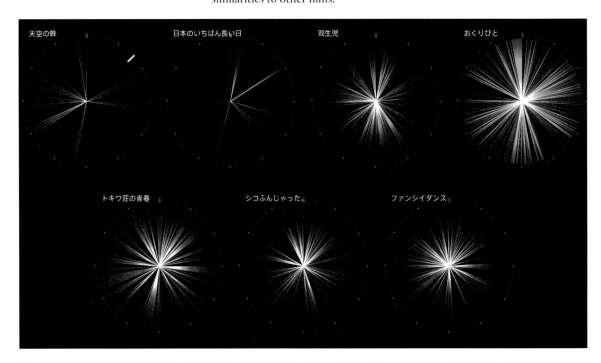

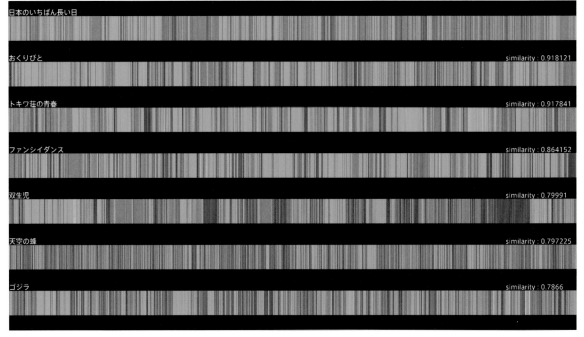

Tokyo Tokyo FESTIVAL Special 13
Light and Sound Installation "Coded Field"

2019

浄土宗大本山増上寺（東京・港区芝）とその周辺を舞台にした、光と音が織りなすパブリックアートプロジェクト。会場の建築データや地形データを解析した情報が、独自開発したバルーン型デバイスを用いて現実空間の光や音に変換され、大勢の参加者が広範囲な場所で同時に楽しめるインスタレーションを展開した。

Public art project interweaving light and sound, set in the vicinity of Zojoji Temple at the foot of Tokyo Tower. The venue's architectural data and topographical analytics were transformed into real world light and sound by a proprietary balloon-shaped device, creating an installation that could be enjoyed simultaneously by a large crowd of participants spread out over an expansive area.

Lucid Motion

2019 　ARTECHOUSE DCで行われた個展。[#1] 大型イマーシブ環境で、流体シミュレーションな
どのアルゴリズムでダンスデータを映像に変換（左）。[#2] iPadでARオブジェクトを見ると、オブ
ジェクトの周囲でCGのダンサーが踊り出すインスタレーション（右上）。[#3] Style Transferなど
のディープラーニング技術で、観客のシルエットからインタラクティブ映像を生成（右中・右下）。

A solo exhibition presented at ARTECHOUSE DC. [#1] Dance data was converted into imagery using fluid mechanics and other simulation techniques, for presentation in a large-scale immersive environment. (light) [#2] Installation combining AR and iPads. As visitors watched objects on their iPads, a CG dancer appeared, and danced around the object. (right top) [#3] Style Transfer and other deep learning technologies were used to generate interactive imagery based on the viewer's silhouette. (right middle / bottom)

phenomena – quarantine version

2020 エレクトロニックミュージックとデジタルアートのフェスティバルを展開するMutekのブランチ Mutek San Franciscoがバーチャル空間の中に構築した美術館に、作品を発表するという 形でプロジェクトに参加した。コロナ禍の中で今できることを検討し、配信の形態で公開でき る作品の制作に挑戦した。

Participated in an exhibition hosted at the virtual art museum created by Mutek San Francisco. The project explored new modes for the presentation of work amid the coronavirus pandemic.

Social Distancing Communication Platform

2020

コロナ禍における、大人数でのオンラインコミニュケーションの新しい可能性を探る実験的なプロジェクト。最初のテストケースとして、音楽イベントをモチーフにしたプロトタイプが作られた。リアル空間と同様に、ユーザー間の距離が近いか遠いかによって音量が変化する仕様になっている。

Experimental project exploring new frontiers for online communication accomodating large groups of people amid the coronavirus. This prototype was created as an initial test case that simulated attendance at music events during the pandemic. As in the real world, the audio volume varies depending on the user's distance from the stage.

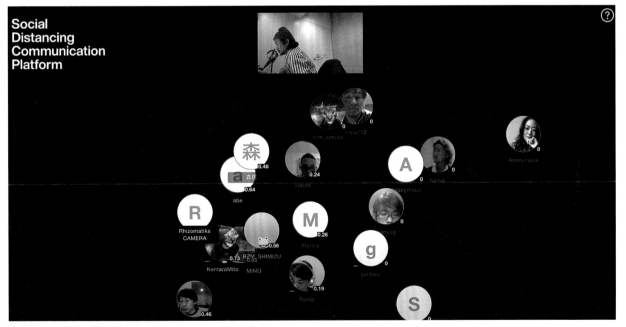

Messaging Mask

2020

小さな声やささやき声を音声認識する、マスク型デバイス。ARやプロジェクションによって声をテキスト出力することができ、大きな声を出すことなしに、人々の共感を増幅させることが可能になる。スポーツ観戦やライブハウスなどでの使用を想定し、新しい体験の価値を提供するデバイスとして制作した。

Mask-like device with voice recognition technology that detects whispers and speech as text using AR and projections. The project provided heightened feelings of empathy at low volumes that could offer a new experience at typically raucous sporting events and concerts.

Home Sync Light

2020

エヴィクサー株式会社との共同開発デバイス。可聴音域に埋め込まれた「音響透かし」を内蔵マイクで検出し、映像と光のパターンの同期を実現。電源を入れるだけで、配信ライブと光が連動する演出を楽しめる。映像中のライトのパターンなどとの同期も可能なため、映像中の演出が部屋に拡張したような演出効果も作りだせる。

Device developed in collaboration with Evixar Inc. with a built-in mic that detected audio watermarks hidden in the audible frequency range and visually synced this audio to light patterns. The device allowed users to enjoy lighting displays synced to any live streamed performance at the press of a button. The device could also synchronize with the performance's own lighting displays, creating an augmented effect that seemed to transport the performance into the viewer's room.

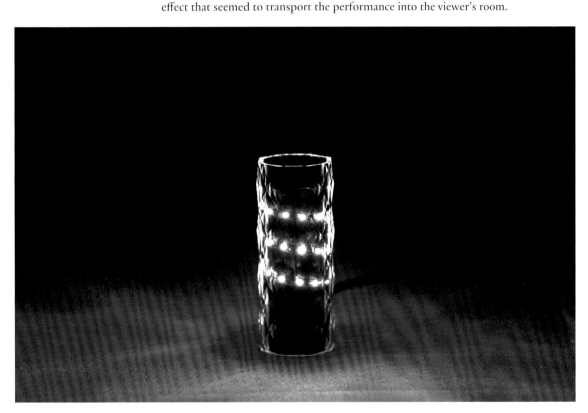

morphechore

2020

脳活動を解析し推定することで振付を生成し、「重力や関節の回転角、筋肉の収縮スピードなど物理的な条件を変化させるとどのようなダンスが作成できるか」という仮定のもと制作されたレクチャーパフォーマンス作品。真鍋がアバターとしてダンスを行い、次第に身体が崩壊していく様子を映像で展開した。

Lecture and performance exploring how dance is affected by changes in physical conditions (such as gravity, the angle of joint rotation, the speed of muscle contraction), in combination with predictive choreography created by analyzing brain activity. The project culminated in a video demonstration of a dancing Daito Manabe avatar that steadily lost control of its digital body as the conditions were loosened.

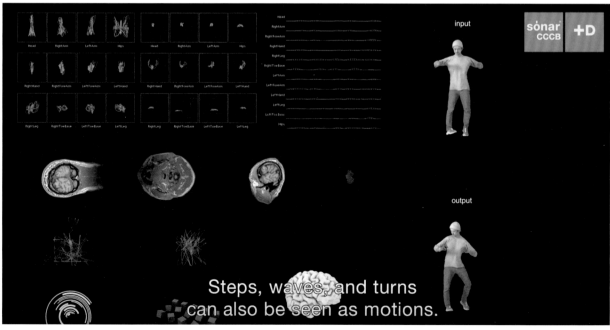

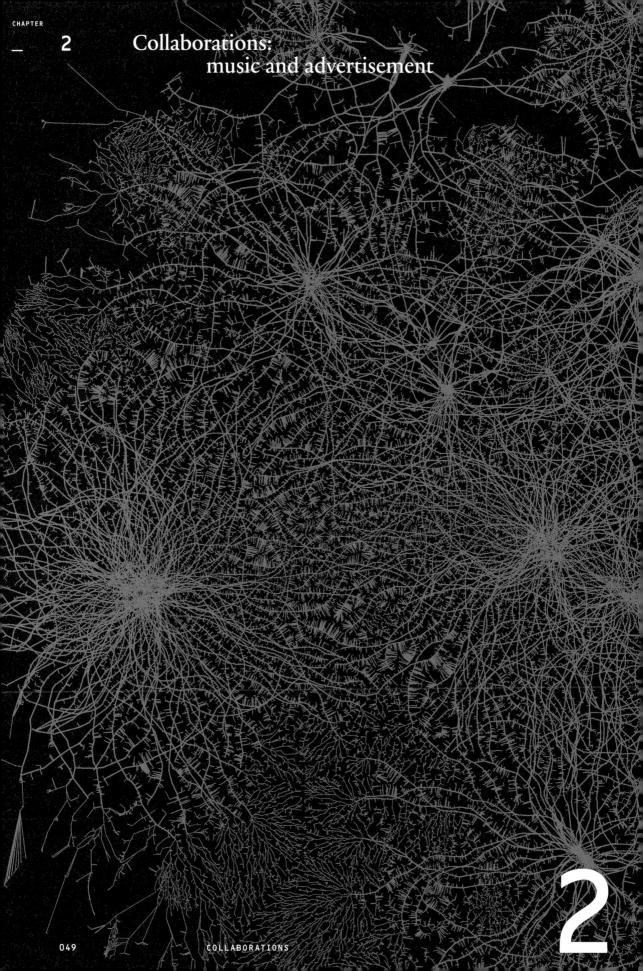

2

8cdbcab9b8f5b0519bcd2b796de91ab83a835dcb0d003d2b5792d3cf16fa7e49

やくしまるえつこメトロオーケストラ "ノルニル" ミュージックビデオ
Yakushimaru Etsuko Metro Orchestra "Nornir" Music Video

2011　楽曲の構成を解析したデータから作成した線路が部屋に敷き詰められ、その上を360度カメラ搭載のロボットが走り、やくしまるえつこを追いかける。360度映像はウェブサイト上でも公開され、マウスで自由に視点を移動したり、自分が視聴した視点の情報をウェブ上で他者と共有できるシステムも開発した。

Music video filmed using a complicated track with a design based on a thorough analysis of the song's structure. A custom 360° camera was affixed to a robot, which ran across the track as if in close pursuit of Etsuko Yakushimaru. The 360° footage was made available on a website where users could adjust the omnidirectional perspective by scrolling with their mouse, and share this unique perspective data with other users online.

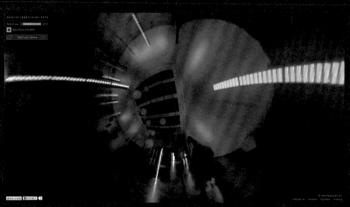

93768dfbf99dcb6e7db99ddd487a9a718c205fcf355bd404b23b497497555cb9

やくしまるえつこ "ロンリープラネット(Post)" ミュージックビデオ
Yakushimaru Etsuko "Lonely Planet (Post)" Music Video

2012　5つのパーツからなる「ロンリープラネット(Post)」バージョンのミュージックビデオ。CGのパーティクルを思わせる表現は、実はハイスピードカメラで撮影した火花であり、工具で鉄を削って発生させた火花を8秒間撮影し、スロー再生した3分弱のミュージックビデオ5種で構成されている。

"Lonely Planet (Post)" version music video consisted of five parts, featuring a CG-esque stream of ephemeral multicolored light particles dissipating into the air. The effect was achieved by filming 8 seconds of steel sparks with a high-speed camera and then replaying the footage in slow motion to create five iterations on a nearly 3-minute-long video.

40b149bf4da1c2ad94b531e3ef41a48025b72ee1055a6e69ded73eaf625f2074

proportion

2011　やくしまるえつこ「少年よ我に帰れ」ミュージックビデオのためのインスタレーション。ロボット
アームに付けた小型プロジェクターで、楽曲の歌詞をイメージした小型オブジェクトに映像を
投影しつつ同時に撮影。壁面投影される映像はすべてリアルタイム映像だが、あたかも編
集済みミュージックビデオのように見える。

Installation for Yakushimaru Etsuko's music video, "Boys Come Back to Me." As the
video was being filmed, a miniature projector attached to a robotic arm projected a
camera feed onto small sculptural objects inspired by the song's lyrics. Although the
images were being projected in real-time, the meta music video has the illusion that it
was post-edited.

8dfb4f8438e51199bf679b518937eb08991be15fe69f2fe252e7dabb051b9d66

LOVE+1+1

2013　やくしまるの声と楽曲情報を用いた歌をリアルタイムに生成するインタラクティブ・インスタレー
ション作品。音声解析と人工知能システムにより来場者が発した言葉を解析して歌詞を自動
生成している。

Interactive installation utilizing voice analysis and an AI system to generate songs with
the voice and music information of Etsuko Yakushimaru in real-time, in response to
speech uttered by visitors.

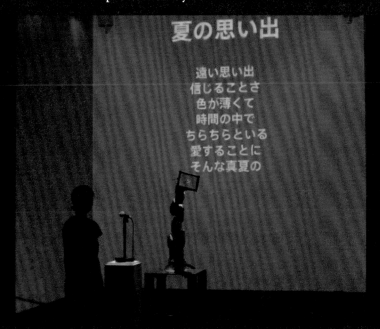

2c099a1843c3cabb03f3905716dccdb286c0469f4ce0e018434558e54101b299

The Human Sized Synthesizer

2014　若く才能溢れるアーティストたちを支援する世界的な音楽学校 Red Bull Music Academy と共同制作した、ヒューマンサイズの巨大シンセサイザー。音色やリズムを生成して手軽に音楽を作ることができるという体験を通して、シンセサイザーのメカニズムを体感的に理解することができる。

A human-sized synthesizer produced in collaboration between Daito Manabe with Rhizomatiks and the Red Bull Music Academy*. The enormous synthesizer allows visitors to create tone and rhythm to easily produce their own musical compositions, while also viscerally experiencing the mechanisms underpinning synthesizer technology. *The Red Bull Music Academy is a world-class music school supporting talented young artists.

cb55c3fd55afb23f3a0a6bdda7dc2e285839715d1eb972ba4b3d395ce24154a8

Björk "Mouth Mantra" ミュージックビデオ Björk "Mouth Mantra" Music Video

2015　Björkのアルバム『Vulnicura』に収録された楽曲「Mouth Mantra」のミュージックビデオを制作した。手術によって一時的に声を失った時の思いを描いたという曲のコンセプトに合わせて、Björkが歌っているパフォーマンスのようすを、彼女の口の中からの視点で見ることができる。

Music video for "Mouth Mantra," a track off of Björk's 2015 album *Vulnicura*. The video takes viewers inside Björk's mouth as she sings the track, based on the temporary loss of her voice following a successful surgery to remove polyps from her vocal cords.

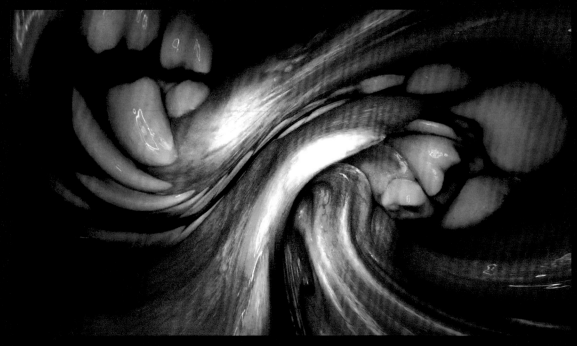

92d921b5d61f570f5b01db9df09768cd805611793ff42cd5e42f0b527700c987

Timo Maas "Tantra" ミュージックビデオ　Timo Maas "Tantra" Music Video

2013　ドイツのプログレッシブ/テクノシーンを代表するDJ兼プロデューサーTimo Maasのミュージックビデオを制作した。楽曲が持っているミニマルな構造を表現するために、落ちてきた球を打ち返すという単純かつ無意味な作業を繰り返し行う装置を制作して撮影を行った。

Music video for DJ/Producer Timo Maas, a seminal figure in the German progressive/techno scene. Reflecting the music's minimalism, the conceptual video consists solely of balls that are dropped from a mysterious gun-like machine, only to be volleyed away by awaiting metal paddles.

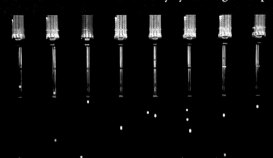

13e33987f2baed9d08d8322e4ada0347de380161974bac63bc96293f94816f06

Squarepusher×Z-MACHINES

2014　スクエアプッシャーとロボットバンドのコラボレーション作品を、真鍋大度が監督したミュージックビデオとして制作した。ロボットバンドの精密な動きによって楽器が演奏される様子を、ロボットアームを使用して撮影するとともに、演奏データを光のパターンに変換する試みも行った。

Music video directed by Daito Manabe, showcasing the collaboration between Squarepusher and a robot band. A robotic arm was used to film the dazzlingly fast and complicated melody line created by the Z-Machines superhuman faculties, while performance data was also transposed into lighting patterns.

Squarepusher "Terminal Slam" ミュージックビデオ
Squarepusher "Terminal Slam" Music Video

2020　「架空のMR（複合現実）グラスを用いて街中から広告を排除する」というコンセプトの真鍋大度監督によるミュージックビデオ。2020年アルスエレクトロニカ佳作入賞。映像作品でありつつもコンセプトの一部はリアルタイムで動作する仕組みを開発し、近い未来、実際に社会実装されることを想定して制作した。

Music video exploring a fictional world in which mixed reality glasses can be used to remove ads from the city. Directed by Daito Manabe, the video was awarded an Honorary Mention in the 2020 Prix Ars Electronica. Branching off from the video, the concept was partially developed into a real-time system, for potential real-world implementation in the not so distant future.

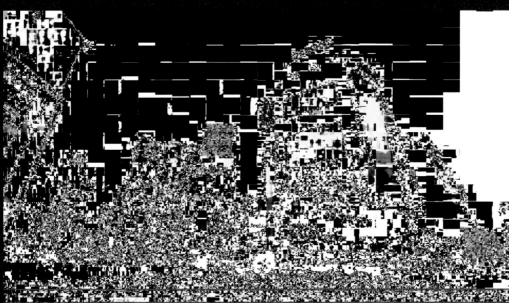

7f6dd2e67fe4e38538d86dc0825a8a765cca40f4a529feed61160997b88cd2f3

Nosaj Thing "Eclipse Blue" ミュージックビデオ
Nosaj Thing "Eclipse Blue" Music Video

2012 LAを拠点に活動するビートメーカーNosaj Thingとの初コラボプロジェクト。タイトルにインスピレーションを得て、太陽と月を表す二人のダンサーによる二つの世界を表現した。太陽のダンサー（スクリーン前面）／月のダンサー（後面）をハイスピードカメラでトラッキングし、その身体の上に映像を投影した。

First collaborative project with the LA based beatmaker Nosaj Thing. Thematically inspired by the juxtaposition of an eclipse and the sun, two dancers each represented their own world as either the sun or the moon. The sun dancer is in front of the screen, while the moon dancer is behind the screen. A high speed camera was used to track the dancers' movements, and projected atop for a whimsical visual effect.

Flying Lotus Presents "The Hit"

2020 Brainfeederの開催によるストリーミングイベントに、真鍋大度がNosaj Thingと出演。グリーンバックによる合成映像制作ではなく、iPad Lidarのみを用いてARライブの映像制作をするという手法や、そのプロセスを確立するために制作した実験的な作品である。

Streaming event hosted by Brainfeeder, featuring Daito Manabe in performance with Nosaj Thing. The experimental project developed processes to create live AR imagery using only iPad Lidar, without greenscreens.

85a090ebaafa5d255e95ecebf4eb3c79a9f502140d8abd6c227b595a573c1fdd

_

Nosaj Thing "Cold Stares ft. Chance The Rapper + The O'My's"
ミュージックビデオ

Nosaj Thing "Cold Stares ft. Chance The Rapper + The O'My's" Music Video

2015   Chance The Rapperのパラノイアを題材とした歌詞から着想を得て制作されたミュージック
ビデオ。ドローンの無人撮影システムを開発し、スタジオにはダンサーとドローンのみが存在
する状態で撮影を行った。映像に3Dデータを重ねることでリアルとバーチャルをシームレス
に往来する仕組みを開発した。

Music video inspired by the lyrics to Chance the Rapper's track Paranoia. An
autonomous drone system made it possible to film the video in a studio populated
only by dancers and drones. 3D data was layered over the resulting footage, seamlessly
transporting viewers between the real and virtual worlds.

COLLABORATIONS

センシング・ストリームズ—不可視、不可聴 Sensing Streams – invisible, inaudible

2014　坂本龍一との初めてのコラボレーション。人間が普段知覚することのできない波長の電磁波を計測し、可視/可聴化した作品。電磁波の流れを多様に顕在化すると同時に、放送局やキャリアに割り当てられた周波数帯に縛られながら、各人が能動的に関わることで形成される一種の「生態系」を可視化した。

The first collaboration between Ryuichi Sakamoto and Daito Manabe, this project sought to visualize imperceptible electromagnetic waves, representing them in both visible and audible form. The ebb and flow of the waves manifested a sort of "ecosystem" encompassing the active involvement of each participant, while constrained by the frequency band assigned to broadcasting stations and carriers.

4e1541e661acfd8cc5ef4b2ba0341f38ecf8872c640b73385019f493298751d5

Ryuichi Sakamoto: Playing the Piano 12122020

2020　　オンラインで開催された、坂本龍一によるピアノコンサート。映画監督、アーティストの
Zakkubalanが撮影監督として参加し、映画のような構図や背景、表現を取り入れた演出と
なっている。また、ボストン・ダイナミクス社の4足歩行ロボット「Spot」の上のデバイスを介した
リモート対談なども演出の一部として行われた。

Online piano concert by Ryuichi Sakamoto, featuring cinematic backdrops, settings,
and other performative elements created alongside director-artist duo Zakkubalan.
A remote talk event was also conducted, using a device atop Boston Dynamics' four-
legged robot "Spot."

OK Go "Obsession" ミュージックビデオ OK Go "Obsession" Music Video

2017　　ロックバンドOK Goの楽曲「Obsession」ミュージックビデオ。567台のプリンターの動きと
カメラの動きを完全に同期させるシステムを構築し、出力される紙の組み合わせで様々なイ
メージを描く演出を行った。撮影は一発勝負であるため、シミュレーターを制作し、綿密にシ
ミュレーションを行った上で撮影を行った。

Music video for "Obsession" by OK Go. The camera was timed to move in perfect sync
with the action of 567 printers, creating recombinant visuals from the paper output
from each printer. As the video can not be retaken, a precise simulator was created to
fine tune the system before filming.

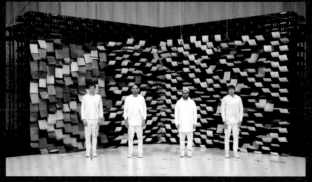

サカナクション SAKANAQUARIUM 光 ONLINE
"ワンダーランド" "ミュージック"
Sakanaction SAKANAQUARIUM HIKARI ONLINE "Wonderland" "Music"

2020　　　ミュージシャンのサカナクションが初となるライブストリーミング公演を開催し、ライゾマティクスはVisual Effectで参加した。従来のライブの制約に捉われず、オンラインライブの表現を再解釈した生配信となった。

First live streaming performance by the band Sakanaction. Visual effects provided by Rhizomatiks challenged the limitations of conventional live performance, presenting an innovative reinterpretation of the live-steamed performance medium.

ef95180c59081f8eab1cab033d5ed9c536099bda1b4c685dc8d035a75dcee04c

NHKスペシャル NEXT WORLD 私たちの未来 −
特設Webサイト SYMPHONY

Website "SYMPHONY" for the NHK Special "NEXT WORLD: Our Future"

2015

2045年のライブを仮定してサカナクションと作り上げた、生配信ライブで使用するリミックス生成のための特設ウェブサイト。人工知能でリミックスを行う企画で、もとになる楽曲と視聴者から集めたデータを用いて、楽曲が遺伝的に進化していく仕組みを開発。実際にリミックスを行った楽曲をTV番組で使用した。

Website developed with the band Sakanaction, envisioning a concert at the time of the "singularity" in 2045, when computers will begin to outsmart humanity. The website used AI to create remixes for use in a live-streaming performance, drawing on musical data and information collected from users in a system that facilitated the genomic evolution of music. A resulting remixed track was featured on the NHK television program, "NEXT WORLD: Our Future."

Rio 2016 Flag Handover Ceremony to Tokyo 2020

2016年リオデジャネイロオリンピックの閉会式で行われた、次の開催都市である東京にオリンピック・パラリンピック旗を引き継ぐセレモニーでのプレゼンテーション。全体のテクニカルディレクション、後半のパフォーマンスパートのフィールド映像の演出と制作、舞台装置制作、AR演出を担当した。

2016

Presentation conducted at the 2016 Summer Olympics closing ceremony to mark the handover of the Olympic flag from Rio de Janeiro to Tokyo. Served as technical director of the flag ceremony presentation, while also overseeing the field visuals, set design, and AR elements in the ceremony's subsequent handover performance.

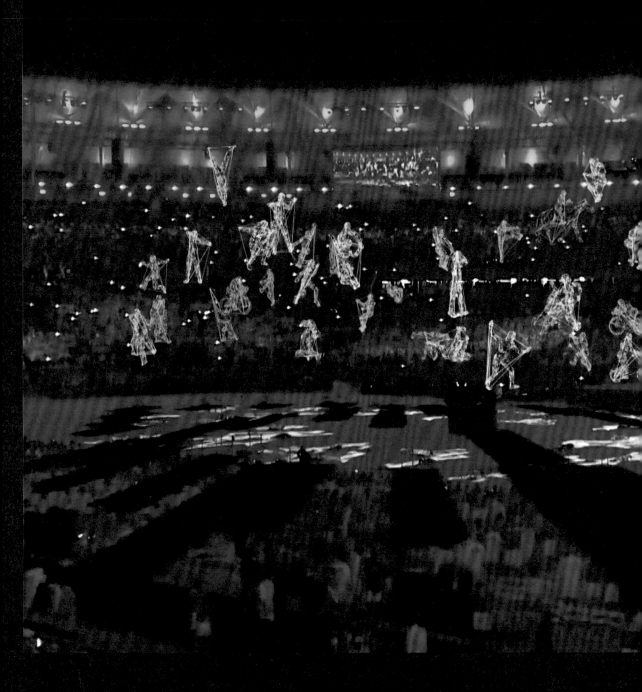

_

FORM

2017　東京国際フォーラムにて上演された、日本の伝統美を最先端テクノロジーで可視化した作品。野村萬斎が演じる舞を3Dスキャンやモーションキャプチャーなど様々なセンサーを用いて解析し、新たな解釈を生んだ。現実と仮想が入り交じる世界で、光によって野村萬斎の身体に再接合し、劇場空間に拡張することを試みた。

Project that used cutting-edge technology to visualize notions of traditional Japanese beauty in performances at the Tokyo International Forum. Dance performed by Mansai Nomura was analyzed via a variety of sensor-reliant techniques, such as 3D scanning and motion capture, to foster a new interpretation of the medium. In a world blending reality and imagination, the projected attempted to combine Nomura's body with light for augmented expansion through the theatre space.

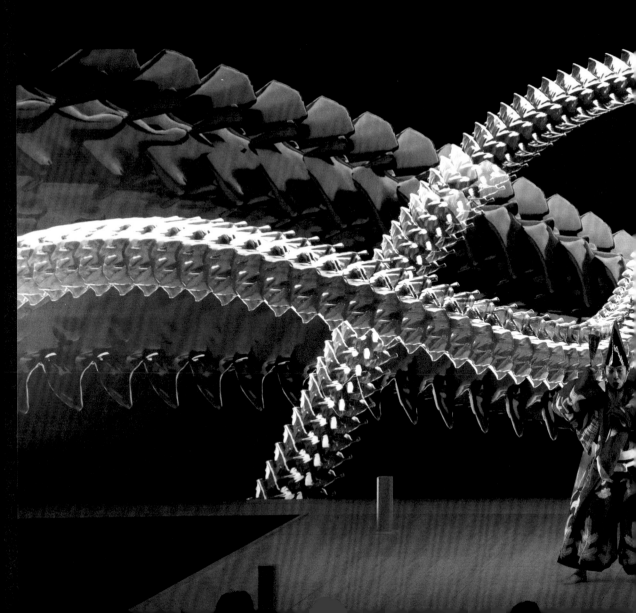

MANSAI ◉ 解体新書 その参拾 特別版『5W1H』

MANSAI:Kaitai-Shinsho No.30 Special Edition "5W1H"

2019

野村萬斎がホスト役となり、アーティストとお互いの専門分野を駆使しながらパフォーマンスとトークを行う「解体新書」シリーズの特別版。人間の行動要素を「5W1H」で記号化、数式で可視化し、人間の「行動」を数学的思考で紐とくと同時に、身体的思考でも捉えることで「生きている人間」を実感することを試みる。

Special 30th instalment of "MANSAI: Kaitai-Shinsho," a performance-and-talk event series hosted by Mansai Nomura which brings together a variety of creators to discuss their respective fields. 5W refers to the five interrogatives; "When, Where, Who, What and Why," while 1H refers to the "How." By converting these factors into numerical information and also drawing on analog thinking, the work attempted to encode humans' attitudes to explore the primitive roots of interpersonal expression, and illuminate the fundamental sources of human behavior.

092c79e8f80e559e404bcf660c48f3522b67aba9ff1484b0367e1a4ddef7431d

echo

2017 / 2018　ダイアログ・イン・ザ・ダーク檜山晃との身体のリサーチより、超音波を発して反響で空間を認識する「エコーロケーション」をヒントにした服をアンリアレイジと共同開発した。服から発した信号で距離を計測し、反響を振動として伝達する。ヨコハマ・パラトリエンナーレ2017、日本科学未来館(2018)等で体験展示を行った(写真は2018)。

Garments developed in collaboration with experimental fashion label ANREALAGE, building on research conducted with Akira Hiyama of the Dialogue in the Dark project. Inspired by bats' ability to use ultrasound to navigate in pitch darkness in a process known as echolocation, the clothing itself emits signals that are then measured to gauge distance and send vibrations back to the wearer in the form of a vibration, or "echo," that provided a new experience of spatial awareness. The project was presented in interactive exhibitions at the Yokohama Paratriennale 2017 and the National Museum of Emerging Science and Innovation in 2018 (pictured).

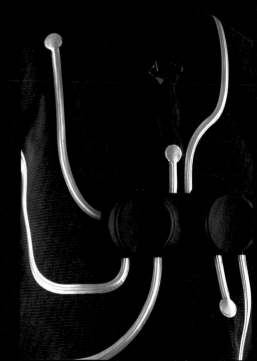

Dolce&Gabbana Fall Winter 2018/19 Women's Fashion Show

2018

ドルチェ＆ガッバーナ 2018-2019 秋冬 ウィメンズ コレクションにおけるファッションショー
の冒頭シーン。ファッションモデルがバッグを手にして歩くかわりに、新作バッグを搭載したド
ローンが隊列を組み、ランウェイを飛行する。その姿をとらえた映像は、インターネットを通じて
世界中に拡散された。

Opening segment for Dolce&Gabbana fall/winter 2018/19 women's fashion show. In
the opening scene, instead of fashion models walking with a bag, drones equipped
with the new bag form a formation and fly down the runway. The video that captured
this scene attracted worldwide attention via the Internet.

エイブルpresents第73回全日本フェンシング選手権大会
Fencing Visualized Project

The 73rd All Japan Fencing Championship presented by ABLE　Fencing Visualized Project

2020　AR技術を用いてフェンシングの剣先の軌跡を可視化する「Fencing Visualized Project」のシステムを開発した。2012年から様々な開発プロセスを経て、現在では深層学習を用いて、マーカーを使用しない剣先の検出や可視化が可能となった。2020年には全日本選手権大会決勝戦にて実戦採用され、ABEMA（アベマ）で生配信された。

Fencing Visualized Project was the system with AR technology for visualizing the trajectory of a fencing sword tips. Since 2012, through the various development by using deep learning, now it become possible to detect and visualize sword tips without using markers. The project was deployed at the All Japan Fencing Championship in 2020 and also streamed live on Abema TV.

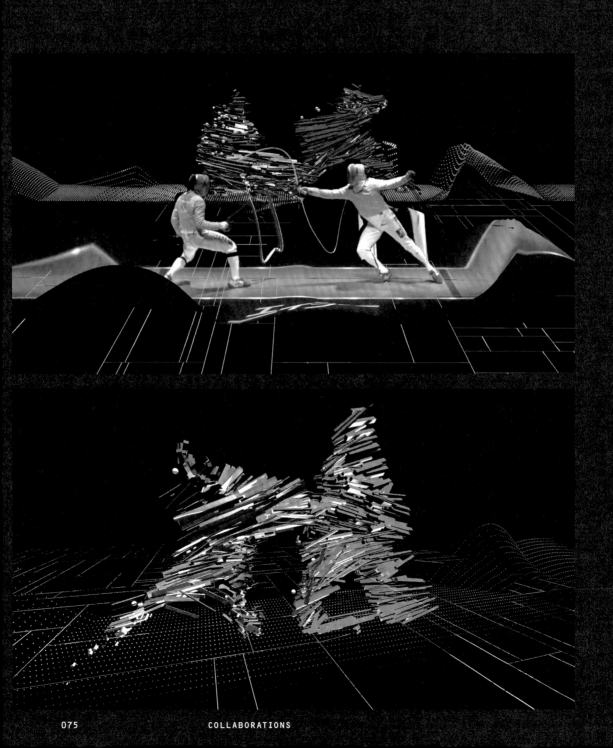

COLLABORATIONS

_

White Mountaineering | 2021 Spring / Summer Collection Paris Fashion Week©

2020　オンラインで開催された、White Mountaineering 2021年春夏パリ・コレクションのショーの演出、及び映像、音楽制作を手がけた。フォトグラメトリー技術を用いて、モデルが歩く姿を3Dデータ化し様々な視点で衣装を見せる演出を行った。また、衣服のパターンデータによって服が出来るプロセスを可視化するなど、服を媒体とした挑戦も行った。

Online fashion show for White Mountaineering, held as part of Paris Fashion Week for spring/summer 2021. Photogrammetric technology was used to render models as 3D data, showcasing the clothing from a range of angles. Garment pattern data was further used to visualize the processes that went into the making of the outfits and displayed as the models walked down a digitally augmented runway, epitomizing the brand's distinctively functional fabrics and advanced cuts.

ThermoArt by DAITO MANABE | UNIQLO HEATTECH JP |

2020

被写体の動きと赤外線放射エネルギーとを解析してグラフィック生成する作品。ネガティブチェックにも使用されるサーモカメラを、データのセンシングのみならずグラフィック素材生成のデバイスとすることによって、「体温を測る」行為を楽しいものに変化させている。

This project generated graphics based on a subject's movements and infrared radiation. Whereas thermographic cameras are often used in "negative" contexts—for example, to gauge body temperatures at times of illness—this project sought to go beyond the device's data sensing function by adding a positive element of graphical play to the routine task of taking one's temperature.

Takeaways from Using Human Heat

It's quite personal and intimate data.

It could feel rather intimidating even, for the models.

where the excitement of this method lies,

ンスにアーティストとして客演参加した。筋電位センサーや喉頭マイクをArcaの身体に取り付け、多様な音に変換を行った。パフォーマンスは即興で行われ、4日のあいだ、毎日違うパフォーマンスを披露した。

Participated as a guest artist in a new performance by Arca, created and presented at The Shed, a creative arts center in New York. Arca was outfitted with myoelectric sensors and a throat microphone that were used to create a range of manipulated sound. Each performance over the four-day series was unique.

fb9e0b5e276436ab046597a7b437591fd912e4007bcdb4474a5e3370ae265c53

KAZU "Come Behind Me, So Good! (Official video by Daito Manabe + Kenichiro Shimizu)"

2020

Kazu Makinoのミュージックビデオ。ダンサーのフォトグラメトリーデータと、レーザースキャナーでスキャンした地形データを同じ3D空間に存在させることで、シームレスな風景を創り出した。作品中では、広大な地形データと複数のダンサーが、違和感なく同じ3D空間に存在している。

Music video for Kazu Makino combining a complex trove of photogrammetric dancer data and laser-scanned topographical data to create a seamless digital landscape in 3D space.

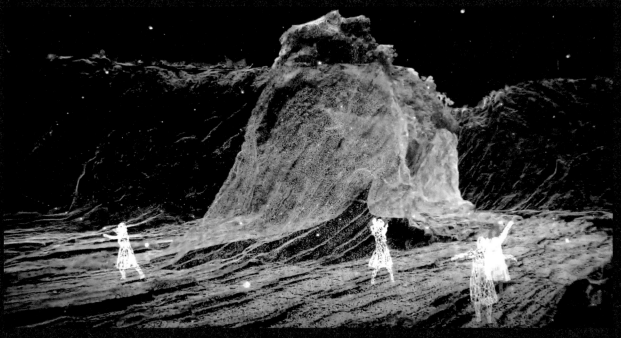

a162f31afebe139b84fda776d24bb96c411a73ce70613dfe4139c4da8cfbd670

YOKO KANNO SEATBELTS「オンライン七夕まつり」
"Inner Universe"
YOKO KANNO SEATBELTS Online TANABATA festival "Inner Universe"

2020 「コロナ禍で隔てられた距離を、七夕の伝説のように超えたい」という目的で実施された、菅野よう子による配信。「Inner Universe」の映像演出を担当した。2015年1月17日に他界したシンガーソングライターOrigaのデータを用いて、point cloudでその姿を蘇らせ、菅野との共演を実現させた。

Project by Yoko Kanno, expressing a message of solidarity amid the coronavirus, inspired by the Tanabata legend of the starcroosed lovers separated by the Milky Way are reunited once each year. "Inner Universe" co-starred singer songwriter Origa, who passed away on January 17th, 2015, ressurected with point cloud technology.

274e788d4dafb41aca0d7dac04b786c70236e45cef1e5ec1bb894ef533160b10

CONNECTED WORLD

2020 DJ Krushと真鍋大度のコラボレーション。仮想空間でパフォーマンスを行い、現実空間では表現しきれない音と映像の共感覚体験をTwitchのストリーミングで配信。ターンテーブルやミキサーの動きを解析してスクラッチをビジュアライズするなど、ヒップホップDJスタイル独自のデータを活かした演出を行った。

Collaboration between Daito Manabe and DJ Krush. Streamed on Twitch, the performance conducted in a virtual space blended audio and visuals in a synesthetic experience transcending the physical possibilities of the real world. The movement of turntables and mixers were analyzed to visualize scratching techniques in a performance true to the hip hop DJ style.

2b148c1d849f8d6c0522809ef77083afdb19e1e8fb19041e9f885c1943f41d6d

Staying TOKYO / Playing TOKYO

2020　COVID-19の緊急事態宣言をきっかけに開始された、家にいながら楽しめることを模索する
実験的オンラインイベント。イベントが多数自粛される中、多くのアーティストやクリエイターが
毎回オンラインで参加し、音楽・トークなど表現を行った。緊急事態宣言解除時も《Playing
Tokyo》と名義を切り替え、活動を続けている。

Staying Tokyo was an experimental online event exploring alternative forms of
engagement and entertainment to be enjoyed from the home under lockdown. While
many events were restrained, many artists / creators participated online with their
music and talks. After the state of emergency was lifted, the activity is continuing by
switching with *Playing Tokyo*.

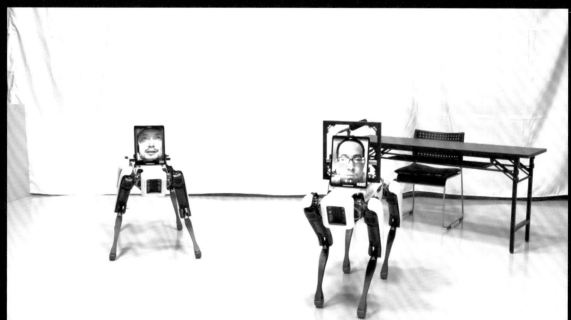

3ba7276d7a5cce874f35711327f2f84e79f6972b33ea33b99e9006dd7c9645aa

非同期テック部 Hidouki Tech Bu

2020 緊急事態宣言中に俳優のムロツヨシ、ライゾマティクスの真鍋大度、ヨーロッパ企画の上田誠ら3人が立ち上げた部活動。ムロが出演、上田が脚本と演出、真鍋がプログラミング・映像・照明などのテックを担当している。ムロのインスタグラム配信に始まり、オムニバス映像作品「緊急事態宣言」にも参加した。

Group founded by Daito Manabe, actor Muro Tsuyoshi, and Europe Kikaku's Makoto Ueda following the declaration of a state of emergency in Japan during the coronavirus. Muro appeared as an actor, Ueda served as director/scriptwriter, and Manabe served as technical director providing the programming, lighting, and visuals. The collaboration began with a live stream on Muro's instagram account, and culminated in the group's participation in an omnibus film about the quasi-lockdown.

非同期テック部
第1回作品発表
＠インスタライブ
May 5, 2020

「ムロツヨシショー、
そこへ、
着信、
からの」

3 Visualization:
post human body

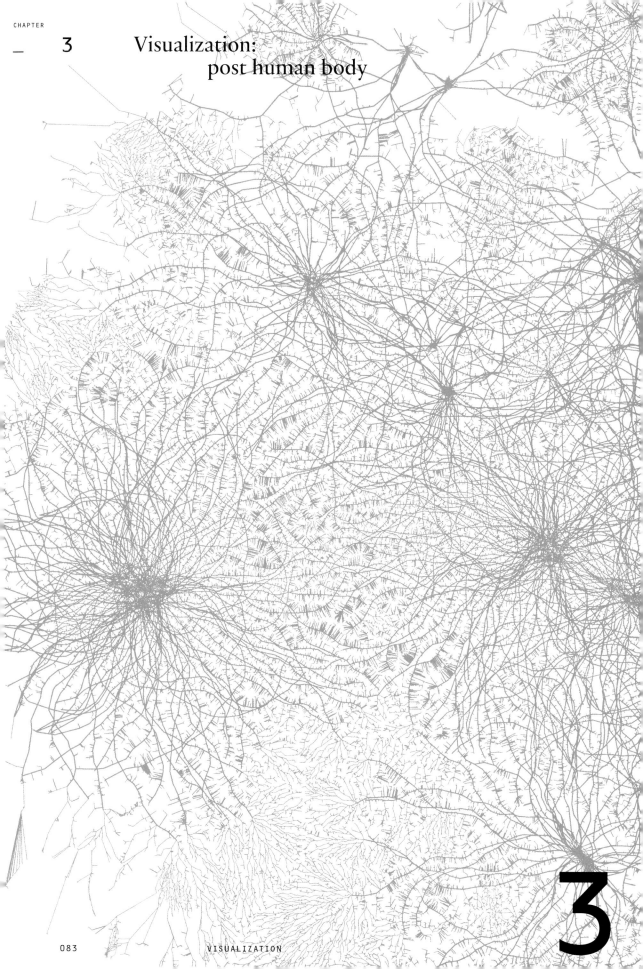

3

d65b18366d1a94896148d7b1f1909fa51d497da727a4f39fe9d200f6874f8728

dot.

2011　Rhizomatiks と ELEVENPLAY との初のコラボレーション作品である《dot.》は、14人のダンサーが iPad を手に持ち、画面上のアニメーションと連携して行ったダンスパフォーマンスである。iPad のカメラを使って本番中に撮影した画像を演出に使用する、iPad を照明の代わりに使用するなど iPad の機能を活用した演出を取り入れた。

ELEVENPLAY's first collaborative work with Rhizomatiks, *dot.*, was a dance performance in which 14 dancers held iPads and perform in sync with animations shown onscreen. The performance incorporated effects that utilized the iPad's functions, such as images taken during the performance with their built-in cameras, and leveraging the iPad's light in lieu of stage lighting.

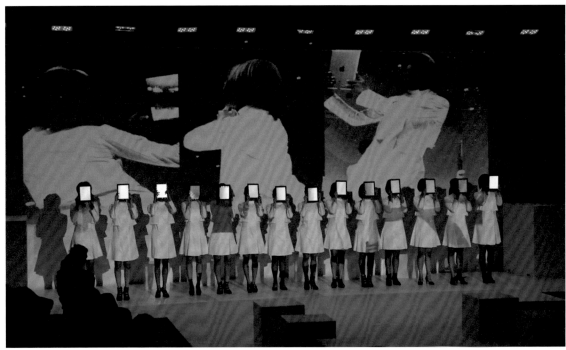

shape

2013

プロジェクションマッピングで、踊るダンサーに映像を投影するダンスパフォーマンス。Kinect
で取得した深度データを使ってリアルタイムにダンサーの身体が存在している領域を判別し
ている。投影の領域に変化を持たせるため、衣装はダンサーの動きに合わせて大きく形が変
化するようなものを制作した。

Dance performance in which images were projection-mapped onto dancers moving
onstage. This entailed determining the dancers' locations in real-time, using depth
data acquired with Kinect. The dancers' costumes were designed to dramatically
change their shape in response to the wearer's movements, adding a further layer of
visual dynamism to the projections.

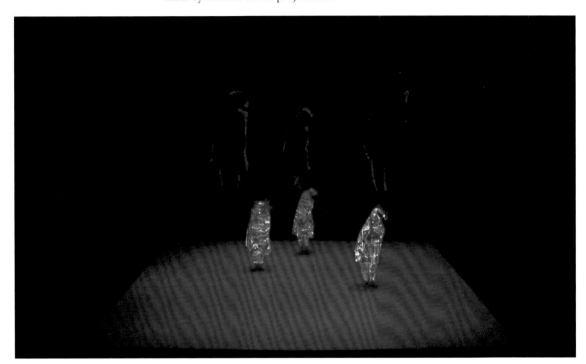

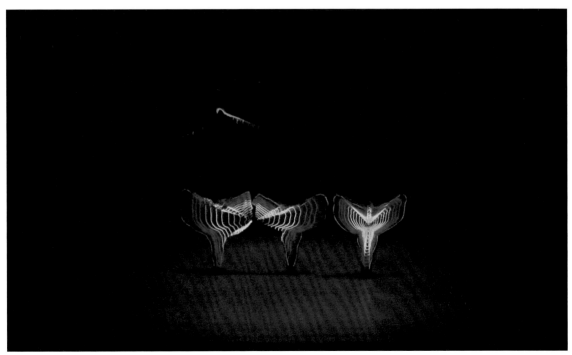

cube

2013

ダンサーとキューブ、プロジェクションを用いたダンスパフォーマンス。それまで個々のオブジェクトを区別して異なる映像を投影することは難しかったが、本作ではキューブに再帰性反射材を使用し、深度カメラの情報と合わせてダンサーの領域とキューブの領域を区別する仕組みを開発し、映像表現を進化させた。

Dance performance combining dancers, cubes, and projections. Projecting disparate images onto individual objects had long posed a considerable technical hurdle. By pairing retroreflective material and depth camera data, this project provided a framework for distinguishing between the dancers and sculptural cubes, unlocking new possibilities for the artistic expression of moving images.

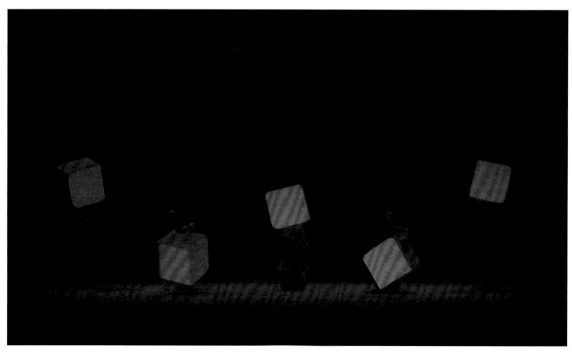

ray

2013

ダンサーとロボットアーム、小型の自作レーザープロジェクターを用いたダンスパフォーマンス。ロボットアームとレーザーを用いて空間を幾何学的なルールに基づき分割し、振付を作成することで、今まで画面の中で映像的に行われていた幾何学的な演出を肉眼で見えるパフォーマンスとして実現した。

Dance performance comprising dancers, robot arms, and a small custom laser projector. Specific geometric rules were used to create choreography and partition the space, an effect heightened by the robots and lasers. The performance revealed geometric processes (geometries that had formerly only been accessible onscreen as filmic representations) in a way that could be seen onstage in real space.

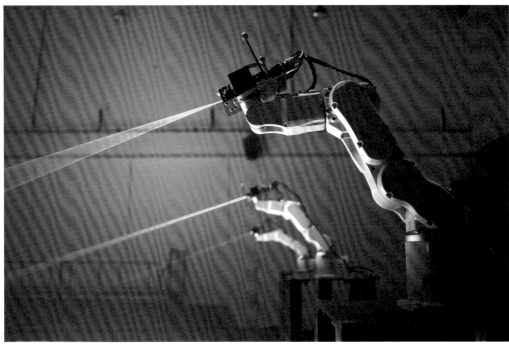

fly

2014 　3台のドローンと3人のダンサーによるダンスパフォーマンス作品。トラッキング技術、ドローンの制御技術を用いてステージ上にオブジェクトを複雑に配置し、その中でダンサーがパフォーマンスすることで新たな身体表現の可能性を模索した。

Dance performance consisting of 3 drones and 3 dancers. Tracking and drone control technology were utilized to place objects complicatedly in actual space around the dancers as they performed, presenting new possibilities in the realm of physical expression.

dcd9895bbd2784dc54007a9d24b4bdfe0937946eb33efa420239a73fa673f6e0

right brain

2014

ダンサーの衣装と手首にマーカーを装着してリアルタイムにその動きをトラッキングし、AR上で軌跡をビジュアライズしたダンスパフォーマンス。映像作品として制作した後に、ステージ上でのパフォーマンスとして展開された。

Dance performance that tracked the movement of dancers and created an AR visualization of their trajectories. Motion-tracking markers were affixed to the dancers' wrists and costumes, and the multiple dancers were all tracked in real-time. The project was first presented as a film, and subsequently performed onstage.

shadow

2014

ドローンに搭載されたスポットライトを、光源位置を自由に配置できる舞台照明として用いた
ダンスパフォーマンス。制御されたドローンから投射される3つの独立した光源が織りなす光
と影が、ダンサーのパフォーマンスとの相乗効果を生み出し、従来のライティングシステムでは
実現できない演出を行った。

Performance illuminated solely by drones equipped with spotlights. The interplay
of three independent light sources projected from each of the drones synergistically
heightened the performative choreography between light, shadow, and dancers,
achieving a dynamic effect and level of creative freedom not possible with
conventional lighting systems.

24 drones

2015　24台の小型ドローンと3人のダンサーによるパフォーマンス作品。大量のドローンがお互いに
ぶつからない安全な距離を常に保ちつつ、美しいコンポジションを生成する。ドローンは編隊
を組みながら飛行するが、その動きはダンサーの動きに連動しており、複雑で有機的なインタ
ラクションを実現している。

Performance piece consisting of 24 small drones and three human dancers. The
large fleet of drones moves autonomously, all the while maintaining a safe distance
to avoid collision and generate an aesthetically beautiful composition. The drones
fly in formation, yet move in synch with the dancers to realize a compex, organic
interaction between man and machine.

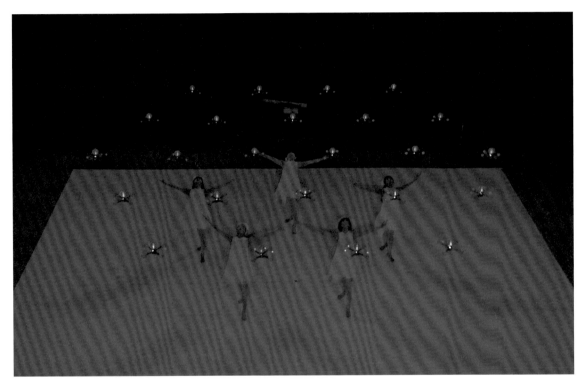

72222ce359f7f1f2e56e4b3e87b8f068feaa2277839e5290d947fb8f4a7e4b44

border / border 2021

2015 / 2021　Rhizomatiks Researchと、演出振付家のMIKIKO率いるELEVENPLAYによるダンスパフォーマンス。観客は動きを完全制御されたパーソナルモビリティ「WHILL」に座り、ヘッドセット型VRディスプレイを装着。VR/ARの虚構の世界とダンサーによって引き戻される現実世界を往来するうちに様々な境界が変容する。《border 2021》ではより高解像度・高臨場感のVRデバイスに合わせ、新しい演出を加えた（図版はすべて《border 2021》）。

Dance performance produced by Rhizomatiks Research and dance company ELEVENPLAY, led by choreographer MIKIKO. The audience sat on "WHILL"—a personal mobility implement whose movement was fully controlled by a program—and given a VR display headset. The innovative performance took the audience on a journey that questioned the delineation between the fictive world of VR/AR and the connection to the real world represented by the dancers. In *border 2021*, a new effect/direction has been added to match the higher resolution and higher realism of VR devices (All the plates are from *border 2021*).

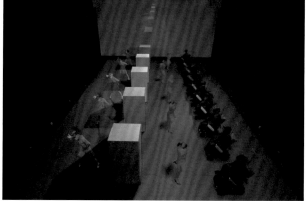

42103a4c378e1130739fac1dacaf1163acf6fa3081d0242b70bb67db08606091

_ border installation ver.

2016 ダンサーのいない無人のステージで、パーソナルモビリティ「WHILL」と舞台装置が無線制御で動いている様子を、独自開発したヘッドマウントディスプレイを使って鑑賞するMR作品。ダンスパフォーマンス作品と同様に、VR/ARの虚構の世界と現実世界をシームレスに行き来するうちに、「境界」が変容していく。

MR work featuring proprietary head-mounted devices that allowed participants to view wirelessly controlled boxes and "WHILL" personal mobility devices moving across a dancerless stage. The project seamlessly blended the boundary between the real world and the "fictional" AR/VR realm.

phosphere

2017　光の結像によって構築された「光のダンサー」と生身のダンサーが共演するダンスパフォーマンス。レーザー光源プロジェクター24台と光軸を増やすための8枚の鏡でステージを取り囲み、32方向からの光を結像させ、スモークを焚いたステージ上に、肉眼で見ることのできる立体的な光のダンサーの姿を構築した。

Dance performance combining human dancers and dancing light. The stage was surrounded by an arsenal of 24 laser projectors and 8 amplifying mirrors that made it possible to form ethereal images out of the light from 32 angles. Light danced across the smoky stage as 3D forms visible to the naked eye.

LEXUS DESIGN EVENT 2019 | LEADING WITH LIGHT

2019

人間のダンサーの動きがプログラムされたロボット、256個の光源、そして1人のダンサーが
織りなすダンスパフォーマンス。通常、スポットライトは光を動かして表現を成り立たせるが、本
作では光軸をロボットで遮り、その動作によって光軸の長さを変化させる演出を取り入れた。

Dance performance interweaving 256 light sources, a human dancer, and a robot
programmed to emulate human dance. Whereas conventional lighting effects are
created by swiveling spotlights, in this experimental performance, the robot was used
to strategically obstruct the light axis, and thus adjust the length of their beams.

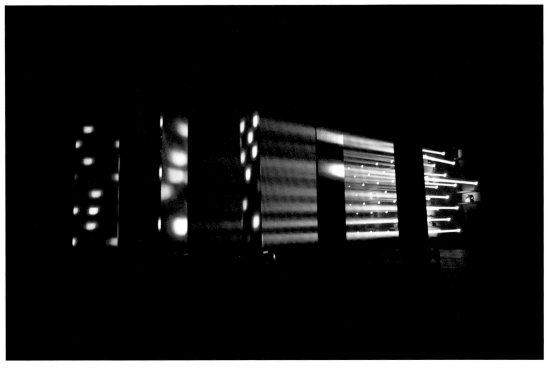

discrete figures

2018 / 2019 　膨大な量の人の動きやダンサーの動きを解析し、機械学習を用いて、ダンスのコレオグラフィーとなり得る動きを生成する試みを行った。また、ステージ上のオブジェクトは全てモーションキャプチャシステムによってトラッキングされ、ダンサーの身体表現に対応した演出に利用される。

Dance performance that tapped machine-learning to analyze a prodigious trove of human movement and dance data in an experimental attempt to generate movement that could be used as dance choreography. Human dancers shared the stage with sculptural objects that utilized multiple algorithms to relocate in response to the dancers' movements.

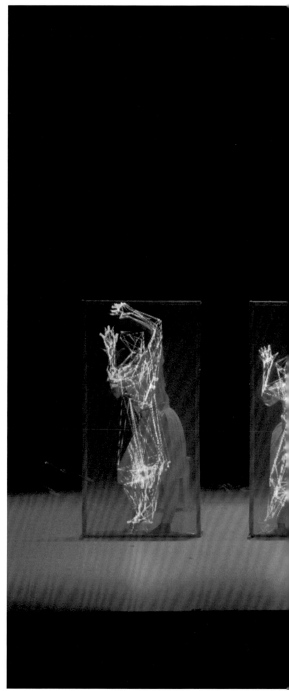

VISUALIZATION

S.P.A.C.E.

2020

ソーシャル・ディスタンスを保ちながら、12kの超高解像度カメラとハイスペックPCによる画像処理を組み合わせて新たな身体表現、映像表現の可能性を提案した映像作品。ダンサーの身体構造と動きで生まれる身体情報を多様なルールで分解し再構築を行い、身体だけでは作ることのできない幾何学的世界を生成した。

This is a new work that proposes new possibilities of physical and visual expression by combining a ultra-high resolution 12K camera device and image processing capability of high spec PC while keeping a social distance.By decomposing and reconstructing information of the dancer's body structure and movements using various rules, this work creates a geometric world that cannot be created by the body alone.

結成10周年、メジャーデビュー5周年記念! Perfume LIVE @東京ドーム 「1 2 3 4 5 6 7 8 9 10 11」Lighting Balloon System

Perfume LIVE @TOKYODOME 1 2 3 4 5 6 7 8 9 10 11

(10th Anniversary as a Group/5th Anniversary on a Major Record Label!) Lighting Balloon System

2010

Perfumeの結成10周年、メジャーデビュー5周年記念として、2010年11月3日に行われた東京ドームでのライブ公演。楽曲に合わせて、東京ドームのバックスタンドで光る、直径5メートルのLED内蔵のバルーンを製作した。

Live performance held at the Tokyo Dome on November 3rd, 2010 to commemorate Perfume's 10th anniversary as a band and 5th anniversary since signing to a major record label. The performance featured soaring 5-meter tall balloons illuminated with internal LEDs in various colors remote-controlled by computer.

結成10周年、メジャーデビュー5周年記念! Perfume LIVE @東京ドーム「1 2 3 4 5 6 7 8 9 10 11」Interactive Visuals

Perfume LIVE @TOKYODOME 1 2 3 4 5 6 7 8 9 10 11

(10th Anniversary as a Group/5th Anniversary on a Major Record Label!) Interactive Visuals

2010 　 Perfumeの結成10周年、メジャーデビュー5周年記念として2010年11月3日に行われた東京ドームでのライブ公演にて、"Perfumeの掟"でメンバー登場前の映像演出を行った。流体力学、衝突演算など物理シミュレーションを用いた映像ソフトウェアが開発され、リアルタイム表現による映像演出が行われた。

Produced a visual segment, "Perfume no Okite," featured at a Tokyo Dome concert held on November 11th, 2010 to commemorate the 10th anniversary of the group Perfume, before the singers took the stage. The real-time performance consisted of video imagery and proprietary video software drawing on physical simulations (fluid mechanics, collision computations, and more).

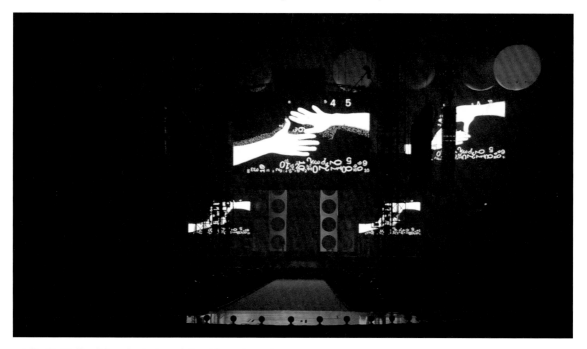

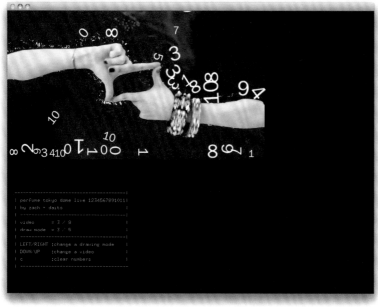

結成10周年、メジャーデビュー5周年記念! Perfume LIVE @東京ドーム 「1 2 3 4 5 6 7 8 9 10 11」Balloon Explosion System

Perfume LIVE @TOKYODOME 1 2 3 4 5 6 7 8 9 10 11
(10th Anniversary as a Group/5th Anniversary on a Major Record Label!) Balloon Explosion System

2010

Perfume結成10周年、メジャーデビュー5周年記念として2010年11月3日に行われた東京ドームでのライブ公演にて、あ～ちゃんがレーザー銃を撃つタイミングに合わせ、LEDを内蔵した光るバルーンを破裂させる演出を行った。バルーンは、レーザーではなく実際には電熱線によって破裂させている。

Live performance held at the Tokyo Dome on November 3rd, 2010 to commemorate Perfume's 10th anniversary as a band and 5th anniversary since signing to a major record label. During the performance, a band member wielded a laser gun, pulling the trigger to seemingly burst a balloon illuminated by internal LEDs. However, the balloon was actually popped by a heating wire, rather than a laser. Tied to a mannequin's hand, the balloon was connected to wire timed to heat at the precise moment when A~chan took aim.

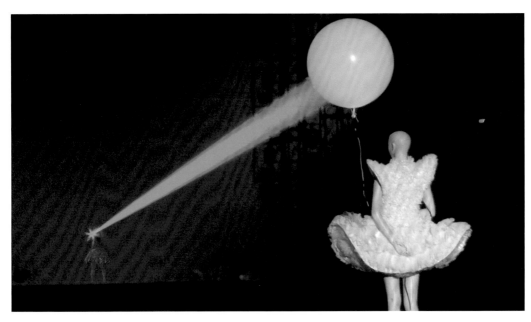

結成10周年、メジャーデビュー5周年記念! Perfume LIVE @東京ドーム 「1 2 3 4 5 6 7 8 9 10 11」3D Scan Visuals

Perfume LIVE @TOKYODOME 1 2 3 4 5 6 7 8 9 10 11
(10th Anniversary as a Group/5th Anniversary on a Major Record Label!) 3D Scan Visuals

2010 　Perfumeの結成10周年、メジャーデビュー5周年を記念して行われた東京ドームでのライブ公演にて、カラーの3Dデータを用いて制作した映像を、ライブパフォーマンスで使用した。工業用の深度カメラで取得した深度データとカラーカメラのデータを合わせ、カラーの3Dデータを合成する仕組みを作った。

Live performance held at the Tokyo Dome on November 3rd, 2010 to commemorate Perfume's 10th anniversary as a band and 5th anniversary since signing to a major record label. Perfume was filmed with an industrial depth camera and color cameras, producing the world's first live performance with 3D color video imagery.

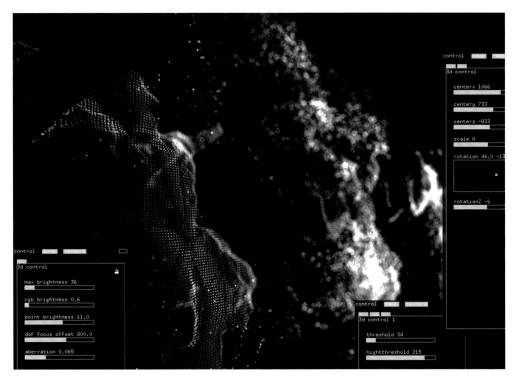

Perfume global site project #001

2012

Perfumeの世界デビューを記念して、ファンとクリエイターの手によって世界へ羽ばたくことを
テーマとしたWebプロジェクト。ダンスのモーションキャプチャーデータや楽曲などを提供して
ファンが作る二次創作をオフィシャルで認め、さらに二次創作コンテンツの著作権を作成者
に帰属するという試みが行われた。

Inaugural edition of a web project commemorating Perfume's worldwide debut. Conceived to highlight the partnership between artists and fans, this open source project provided fans with a range of data for secondary creation. Motion capture was used to digitize Perfume's dancing, with fans given extensions and sample codes to manipulate this data. Whereas fan-created content conventionally runs afoul of copyright laws, this experimental project officially condoned participation, and went so far as to grant fans the copyright to their creations.

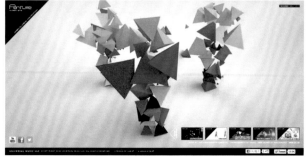

Perfume 3rd Tour「JPN」"Spring of Life"

2012

ミュージックビデオ「Spring of Life」の制御デバイスをもとに、LEDの衣装をライブ仕様に
アップデートした。電源を有線からバッテリー駆動にしたことに加え、ライブ中の早着替えに対
応するために配線ほか細部を改良した。

Live performance featuring updated versions of LED costumes based on control devices featured in the "Spring of Life" music video. The LED costumes underwent a number of refinements. Notably, the change to a battery-powered design cleared the way for less restrictive wiring, a valuable detail when making quick costume changes during a performance. Further improvements included added durability, smaller devices, and a firmware update.

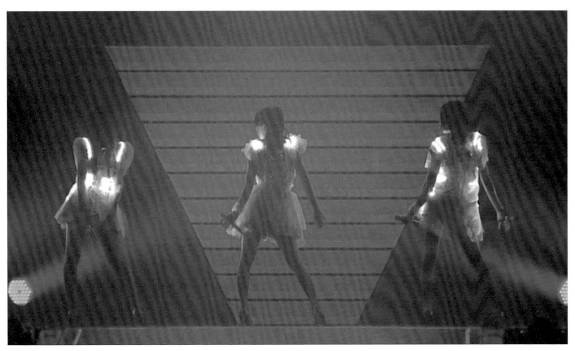

Physicalizing Data by Rhizomatiks Inspired by Perfume

2012 「TOKYO DESIGNERS WEEK2012」に出展された、Perfumeを3Dスキャンしたデータから生まれた等身大のフィギュアと、AR映像とを組み合わせたインスタレーション作品。リアルとバーチャルの境界に存在する「Perfume」というアーティストの姿が体現されている作品を目指した。

An installation piece for TOKYO DESIGNERS WEEK 2012 combining AR imagery with life-sized figures created from 3D scans of Perfume. The project was a literal embodiment of Perfume's artistry straddling the border of both the real and virtual worlds.

Rhizomatiks inspired by Perfume

2013　　NTTインターコミュニケーション・センター［ICC］で、ライゾマティクスがこれまで手がけた
Perfumeのテクノロジー演出術を紹介する初めての展覧会が開催された。Perfumeの3D
スキャンデータがホログラム風の映像でリアルに迫ってくるインスタレーションや、3人が実際
に着用したLED衣装などが展示された。

A debut exhibition shining a spotlight on the innovative technological performances
developed in collaboration between Perfume and Rhizomatiks. Held at the NTT
Intercommunication Center in the Tokyo Opera City Tower, the event offered a
comprehensive up-close look at this unique partnership to date. Visitors were greeted
by surreal, hologram-esque video created by 3D scanning Perfume's members in
the Physicalizing Data by Rhizomatiks Inspired by Perfume installation. Displays
included the LED-filled costumes, illuminated high heels, and glowing nails worn
during a live performance of "Spring of Life," as well as the motorized, mobile
costumes worn during the Cannes Lions International Festival of Creativity. The
exhibition also highlighted interactive contributions such as fan-submitted posts to
the Global Site Project.

Perfume WORLD TOUR 2nd "Spending All My Time"
Dynamic projection system

2013　《Perfume global site project #003》にて登場したデザインツールを活用して、ファンが
制作したグラフィックやファンのツイートを素材にしたグラフィックを、形を変えていく衣装に映
し出し、踊るPerfumeメンバーたちの動きにぴったりと合わせたプロジェクションを行った。

Fan tweets and graphics submitted to the *Perfume global site project #003* were
used to create visuals that were projected onto the trio's costumes. Their pure white
garments became an ideal screen for the vivid graphics coordinated to align precisely
with the choreography.

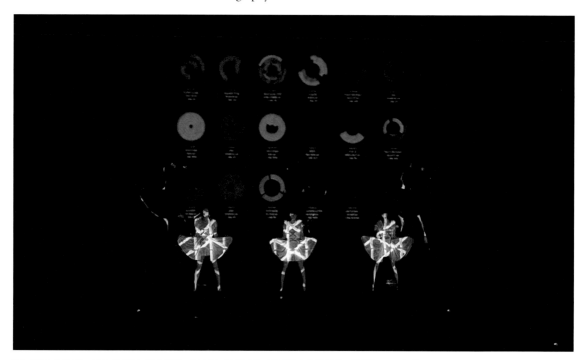

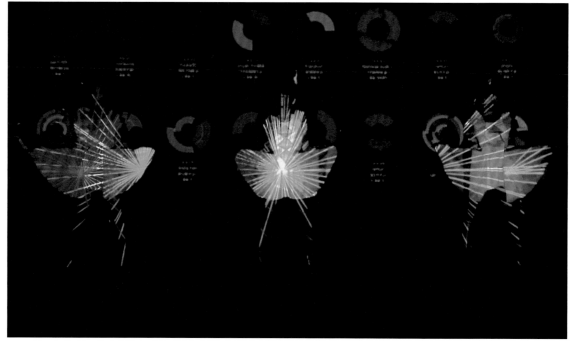

e4477e5c79173d2cc37bebc1fb2ed9587f38e51e4d9a7d85bad9b9b834f9ff8a

Perfume Cannes Lions International Festival of Creativity

2013 　2013年6月20日にフランス・カンヌにて行われた「カンヌライオンズ国際クリエイティビティ・フェスティバル」にて、Perfumeが日本人アーティストとして史上初のパフォーマンスを行った。変形する衣装は、肩部分の開閉はモーター制御、腰部分はサーボ（位置、速度等を制御するモーター）によって開閉している。

On June 20th, 2013, Perfume became the first Japanese artists to ever perform at the Cannes Lions International Festival Creativity held in Cannes, France. The projection mapping was deployed on shape-shifting costumes that opened and closed with motor-controlled shoulders and waist servos (motors that control factors such as position speed).

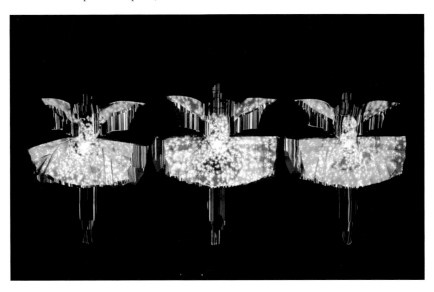

fefea904cce885e1751d3e8d9b1efcd027a58e800695499e91237501dc0ac45e

Perfume 4th Tour in DOME「LEVEL3」"Spending all my time"

2013 　Perfume global site project #003にて登場したデザインツールを使ってファンが制作したグラフィックや、ファンのツイートを素材にしたグラフィックを変形する衣装に映し出し、踊る彼女たちの動きにぴったりと合わせた投影を行った。

Fan tweets and graphics submitted to the Perfume global site project #003 were used to create visuals that were projected onto the trio's costumes. Their pure white garments became an ideal screen for the vivid graphics coordinated to align precisely with the choreography.

Perfume 4th Tour in DOME「LEVEL3」"Sleeping Beauty"

2013   Perfume 4th Tour in DOME「LEVEL3」の演出を担当した。公演前に取得したライブ来場者の3Dスキャンデータを用いて映像を制作し、「Sleeping Beauty」の演出として上映した。映像内に3Dスキャンされた観客が登場することに加え、映像の中のPerfumeが観客を「つまみ上げる」という演出も行われた。

Perfume's 4th Tour in DOME LEVEL3 involved an ambitious 3D scanning project over a series of concerts. Booths installed outside the two largest dome auditoriums in Tokyo and Osaka obtained 3D body scan data of audience members as they arrived for the concert. This data was then used to create video imagery that was screened during "Sleeping Beauty," allowing audience members to become part of the performance. In an additional video segment, Perfume's members seemingly plucked the 3D spectator scans out of the audience and placed them onstage.

Perfume WORLD

2014 「Cling Cling」のリリースを記念してオープンした、Perfumeのアバターが生活するファン参加型オープンワールド。その世界の中での住所取得も可能になっている。実際のPerfumeの活動から、アバターの状態も変化した。「エレクトロ・ワールド」ミュージックビデオのシーンをサンプリングしオマージュとした。

A website commemorating the release of the single "Cling Cling," Perfume WORLD is a virtual world that's home to Perfume's avatars and open to fan participation. Avatar status and movement is determined by Perfume's real-world activities and information exchange on the platform. When fans login from their Twitter or Facebook accounts, they can receive their own unique address in Perfume WORLD. Posts submitted on the site were even used in the intro sequences during live performances.

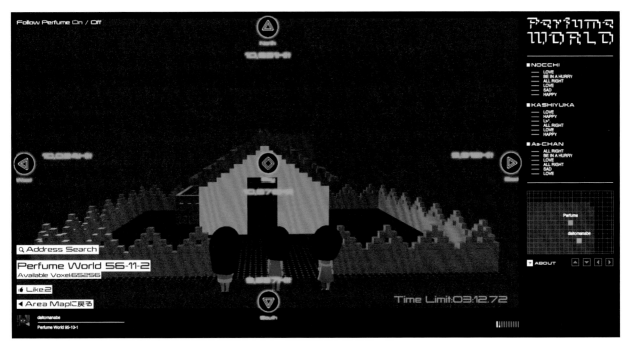

6a1a1cf96f32a2f3752bcddfe5628b9608428dd3053979a24379468012dd2e05

Perfume 5th Tour 2014「ぐるんぐるん」"intro"

Perfume 5th Tour 2014「Gurun Gurun」"intro"

2014　《Perfume World》で作られた1万人を超える参加者のデータを用いて、ライブのイントロ映像を制作した。バーチャルな世界からリアルのライブ会場へシームレスにトランジションする演出を試みた。

Live intro imagery created using data from over 10,000 fans collected during the *Perfume World* project. The performance aimed to facilitate a seamless transition from the virtual world into the real-world concert venue.

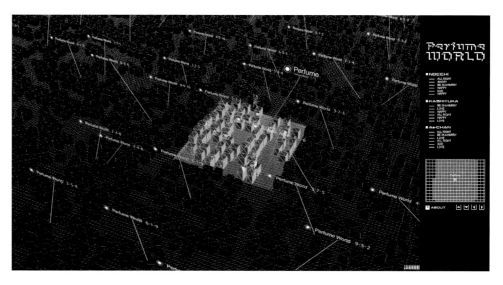

7e378c90ad3d00f324e6e5e84755b03546a49c11625df8bea718c2856b117337

Perfume 5th Tour 2014「ぐるんぐるん」"エレクトロ・ワールド"

Perfume 5th Tour 2014「Gurun Gurun」"Electro World"

2014　《Perfume World》で作られた1万人を超える参加者のデータを用いて、ステージの背景LEDパネルに映し出される「エレクトロ・ワールド」の映像を制作した。「エレクトロ・ワールド」のミュージックビデオへのオマージュといえる演出を行った。

Visuals for "Electro World" created using data from over 10,000 fans collected during the *Perfume World* project. Imagery was displayed on LEDs set up behind the trio in an homage to the "Electro World" music video.

Perfume live "SXSW 2015"

2015　米テキサスで行われた「SXSW」で披露したライブ。会場の3Dスキャンデータとフォトグラメトリーで作成したPerfumeの3Dデータを用い、CGの映像とリアルタイムの映像を切り替え、リアルとバーチャル空間をシームレスに往来するAR演出や自由視点映像、ハーフスクリーンへの投影を中継した。

Live performance at SXSW, the technology and music festival held annually in Austin, Texas. Streamed live on YouTube, this AR performance incorporated a complex combination of 3D scanning and photogrammetry techniques to create seamless transitions between CG imagery and real-time camera video. Semi-transparent video imagery was projected onto a half screen in real-time, and online viewers were able to freely adjust the camera angle on their live-stream feeds.

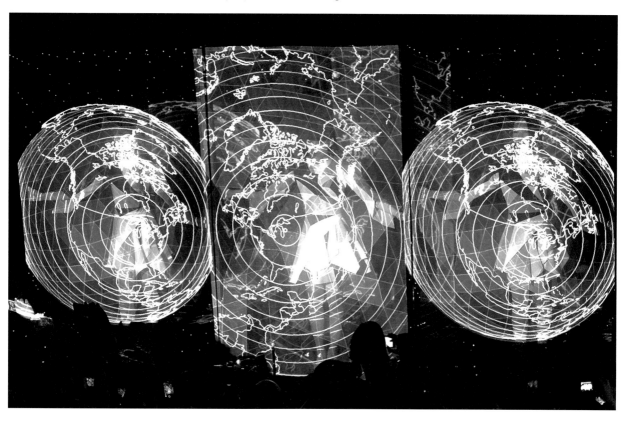

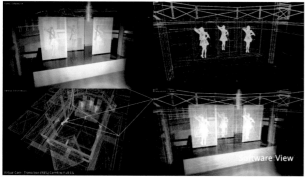

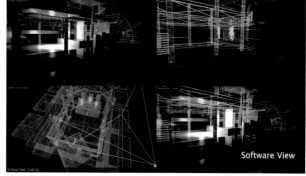

30周年記念特別番組 MUSIC STATION ウルトラFES 2016
Perfume "Spending all my time" Dynamic VR Display

Music Station Ultra Fes 2016 Perfume "Spending all my time" Dynamic VR Display

2016

平面的なディスプレイが別の空間につながる窓のように変化する「ダイナミックVRディスプレイ」を使用した演出が行われた。カメラの位置に合わせた映像をリアルタイムに生成しディスプレイへ送出することで、空間的な奥行きや広がりを感じる演出を行った。

In this live televised performance, a dynamic VR display transformed behind the dancers as if a window into another world. The production featured mobile LED displays outfitted with position-tracking markers that enabled the real-time generation and transmission of video imagery, based on rapid analysis on calibration of their movement.

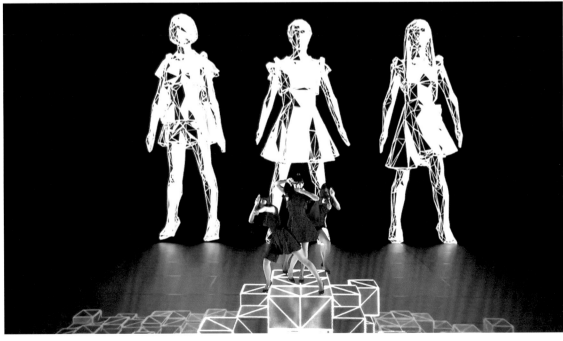

【docomo×Perfume】FUTURE-EXPERIMENT VOL.01
距離をなくせ。
[docomo × Perfume] FUTURE-EXPERIMENT VOL.01 Eliminate the Distance

2017　NTTドコモの5Gをはじめとした通信テクノロジーを活用したプロジェクト。東京、ニューヨーク、ロンドンの3都市に分かれたPerfumeのメンバーが「FUSION」を踊り、リアルタイムでそれぞれの場所の映像をタイムラグなく組み合わせたコンテンツを、全世界へインターネットでストリーミング生中継配信した。

The FUTURE-EXPERIMENT project seeks to provide new modes of immersive, experiential entertainment using NTT DOCOMO's communication technology including 5G. In this inaugural installment, Perfume simultaneously danced to "FUSION" on three different continents: Kashiyuka in London, A~chan in Tokyo, and Nocchi in NY. Video from each location was stitched together in real-time to achieve a group dance act without any time lag. The project was produced by DENTSU, with performance direction by MIKIKO. Rhizomatiks handled performance planning, operation, video creation, technical design/development, and lighting design.

Perfume×TECHNOLOGY presents Reframe

2018　　Perfumeが生み出してきたパフォーマンスの「再構築」をテーマとしたライブ公演。3人の仮想の影を使った「FUSION」、ファンが撮影した"大切な写真"をデータ解析し、ミュージックビデオの一部に融合させた「願い」、ドローンとARによる「無限未来」など、Perfumeに由来するデータから多様な試みが生まれた。

Live performance executed in collaboration with the choreographer MIKIKO. Rhizomatiks Research provided the interaction design, technical development, and video imagery. The title "Reframe" denotes reconstruction, a new framework for contextualizing Perfume's diverse corpus. Data from all Perfume's performances to date became the basis for an experimental reinterpretation of three tracks. "FUSION" utilized massive shadows of the trio, projected onstage. For "NEGAI," fan-submitted photographs were analyzed and matched with music video segments. Meanwhile, "MUGEN MIRAI" featured drones and AR technology.

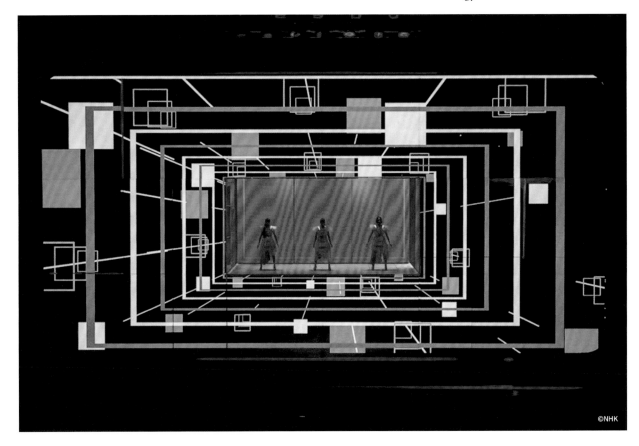

©NHK

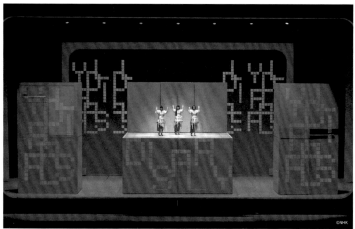

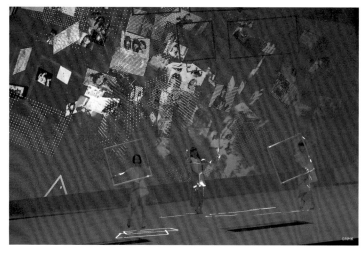

Reframe 2019

2019   Perfumeの活動から生まれた映像、音声、振付、歌詞データを解析し新たな視点から再構築したライブ。LINE CUBE SHIBUYAのこけら落とし公演として前年の初演からアップデートした。当日に撮影した観客の動画を解析し、「VOICE」のモーションデータに類似した画像データを抽出して1つの振付にする試みなどが行われた。

Live performance that analyzed video, audio, choreography, and lyrics created over Perfume's career, "reframing" this data from a new perspective. This project was an updated version of 2018's project, commemorating the first performance held at the newly renovated former Shibuya Public Hall (aka "Line Cube Shibuya"). Video taken of the crowd during the performance was analyzed to extract images correlating with motion data from "VOICE," which were then melded as a single cohesive choreography.

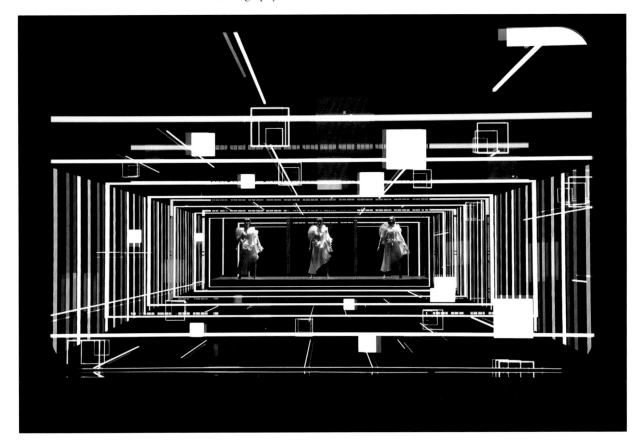

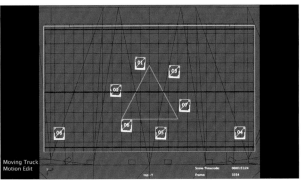

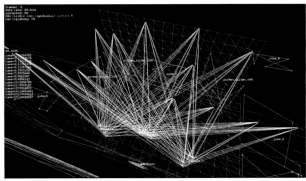

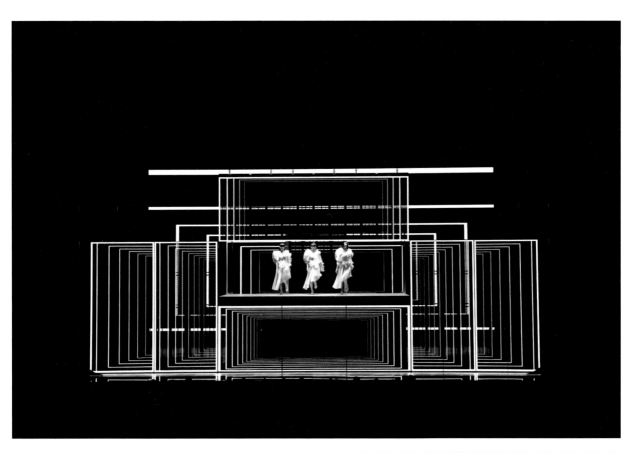

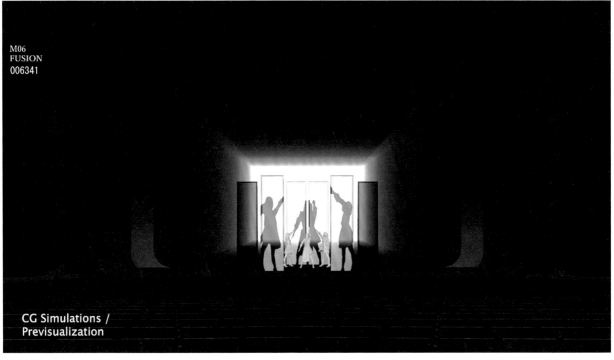

M06
FUSION
006341

CG Simulations /
Previsualization

【docomo×Perfume】FUTURE-EXPERIMENT VOL.04
その瞬間を共有せよ。

[docomo×Perfume] FUTURE-EXPERIMENT VOL.04 Share that moment

2018 「Perfume 7th Tour 2018『FUTURE POP』」のカウントダウンライブ内で行われた、NTT ドコモとのプロジェクト。Perfumeの手の動きを解析し、会場内のデバイスの光を制御する システムや、Perfumeが持つタブレットと観客のスマートフォンを双方向で通信し、アンケー トを送るシステムなどを実現した。

Project with NTT DOCOMO conducted as part of the countdown performance leading up to Perfume's 7th tour "Future Pop" in 2018. Created systems that controlled lighting devices inside the venue in response to Perfume's hand movements, and sent surveys between spectator smartphones and tablets held by Perfume onstage.

Perfume Live at Coachella Valley Music and Arts Festival 2019

2019　フェスティバルで行われたライブにおいて、機械学習技術を用いたリアルタイムグラフィックの生成や、モーションキャプチャーシステムを使った映像を、ステージ上で動くスクリーンに投影する演出などを行った。配信映像では、ARや自由視点移動映像などを組み合わせた複合的な映像演出を行った。

Presentation combining machine learning and motion capture to generate real-time graphics that were projected onto a screen moving onstage. Image compositing also allowed live-stream viewers to freely adjust their vantage point and enjoy the performance with additional AR enhancement.

345277b5f26db0e4dd45024e243dea75ccc12b28303ce62f01a46665e4f7e67f

Rhizomatiks inspired by Perfume 2020

2020 渋谷のPARCO MUSEUM TOKYOにて開催された、ライゾマティクスがこれまで手がけた Perfumeのステージ演出技術や、データを二次利用して制作した新作を含む映像インスタ レーションなど紹介する展覧会。独自開発のデバイスやソフトウェアの展示の他に、作品の 体験スペースなども設置された。

Exhibition held at the Parco Museum Tokyo, showcasing past stage technology from the collaboration between Rhizomatiks and Perfume, as well as new video installations and other work created from data collected over the years. Custom-made devices and softwere were also displayed along with a space where visitors could experience interactive works.

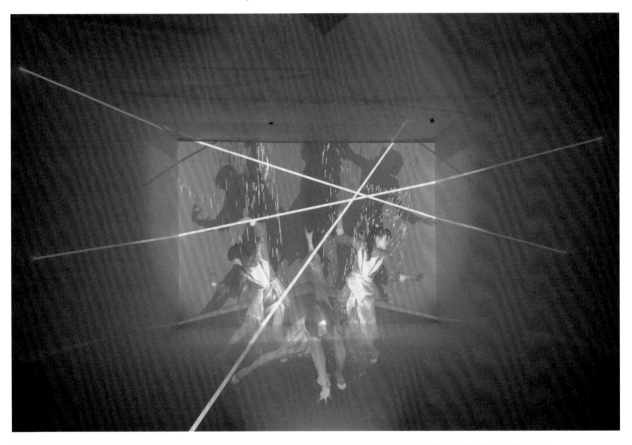

Rhizomatiks
inspired by Perfume 2020

Perfume 8th Tour 2020 "P Cubed" in Dome

2020　　　　Perfume結成20年、メジャーデビュー15周年の節目の年に行われたドームツアーに、演出サポートとして参加。Reframe 2019からバージョンアップした「Kiseki - Visualization」や、Coachella Valley Music and Arts Festivalで披露した姿勢推定を用いたリアルタイムエフェクトのアップデート版なども披露された。

Production support for Perfume's Tokyo Dome tour to celebrate their 20th anniversary as a band and 15th year since making their major label debut. Included a new "Kiseki-Visualization" that evolved from Reframe 2019, as well as an updated version of the motion-predicting real-time effects featured at Coachella 2019.

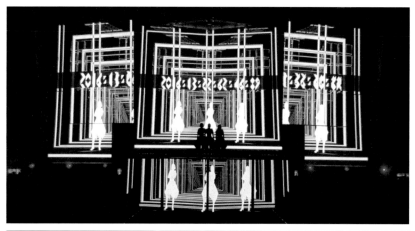

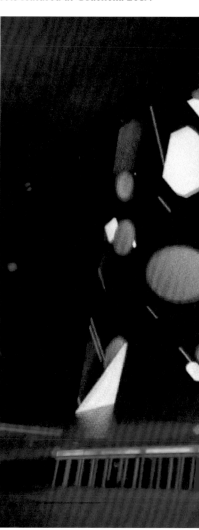

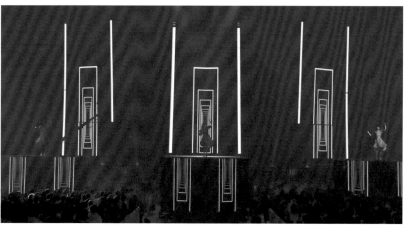

VISUALIZATION

Perfume Imaginary Museum "Time Warp"
@P.O.P. (Perfume Online Present) Festival

2020

Perfumeメジャーデビュー15周年、結成20周年を迎える2020年9月21日、オンラインフェスティバルで行われたライブ。"P Cubed"ツアーの千秋楽(同年2月26日)中止後に「行き場のなくなった観客の想いをどうやってオンラインで発表していくか」を、かつてない多数の映像作家が参加して表現した。

Live performance conducted on September 21st as part of an online festival commemorating Perfume's 20th anniversary as a group and 15th year since making their major label debut. Following the cancellation of the P Cubed tour (originally scheduled for February 26th) the online event offered a challenging platform for capturing the same energy as the originally planned concert, and involved the participation of an unprecedent number of video artists.

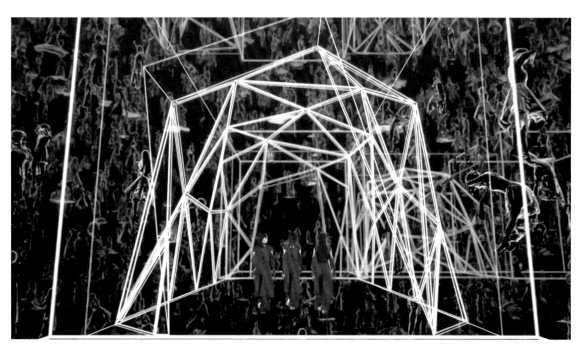

_ Rhizome

2021

natiks

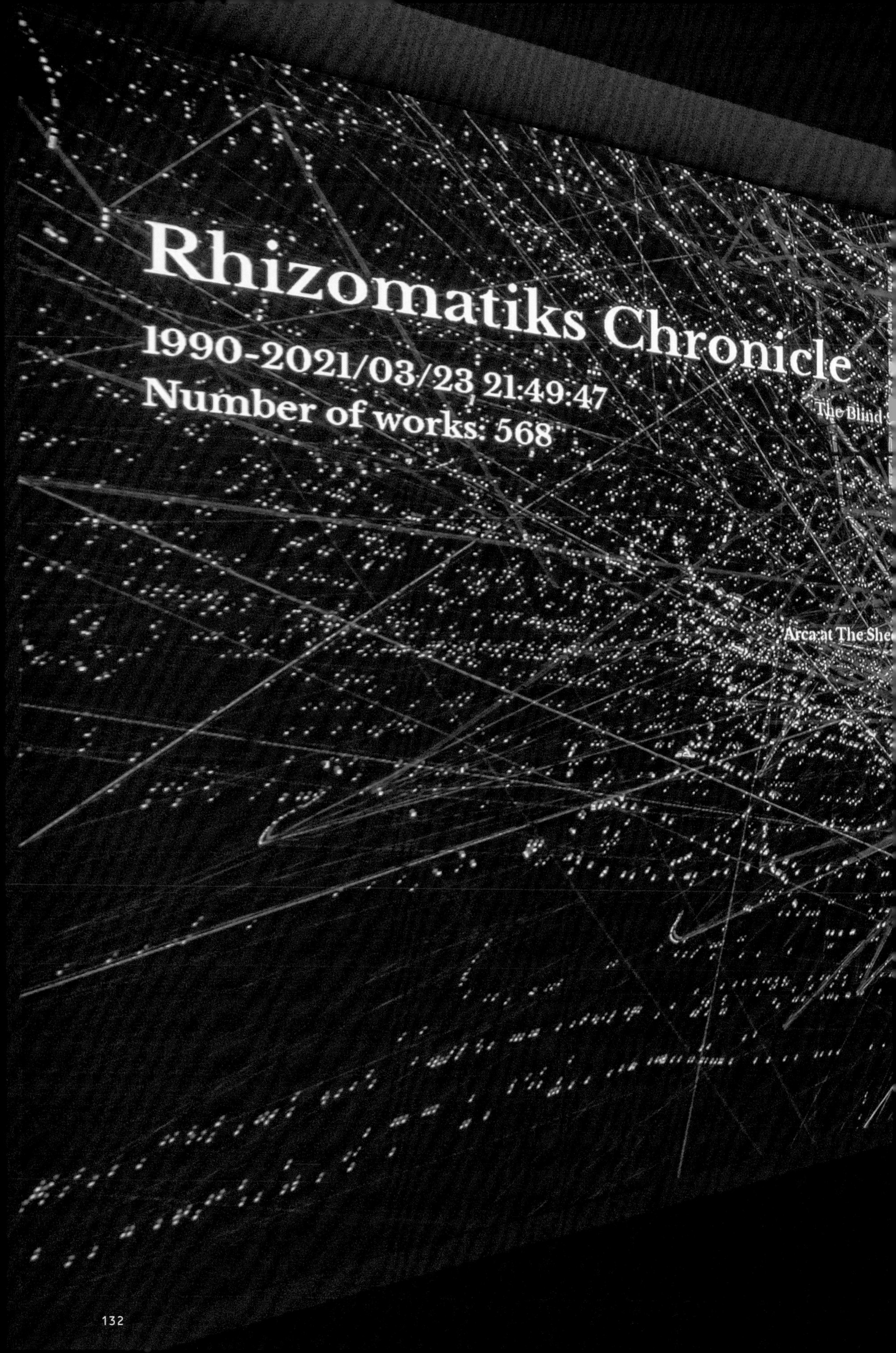

Rhizomatiks Chronicle
1990-2021/03/23 21:49:47
Number of works: 568

The Blind

Arca at The She

aa8a770f99720834a62d72dc273c8bf650ff2a5b01f1565b8ebcdc13fb020dc7

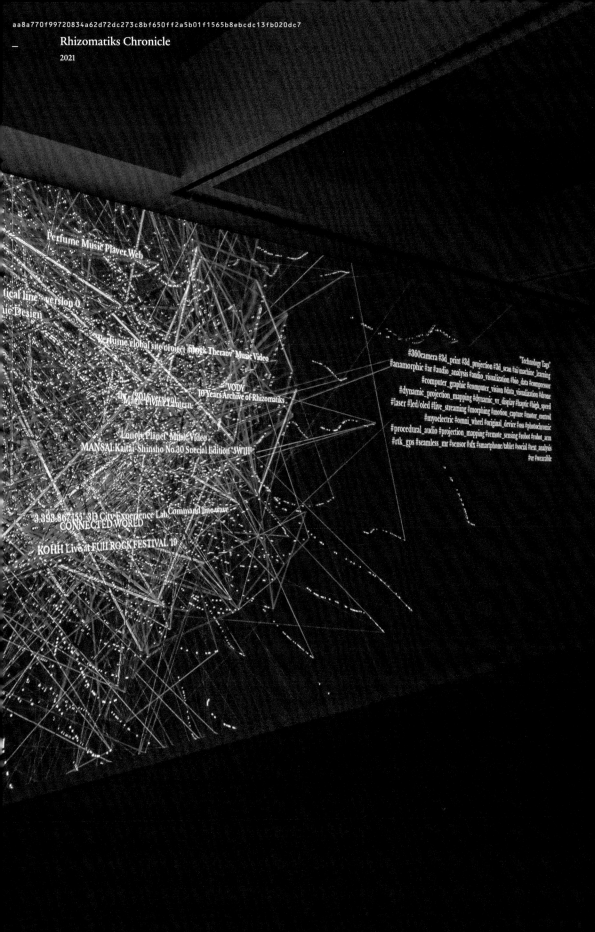

'Technology Tag'
#360camera #3d_print #3d_projection #3d_scan #ai/machine_learning #anamorphic #ar #audio_analysis #audio_visualization #bio_data #compressor #computer_graphic #computer_vision #data_visualization #drone #dynamic_projection_mapping #dynamic_vr_display #haptic #high_speed #laser #led/oled #live_streaming #morphing #motion_capture #motor_control #myoelectric #omni_wheel #original_device #os #photochromic #procedural_audio #projection_mapping #remote_sensing #robot #robot_arm #rtk_gps #seamless_mr #sensor #sfx #smartphone/tablet #social #text_analysis #vr #wearable

Perfume Music Player.Web

tical line version 0
ic Design

Perfume global site project #book Theranov' Music Video

VODY
'Magic Living Lantern 10 Years Archive of Rhizomatiks

'Lonely Planet' Music Video
MANSAI Kaitai-Shinsho No.30 Special Edition "5W1H"

'3,393,867,155' 3D City Experience Lab.Command line.wave
CONNECTED WORLD

KOHH Live at Full ROCK FESTIVAL '19

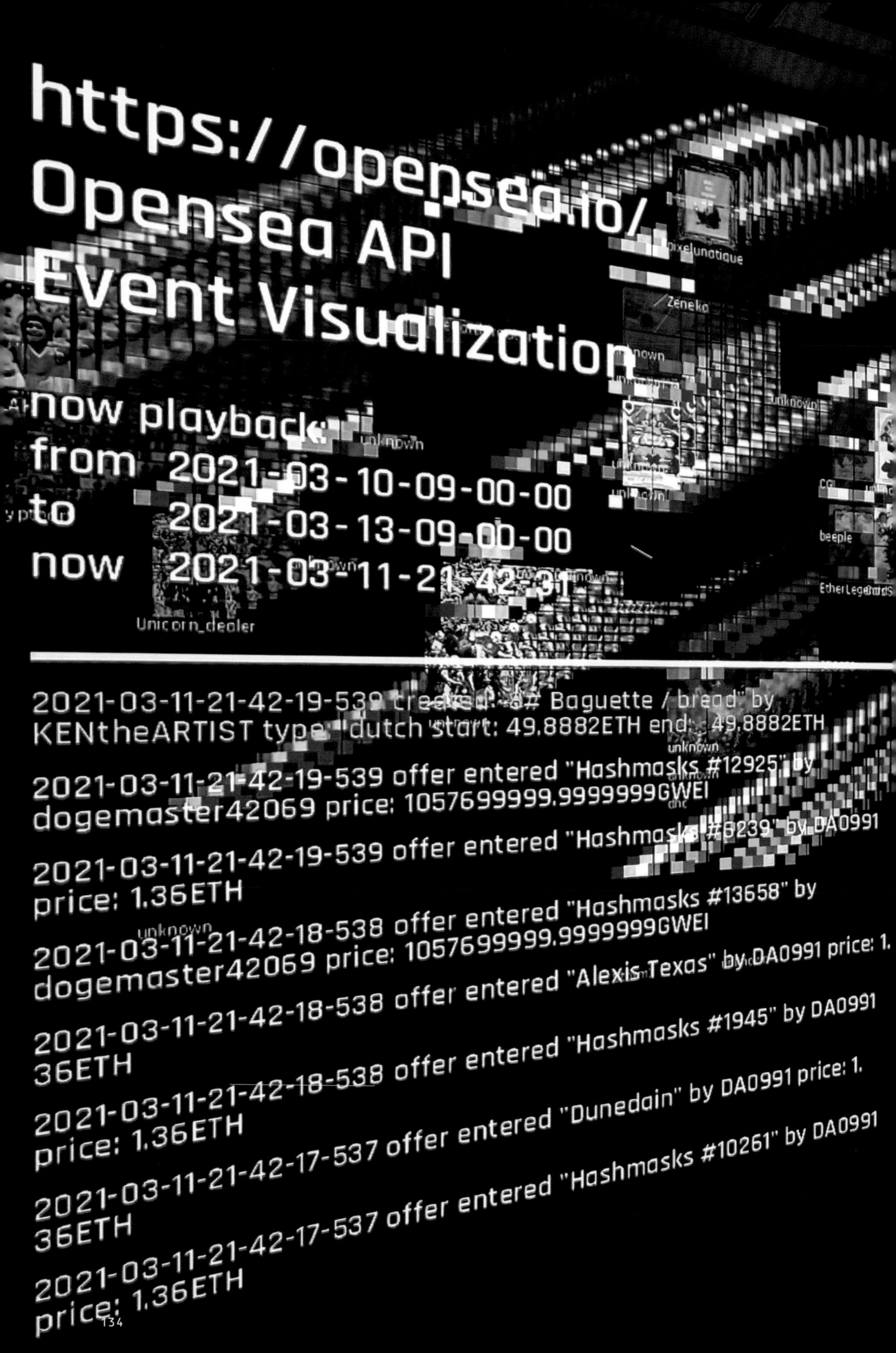

https://opensea.io/

Opensea API
Event Visualization

now playback:

from   2021-03-10-09-00-00
to   2021-03-13-09-00-00
now   2021-03-11-21-42-31

2021-03-11-21-42-19-539 created "# Baguette / bread" by KENtheARTIST type "dutch start: 49.8882ETH end: 49.8882ETH

2021-03-11-21-42-19-539 offer entered "Hashmasks #12925" by dogemaster42069 price: 1057699999.9999999GWEI

2021-03-11-21-42-19-539 offer entered "Hashmasks #8239" by DA0991 price: 1.36ETH

2021-03-11-21-42-18-538 offer entered "Hashmasks #13658" by dogemaster42069 price: 1057699999.9999999GWEI

2021-03-11-21-42-18-538 offer entered "Alexis Texas" by DA0991 price: 1.36ETH

2021-03-11-21-42-18-538 offer entered "Hashmasks #1945" by DA0991 price: 1.36ETH

2021-03-11-21-42-17-537 offer entered "Dunedain" by DA0991 price: 1.36ETH

2021-03-11-21-42-17-537 offer entered "Hashmasks #10261" by DA0991 price: 1.36ETH

134

504bf4f68f834a218eaa6def106efb723448189671f1c98de2b8cda712578523

2021-03-11-21-42-17-537 offer entered "Hashmasks #15677" by DA0991 price: 1.36ETH

2021-03-11-21-42-17-537 offer entered "Elon Husk" by DA0991 price: 1.36ETH

2021-03-11-21-42-17-537 offer entered "Hashmasks #16083" by DA0991 price: 1.36ETH

2021-03-11-21-42-17-537 offer entered "LIZA KOSHY" by HugMe price: 1.72686GWEI

2021-03-11-21-42-17-537 offer entered "Hashmasks #567" by DA0991 price: 1.36ETH

2021-03-11-21-42-17-537 offer entered "Hashmasks #8663" by DA0991 price: 1.36ETH

2021-03-11-21-42-17-537 offer entered "Hashmasks #10263" by DA0991 price: 1.36ETH

2021-03-11-21-42-17-537 offer entered "Conroy" by DA0991 price: 1.36ETH

2021-03-11-21-42-17-537 offer entered "owl" by DA0991 price: 1.36ETH

2021-03-11-21-42-17-537 offer entered "Udi Wertheimer" by DA0991 price: 1.36ETH

2021-03-11-21-42-17-537 offer entered "Hashmasks #9845" by DA0991 price: 1.36ETH

2021-03-11-21-42-17-537 offer entered "Hashmasks #9117" by DA0991 price: 1.36ETH

2021-03-11-21-42-17-537 offer entered "Hashmasks #3995" by dogemaster42069 price: 1057699999.9999999GWEI

2021-03-11-21-42-16-536 offer entered "Le Petit Prince" by 38CD7 price: 1.183ETH

2021-03-11-21-42-11-531 offer entered "Hashmasks #10480" by dogemaster42069 price: 1001899999.9999998GWEI

2021-03-11-21-42-11-531 offer entered "Hashmasks #15489" by DA0991 price: 1.36ETH

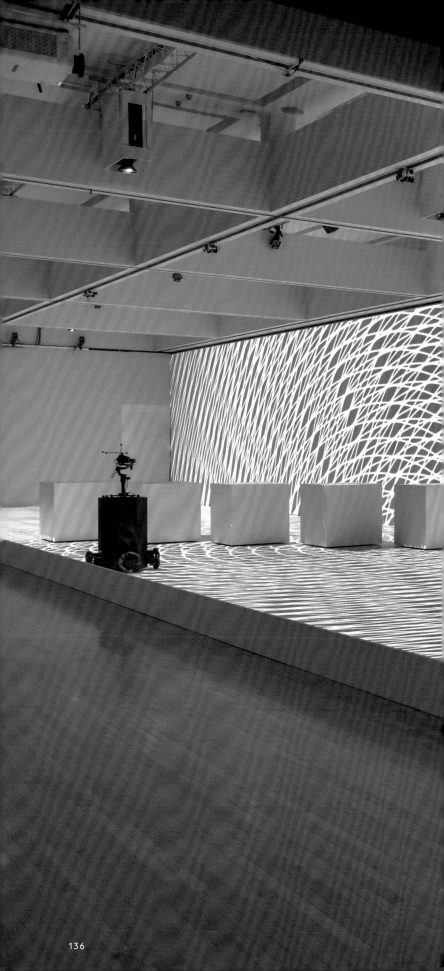

Rhizomatiks × ELEVENPLAY "multiplex"

2021

Rhizomatiks × ELEVENPLAY "multiplex"

2021

_
Rhizomatiks × ELEVENPLAY "multiplex"
2021

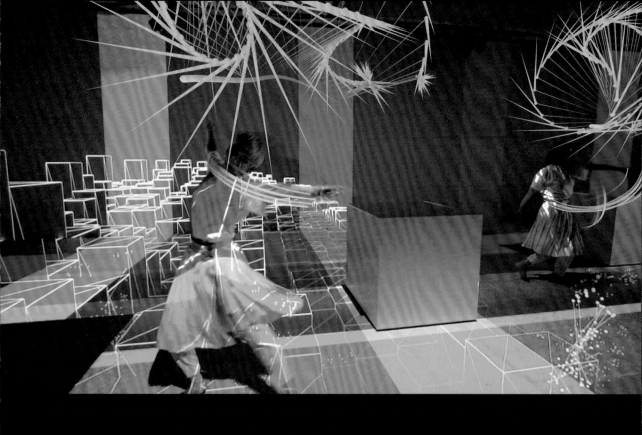

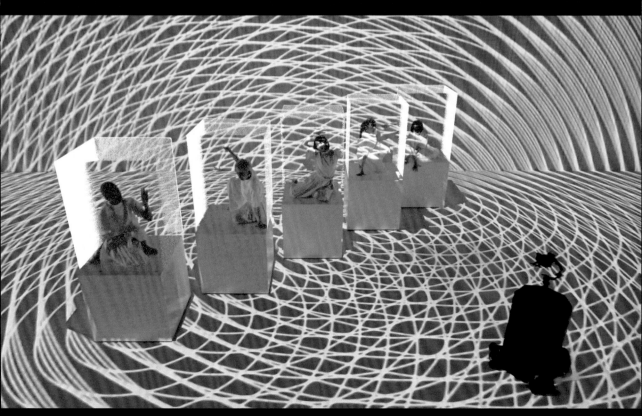

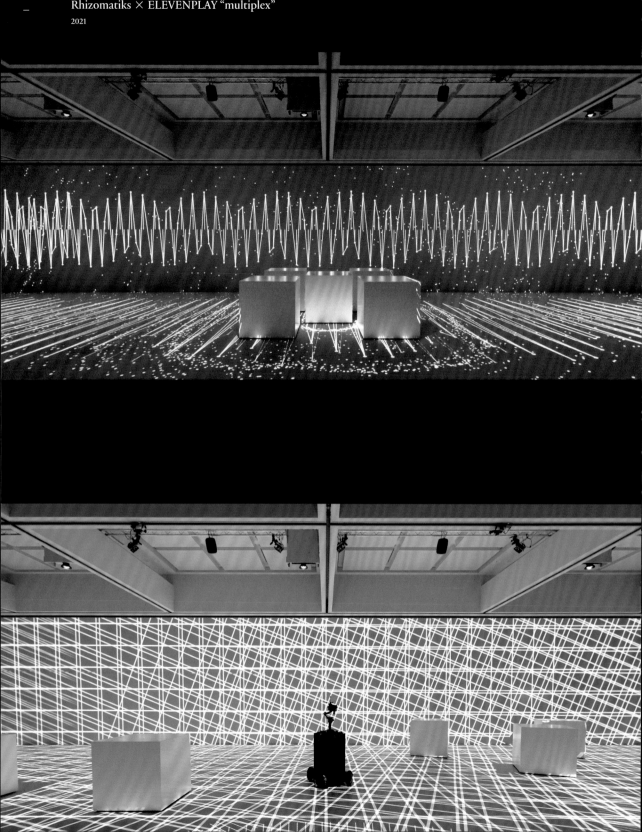

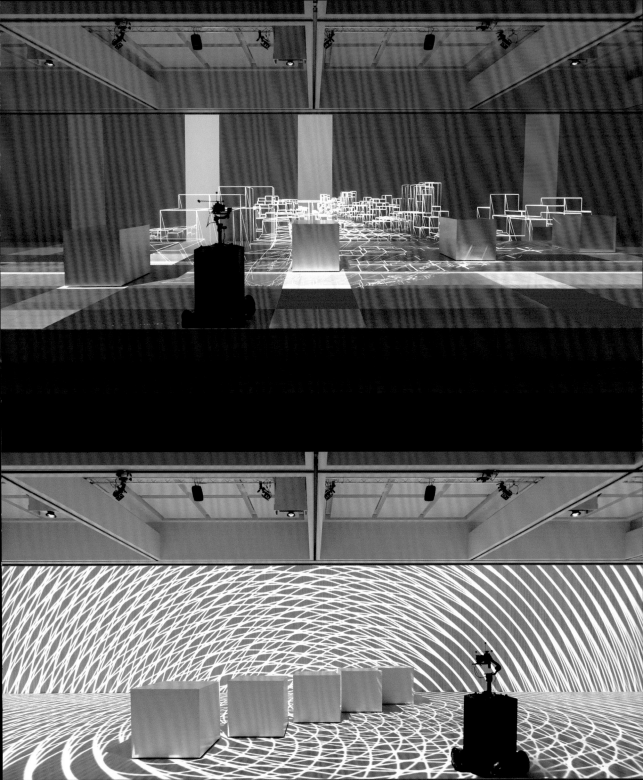

145

R&D (Research & Development)

2021 –

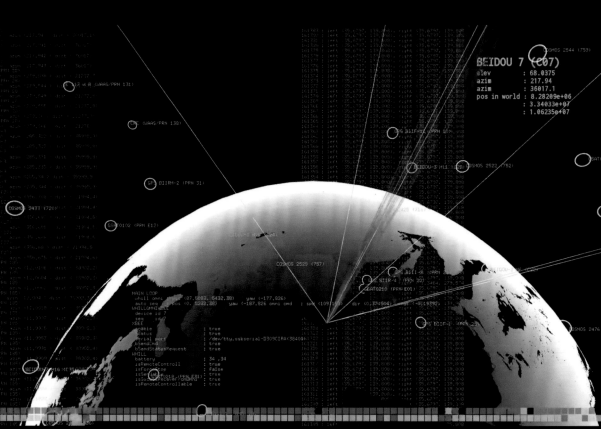

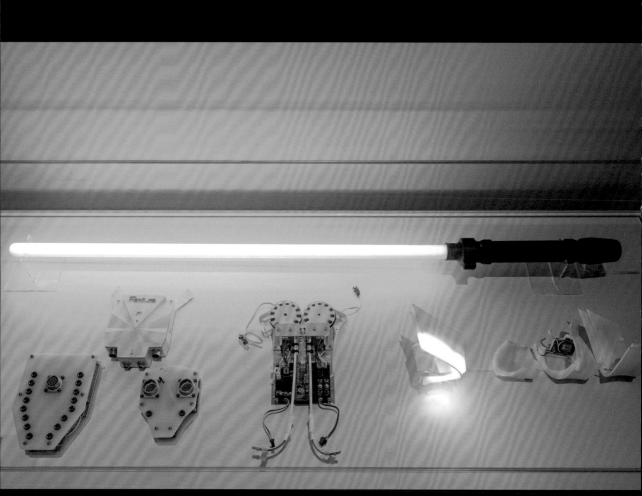

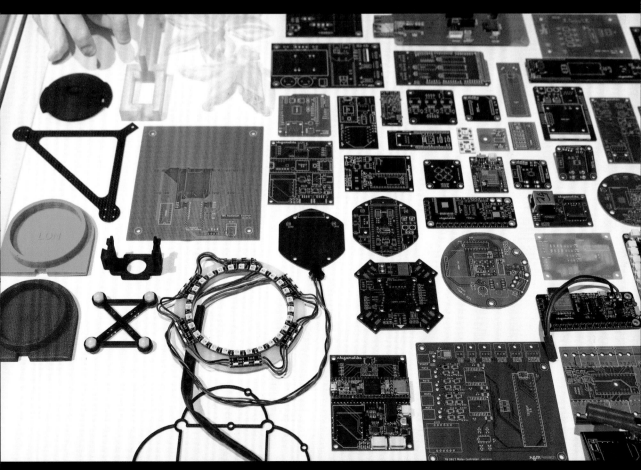

_ particles 2021
2021

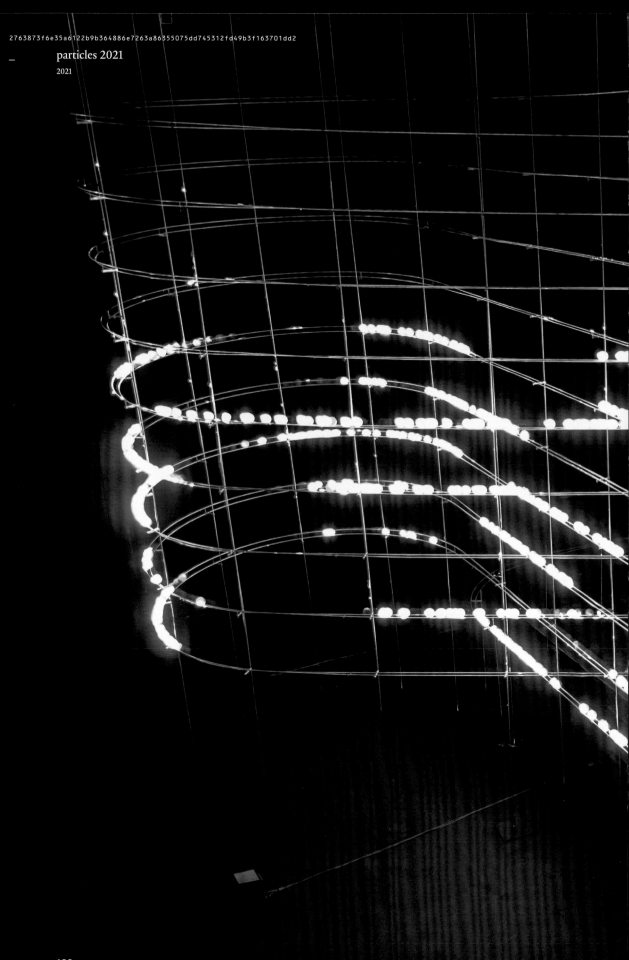

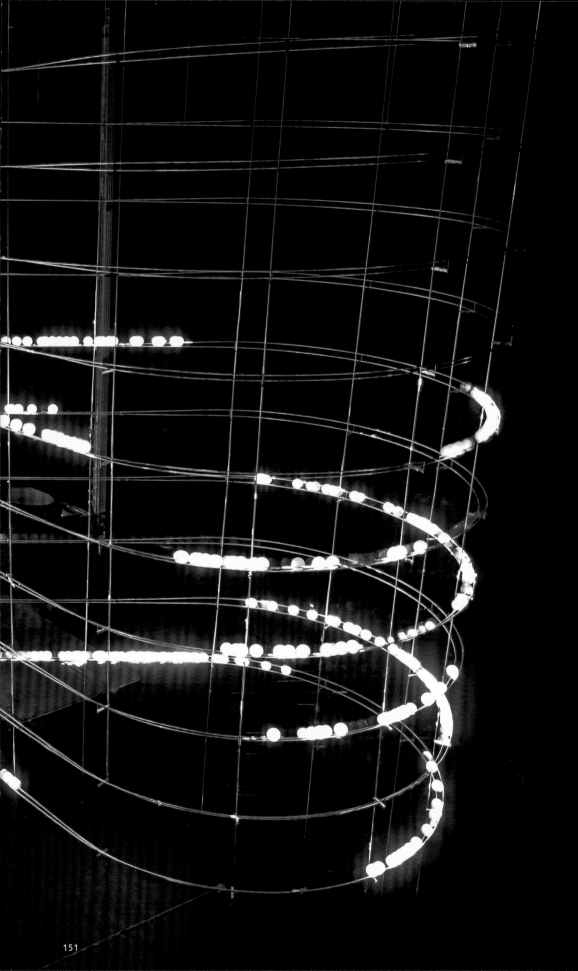

2763873f6e35a6122b9b364886e7263a86355075dd745312fd49b3f163701dd2

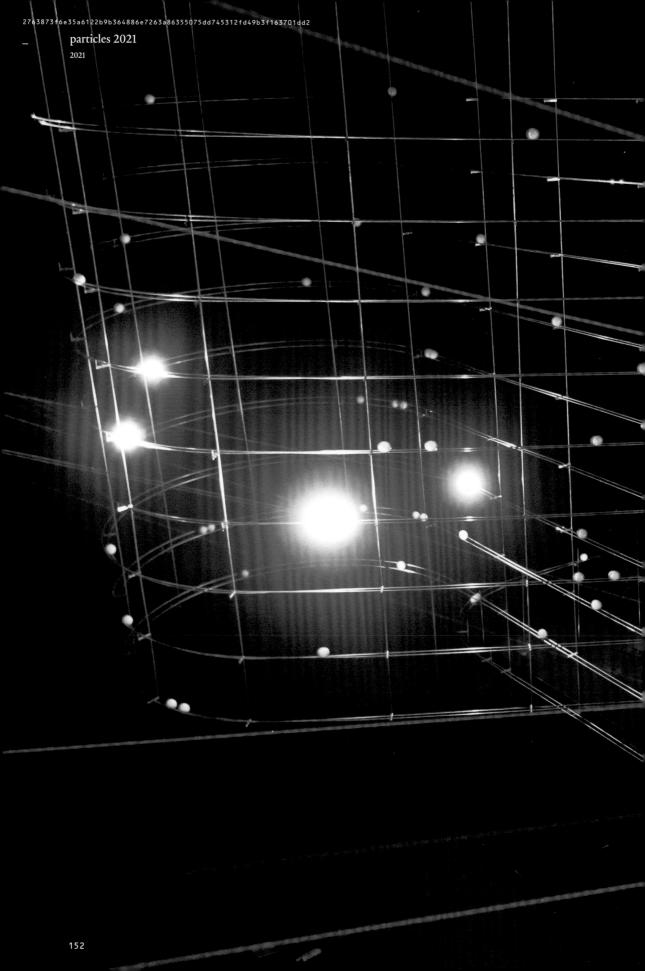

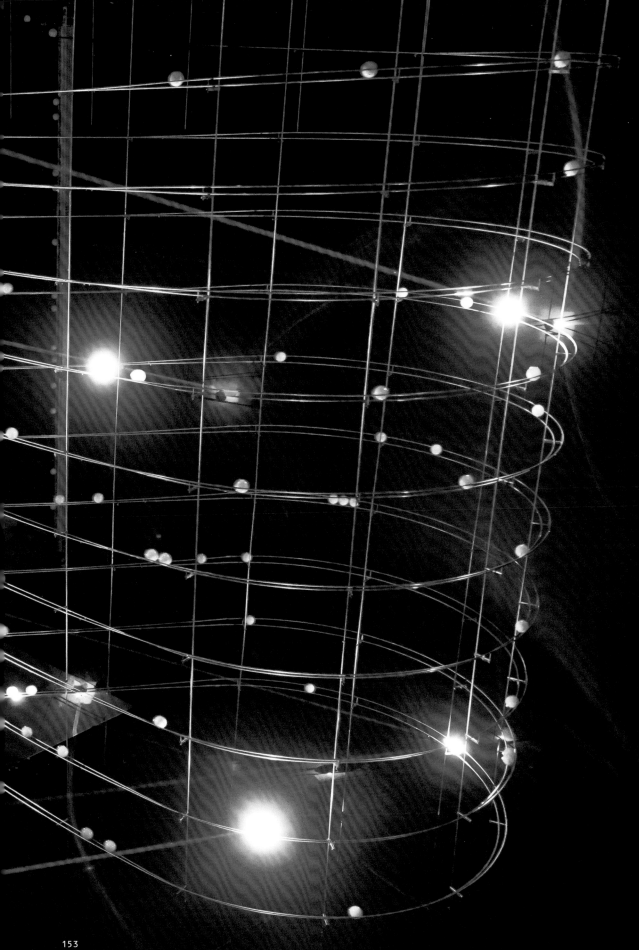

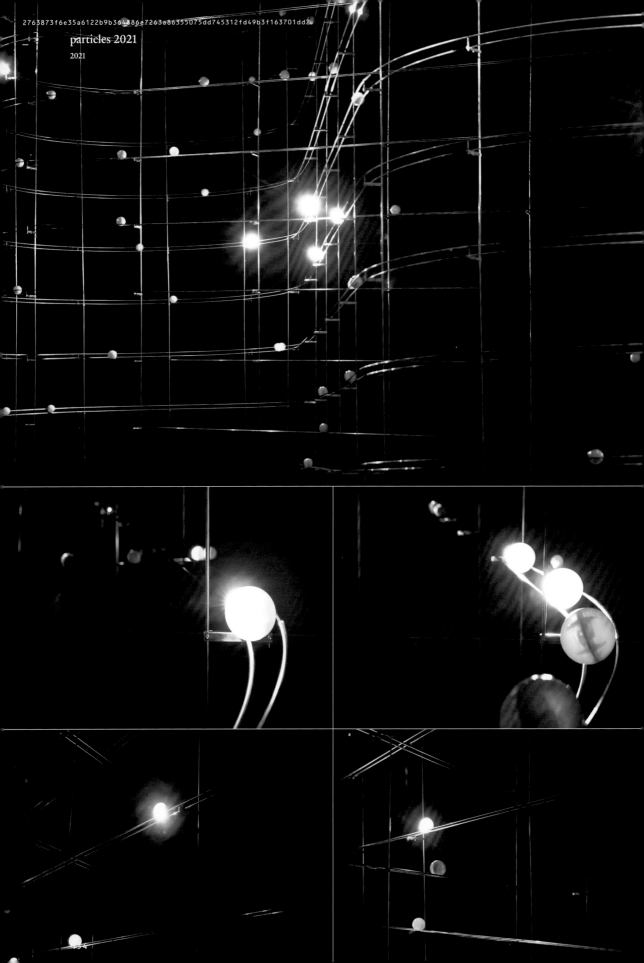

2763873f6e35a6122b9b364386e7263a86355075dd745312fd49b3f163701dd2

particles 2021

2021

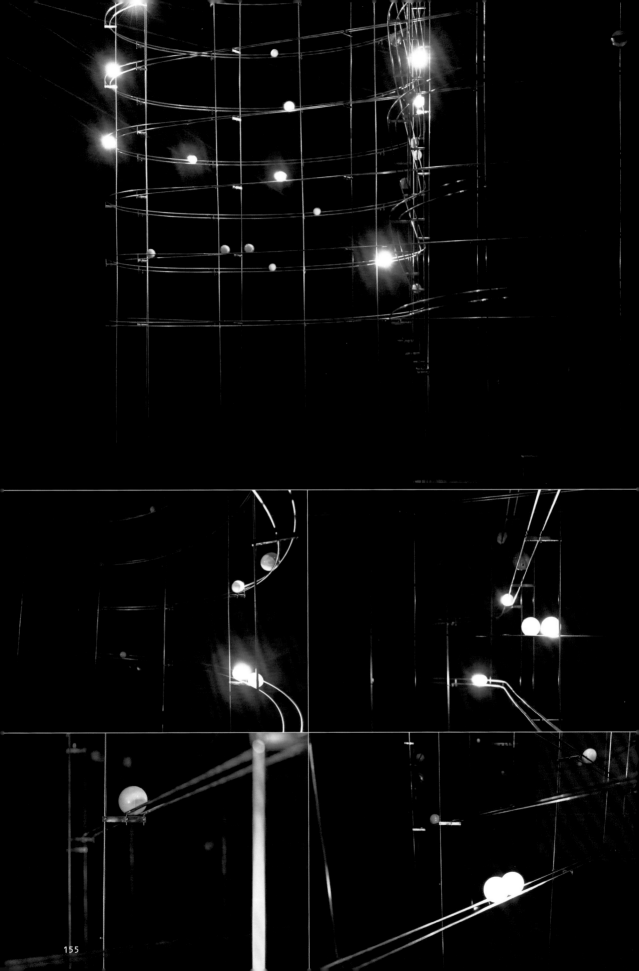

Epilogue

2021

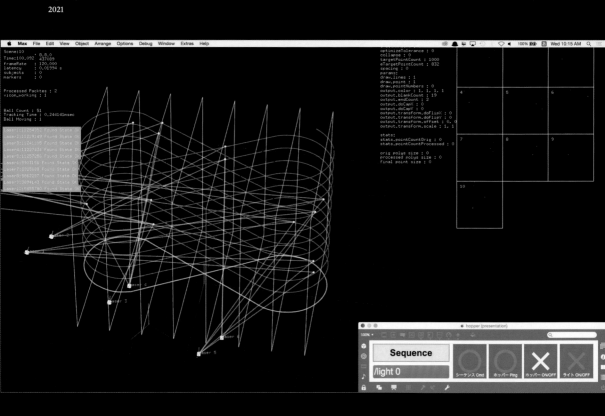

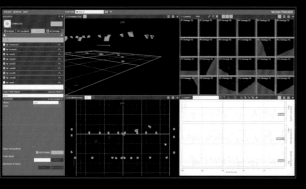
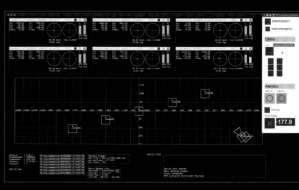

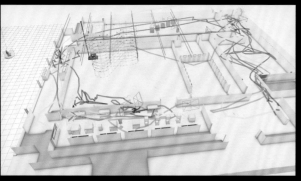
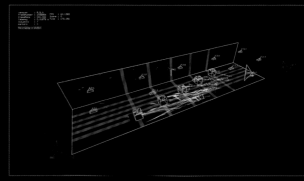

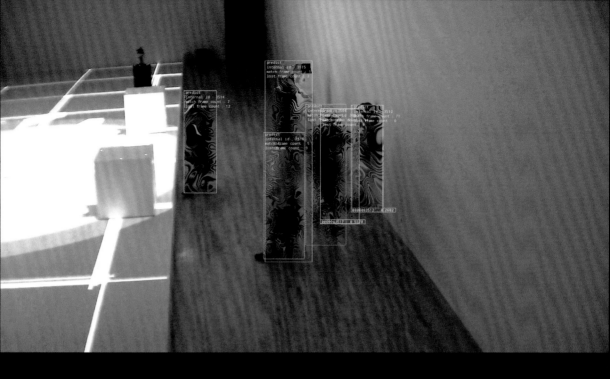

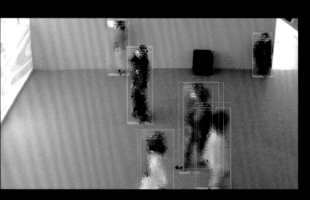

rhizomatiks_multiplex online

2021

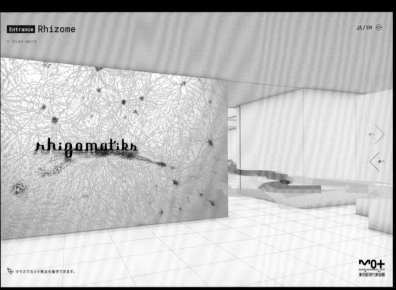

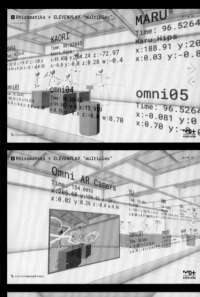

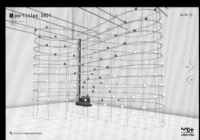

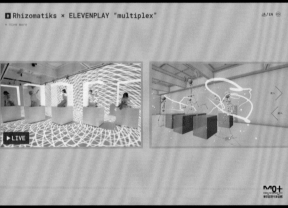

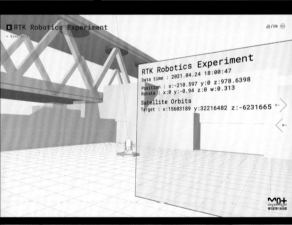

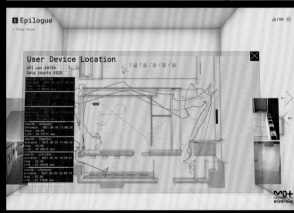

インタビュー｜真鍋大度＋石橋素

聞き手｜長谷川祐子

メディアアート・コレクティブとしてのライゾマティクス

—— 結成されて15年ということですが、結成の動機や、コレクティブとして形作られていった経緯はどのようなものでしたか?

真鍋[1]　結成は2006年でした。当時はアドビのフラッシュなど、ウェブのコンテンツ制作が全盛の頃で、ライゾマでは基本的に僕以外の最初のメンバーはフラッシュを使っていました。石橋(素)[2]さんはまだライゾマに入っていなかったのですが、僕は石橋さんとの仕事が一番多くて、いまやっていることにつながるようなことを、当時はICC(NTT インターコミュニケーション・センター[ICC])やYCAM(山口情報芸術センター[YCAM])でやりつつ、一方でそれだけでは制作費も捻出できないのでクライアントワークもやっていました。クライアントワークでは、商業施設のエントランスにインタラクティブな映像を入れたり、ファッションブランドのイベントでインスタレーションを展示したり。そこのラインはいまもそんなに変わっていないという感じです。ウェブチームはフラッシュが廃れていったのでだんだんとなくなっていって、彼らも実空間の展示やインスタレーションをやるようになっていきました。

—— ライゾマという名前は、「リゾーム」から来たということですが、それはみなさんでディスカッションして決めたんですか?

真鍋　ライゾマティクスという名前は2000年くらいに大学を卒業する頃にはもうありました。僕の記憶と齋藤(精一)[3]の記憶が微妙に違うところがあるので、お互い別々のことを言っているかもしれませんが、僕の記憶だと大学のときに作っていた名刺にすでに「ライゾマティクス」と書いてありました。齋藤は建築をやっていて、僕は音楽と数学をやっていて、クセナキスの影響を受けて建築と音楽と数学で何か表現活動をしようと話していたんです。大学時代から二人でファッションイベントなどの映像や音楽を作ったりしていました。

　　　ライゾマティクスという名前は齋藤が考えたものですが、経緯としては、僕は数学科だったので、「マスマティクス」という響きを取り入れつつ、齋藤のドゥルーズの影響から「リゾーム(rhizome)」と、主義や主張といった印象を生み出す英語の「ティクス(-tics)」を掛け合わせた(=tiks)、というものになります。ヒエラルキーや今までの関係性とは違うということを念頭に置いて活動していこうというコンセプトでした。

1　真鍋大度(まなべ だいと)
1976年東京都生まれ。アーティスト、インタラクションデザイナー、プログラマー、DJ。東京理科大学数学科、国際情報科学芸術アカデミー(IAMAS)卒。2006年株式会社ライゾマティクス設立、2015年よりライゾマティクスの中でもR&D的要素の強いプロジェクトを行うRhizomatiksResearchを石橋素と共同主宰。身近な現象や素材を異なる目線で捉え直し、組み合わせることで作品を制作。高解像度、高臨場感といったリッチな表現を目指すのでなく、注意深く観察することにより発見できる現象、身体、プログラミング、コンピュータそのものが持つ本質的な面白さや、アナログとデジタル、リアルとバーチャルの関係性、境界線に着目し、デザイン、アート、エンターテイメントの領域で活動している。

2　石橋素(いしばし もとい)
1975年静岡県生まれ。エンジニア、アーティスト。東京工業大学制御システム工学科、国際情報科学芸術アカデミー(IAMAS)卒。デバイス制作を主軸に、数多くの広告プロジェクトやアート作品制作、ワークショップ、ミュージックビデオ制作など精力的に活動を行う。過去に、ArsElectronica優秀賞、文化庁メディア芸術祭優秀賞受賞。2015年よりアート、テクノロジー、エンターテイメントを活動の中心とした研究開発部門「RhizomatiksResearch」を真鍋大度と共同主宰する。

真鍋 　会社になったときは社員1人で役員が3人だったんですが、役員3人は全員同じ大学（東京理科大学）なんですよ。齋藤は建築学科で大学の頃から一緒に音楽と建築と数学みたいなことをやっていて、もう1人の千葉（秀憲）[4]というのが数学科の研究室が一緒で、そのあとの会社も一緒だったんです。もう1人の堀井（哲史）[5]というメンバーは僕が岐阜のIAMAS（国際情報芸術アカデミー）に行ったときに、学年は違うんですけど一緒にオーディオ・ビジュアルのパフォーマンスや展示をやっていました。最初は僕がハブになって、一緒に仕事をしていた人たちが集まってきて初期のライゾマができていったという感じです。

―― いろいろなメディアやテクノロジーの知識やスキルを生かしながらクリエイションをやっていくためのコレクティブだったと。誰かがディレクターとして指示を出すというかたちではなく、それぞれが建築的なことをやる、オーディオのことをやるといった、ヒエラルキーのない構造ですね。

真鍋 　広告の仕事をやると、すごく分業されているんですよね。コピーライター、アートディレクター、クリエイティブディレクターみたいに。それに比べるとメディアアートの制作の場合、肩書きを付けるのが難しいくらい、1人で何役もやっていると思います。そういうコラボレーションのかたち自体が、いまとなっては普通なのかもしれないですけど、当時はすごく新しい関係性で作っていたなと思います。メディアアートの世界にいる人からするとごく当たり前なんですけど、広告やコマーシャルの世界の人から見ると、「肩書きは何ですか？」という問いに対して、「プログラムも書いて映像も作って、今回は音楽もやっています」というようなあり方は当時はすごく珍しかったのではないかと。

プログラムの潜在的な可能性を他者と共有するメディアアート

―― 数学をされていたところからクリエイションにつながっていったというのは、プログラムを書くということが画を描くようなものだったのかなと思いますが、そのテクノロジーの可能性を他者と共有でききるようなかたちへと、どのように拡げていかれたのでしょうか？

真鍋 　一番最初に拡がっていったのは広告で、YouTubeの登場が大きかったです。YouTubeが出る前は、メディアアーティストの表現や、リアルタイムでインタラクティブに映像を生成することの価値が、まだそれほど世の中に伝わっていなかった気がします。もちろんDVDを焼いて配ったりもしていましたが、YouTubeが出てきたことで、広告のプロジェクトのアプローチが変わった。それまでの広告でははものすごいお金をかけてCGの映像を作ったりしていたと思うのですが、そうではない作り方があるということに広告の人たちが気づいた。YouTubeを使えば、いまで言うところの「バズ映像」みたいなものを作れる、と。彼らがそれに気づいたのが2009−10年ぐらいだったと思います。なので2010−11年は、カンヌ国際広告祭〔編注：現在の名称は「カンヌライオンズ 国際クリエイティビティ・フェスティバル」〕などはそういっ

3　齋藤精一（さいとうせいいち）
1975年神奈川県生まれ。クリエイティブディレクター、デザイナー。建築デザインをコロンビア大学建築学科（MSAAD）で学び、2000年からニューヨークで活動を開始。2003年の越後妻有アートトリエンナーレでアーティストに選出されたのを機に帰国。フリーランスとして活動後、2006年株式会社ライゾマティクス（現：株式会社アブストラクトエンジン）を設立。2016年から社内の3部門のひとつ「アーキテクチャー部門」を率い、2020年社内組織変更では「パノラマティクス」と改める。2018−2021年グッドデザイン賞審査委員副委員長。2020年ドバイ万博 日本館クリエイティブ・アドバイザー。2025年大阪・関西万博 People's Living Lab クリエイター。

4　千葉秀憲（ちばひでのり）
1976年茨城県生まれ。プロデューサー。東京理科大学理学部卒。株式会社ライゾマティクスの創設メンバー。経営実務担当兼プロデューサーとして、国内外の大規模な案件に従事。数多くのプロジェクトのプロデュースのほか、会社全体を俯瞰し、企業経営を行ってきた。2019年、これまで培ってきた表現のための研究開発、企業とのコラボレーションをベースとしたクリエイションを活かし、社会実装・還元を目的とした株式会社フロウブラトウを設立。

5　堀井哲史（ほりい さとし）
1978年埼玉県生まれ。ビジュアルアーティスト、プログラマー。プログラミングを主体にインタラクティブな作品、映像制作を行い、インスタレーション、ライブ・パフォーマンス、VJ、コマーシャルなどさまざまな形態での作品発表、デザインワークを手がける。2006年にライゾマティクスに参加以降は、動的な絵作りからシステム設計、その実装までを担当している。第16回文化庁メディア芸術祭大賞。カンヌ国際広告祭銀賞など。

たインタラクティブな映像ばかりでしたね。僕たちはそれにすごく良いタイミングで乗ることができたので、『NIKE MUSIC SHOE』やインテルの『The Museum of Me』など、ライゾマが企画や制作で関わった案件でカンヌの賞はたくさん獲りました。2010–13年くらいは、ライゾマだけではなくて、いろいろなメディアアーティストたちがカンヌ広告祭で受賞していましたが、広告は流行り廃りがすごく早いので、2014年にはもう廃れていましたね。

—— その流行の後、広告はどこにいったんでしょう?

真鍋　広告は「ソーシャルグッド」のような概念に徐々に移行していって、またストーリーテリング重視のフィルムに戻っていったという感じかと思いますが、ここ5年はカンヌも行ってないので最新情報は分からないです。ただ、流行り廃りが早い印象はあります。

—— なるほど。

真鍋　メディアアート自体、応用しやすいものが多いので、例えばいまのiPhoneの親指で操作するようなインターフェースも、メディアアーティストのマルコス・アロンソが作っていたり、アップルのビジュアライザーもロバート・ホジンという作家が作っていたりして、応用しやすく社会実装しやすいものが多いので、それが2010年前後からどんどん加速されていったということがあります。2、30年後に振り返られたときに、メディアアートへの社会的関心が高まり、経済的効果も認められた結果アップルやグーグルにどんどん吸収されていったという時代になるのかもしれません。1966年に設立されたE.A.T.(Experiments in Art and Technology)の時代の、ベル研究所とメディアアーティストの関係とは異なります。当時の最先端のテクノロジーは軍事など国家プロジェクトであり誰でも使えるものではありませんでした。ところが今はテクノロジーは特殊なものではなく、誰もが使えるものになった。オープンソース化も進んでいます。現在でも特権、または経済力が無いと扱えないテクノロジーを用いて作品制作をする人もいますが、むしろ珍しいでしょう。2010年代、2020年代のメディアアーティストの多くは巨大なIT企業の力を借りないと作れない作品がほとんどでは無いでしょうか。特にここ数年旬となっている機械学習を使った作品はそれが顕著かと思います。実際、グーグルにメディアアーティストが所属した例もあります。2005年にアーロン・コブリンがディレクターとなってグーグルにデータアーツというグループができ、そこから少しずつアップルなどにも拡がって、フェイスブックもいまはスコット＝ソーナ・スニッブという有名なメディアアーティストがARコンテンツのディレクターをやっています。

　　そうやって企業に入る人がいる一方で、インディペンデントでやっている人もいる。例えばカイル・マクドナルド、メモ・アクテンなんかは機械学習を用いた作品を作っていますが、組織に入らず案件ベースでIT企業と仕事をして良い距離感を保っています。

—— 結局、2000年代の始めは、ネオリベラリズムやグローバリゼーション、そこに立脚した経済システムが、ある意味で楽観的に肯定されていたと思います。その時期に、メディアアー

ティストがそういうシステムに吸収されて一緒に使われていき、そのあとさらに、ここ10年くらいはGAFAにメディアアーティストが吸収されているということですね。

真鍋 　そうですね。やはりAIや機械学習は莫大な計算リソースが必要で個人の計算リソースだけでは収まらないため、どうしても大企業のリソースを使用する必要がある。さらに大企業の発明がインスピレーションとなることも多い。それがメディアアートの現状かなという気がします。一方でNFT、ブロックチェーンについては環境保護の観点から一部のメディアアーティストたちが警鐘を鳴らしています。手放してNFTのような新しいテクノロジーを受け入れず、一度俯瞰して実証実験をしながら状況分析をして問題提起をするというのは、メディアアーティストならではのアプローチかなと思います。

エ ン タ ー テ イ ン メ ン ト へ の 展 開 と P e r f u m e と の コ ラ ボ レ ー シ ョ ン

真鍋 　エンターテインメントへの展開は、もともとU2やマッシヴ・アタックが2006−07年くらいから、UVA（United Visual Artists）というイギリスのメディアアート系の人たちとやり始めていました。僕はそのUVAでライブテインメントの担当をやっていたジョエル（Joel Gethin Lewis）と2008年に一緒に仕事をしたんですが、その時にいろいろとノウハウを教わりました。当時、シアターやアートセンターでやっていた演出をPerfumeのライブに展開できたら面白くなるはずと確信して、Perfumeサイドに何度かプレゼンはしていたのですが、実際にPerfumeの演出を担当しているMIKIKOさんから演出技術開発のオファーがあったんです。それが2010年のPerfumeの東京ドーム公演でした。リアルタイムのインタラクティブシステムや自作デバイスを用いた演出を採用した大型の公演は、日本ではその公演が初めてだったと思います。

―― そのときのお客さんの反応やPerfumeの方たちのリアクションはどうでしたか？

真鍋 　かなり大きかったと思います。ツイッターなどのSNSが盛り上がり始めた頃だと思うんですけど。

―― 私は2014年にニューヨークで最初に拝見したのですが、ニューヨークの人たちの反応は驚くべきもので、彼らはデジタルとフィジカルがあんなにマイルドに一緒になっていることにものすごく感動していました。

真鍋 　北米で公演することも多いのですが、PerfumeもELEVENPLAYも、機械やテクノロジーと人間の共存という部分に対する感動が一番大きいようです。それについてのレビューも書かれていました。

―― スピードやシャープさのような、普通の人間やオーガニックの素材ではありえないようなことがデジタルでは可能になる。それと身体が綺麗に合っていくということがやはり驚きだったと思います。

真鍋　それまでシアターでやっていたところからいきなりドームでやっているので、いま思うと全然至らなかったことが多いと思うんですけど。でもこういうのは最初に誰かが切り拓かないと、その業界が進歩していかないので、それは何か切り拓いたなという手応えはありました。

アート／エンターテインメントの対比ではなく、実験的か／そうでないか

真鍋　アートと「エンタメ」は制作のプロセスで共通点が数多くあると思います。最終的なアウトプットの形態や対象が異なりますし、コンセプトやコンテクストも違います。一方で実験的なことをやっているかどうかという観点で言うと、Perfumeのプロジェクトは前例のない身体表現とテクノロジーの組み合わせをコンスタントにやっていると自負しています。Perfumeでなければできないことが我々にとってはたくさんあって、表現力が高いだけでなく、データにした時に非常に良いデータになるということがあります。重心が中心にある／動きがシンクロしているだけでなく、角度や位置の精度が高いんですよね。そのおかげで、ヴァーチャルの世界とリアルの世界がシームレスになるんです。パリ在住のメディアアーティスト後藤英さんと対談した際の話ですが、「海外から見ているとPerfumeみたいな表現の形は他にはないし、ステージパフォーマンスとメディアアートが融合したかたちで発表する機会も成立する土壌もない。Perfumeの作品は純粋なアートフォームとして見てもらえている」とおっしゃっていました。私も海外からの評価は日本とは違うのを肌で感じています。

──「エンタメ」ということを解析していくと、やはりマスが相手なので、期待値に対してより高いパフォーマンス、より異なった種類のスペクタクルを用意してあげるということはあると思うんですね。それがエンタメの定義だとすると、ある意味でものすごくダークなものや、破壊的なものは見せないという予定調和の法則を守ったなかで、どこまでの実験をするかというところなのではないかと思います。ただのエンターテインメントという分け方で括るつもりはなく、差異化と、一種の条件の中でのR&D、ということを考えていました。

真鍋　Perfumeは、ソーシャルという切り口で捉えてもよいのかもしれないですね。ファンの人たちの二次創作をオフィシャルでステージの映像に使ったり、ファンの人が参加することで成立するようなことも結構やっていますが、これはPerfumeでしかできないソーシャルの実験だったなという気がしますね。

スクリーンから空間への変換《particles》

──一方で、実際のハードウェアでいろいろやってみるという関心が空間的に展開したものとして《particles》という作品があるかと思います。スクリーンの中でしか起こらないようなことを、同じスピード感、世界観で実空間に作ってみようと思われたモチベーションはどのようなものだったのでしょう。

真鍋 《particles》[→pp.004-005, 028-029]を制作したのは2011年でした。この作品は、螺旋空間構造をもつ巨大なレールの上をフルカラーLEDと通信装置を内蔵したボールが転がるんですが、点滅する光源が空中を浮遊し、残像を作り出すものです。その当時から今もそうですが、肉眼で見ることができる3D映像の最終ゴールはホログラムなんですね。磁気で浮遊させる技術を使ったり、透明なパネルに画を出して擬似的に3次元の絵を出したり、レーザーを用いたプラズマ発光、スモークとレーザー画を使って実際の3次元上に絵を描く手法もいろいろあるんですけど、そのようなアプローチとは違う立体的な表現を何かできないかと探していたら、この《particles》のかたちになったという感じです。

――― ホログラムが技術的にまだ実現できないから、同じような効果を持つ空中浮遊を作品として見せるということでしょうか。

真鍋 具体的な絵や文字を出す装置を作りたいというよりも、新しい仕組みを作ることによってこれまでとは異なる視覚体験ができたら、というところがモチベーションですね。それを実現するときに、どれだけユニークな方法でやれるかという点が大事なポイントかなと思います。そういうところにどう工夫を入れるかということについては、石橋さんからお話しいただければと思います。

石橋 これは、真鍋が今言ったように、空中に何がしかの像を作り出すというところがモチベーションで、技術的な方法としてどういうことがありえるかをいろいろと考えてやっていったという感じです。最初はスタジオで透明なチューブに光るボールを転がして実験してみたり。要は、空中で光るタイミングをコントロールできれば、像は作れるのではないかという発想です。では何をどうコントロールするのかというところで、《particles》のときは光るボールを転がしてその明滅のタイミングを制御したということですね。

　　　ボールが発光するタイミングと色彩は任意に制御することが可能で、レールの構造とボールの通信制御技術を設計して、それらを融合させることで、空中に立体的な残像を描き出しています。

　　　これはCGのシミュレーションですが fig.1、最初はボールを投げて、光るタイミングをコントロールしてあげれば、こういうことができるだろうと。投げる軌道を計算してコントロールできるので、いろいろと空中に像が出せるのではないかと考えました。

　　　YCAMの展覧会で新作インスタレーションとして展示しましたが、予算的にもとても大変でしたね。

　　　トラッキングについては、ボールがレールの上から下に8の字で降りてくるんですけど、そのレールの両サイドにセンサーがついていて、ボールが通過したときにそのボールが何段目を通過したかがわかる仕組みになっています。センサーは全部で16個あって、1個のセンサーから次のセンサーまで転がるのにかかった時間を毎回計算していて、例えば3番のセンサーを通過したときに、前回3番を通過してから4番までのあいだに何秒かかったから、3番を通過してから4番に行くまでの時間で、いま自分がどのあたりにいるのかということが推測できるようになっています。それに応じて、光を点けたり消したりすることをコントロールするという仕組みです。

fig.1

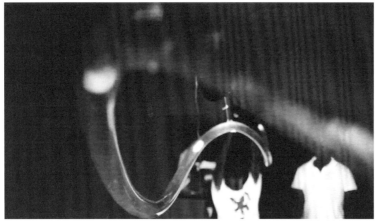

リアルタイムの重要性

—— アート作品としても、またさまざまな分野とのコラボレーションでもお仕事をされていますが、作っていく際の判断の基準のようなものはありますか?

真鍋　リアリティをどう作っていくかという点やフィジカル、メンタル共に自分自身の出来事にしていく点が大事かなと思います。

石橋　例えばメカもそうですけど、メカだけで動かすときと、シアターで演出された状態で見せるときとやはり受け取られ方が全然違います。テクノロジーのポテンシャルやこの先にどういう世界があるかというところまで含めて、受け取る側が基本的にはポジティブに捉えてくれているというか。技術的なアイデアを作品やシアターでのパフォーマンスとして見せることは、テクノロジーの観点で言うととてもメリットが大きい気がしますね。

—— 時間との関係で緊張感を作っていく感じでしょうか。シアターはその場で実際に息を吸っている空間を共有しているので、明らかに自分ごととして捉えやすいんですよね。あまりに先にいってしまっている映像だと、完全に取り残されてしまうので。もちろんイマジネーションはついていくかもしれないですけど、さっきおっしゃった自分ごとというポイントは、非常に重要かなと思いました。

6 真鍋大度・花井裕也「AR/VR技術によるライブ映像演出」、『電子情報通信学会誌』第103号6巻、pp. 564-570、2020年6月。

真鍋　それこそ映画などリアルタイムでない映像ではCGを使ってなんでもできてしまう。そこの塩梅は結構あるかなと思いますね。だからライゾマはすごくリアルタイムにこだわっています。

──　リアルタイムのライブでアクチュアリティをどう伝達するかということについては、「AR/VR技術によるライブ映像演出」[6]という論文に書かれていますね。例えば、何万人ものスタジアムのライブなどでは大型ビジョンの映像が使われますが、客席からはミュージシャン本人はごく小さくしか見えないので、映像を見るしかない。それって、みんな何を見ているんだろうなといつも不思議に思うんです。それだったら家で見ればいいのに、と思ってしまうわけですが、でもやはりそういうものでもないんですよね。多数の観客が「肉眼で一度に体験する」というところが、非常に大きなポイントかなと思います。

真鍋　コロナで失われた体験の一つがリアルスペースでの共有体験ですよね。リモート、VR技術で代わりのものはいろいろ出てきていますが。もともと石橋さんはそういう「インタラクティブもの」を2000年代前半くらいからやっていて、そのときはシアターというよりは美術館などのスペースでお客さん向けにやっているんですよね。

──　美術館でインタラクティブをやっていたということですか。

石橋　体験者というか、お客さんが参加するようなものを、展示や商業スペースで結構やっていたんですけど。インタラクティブと言われていたものは、そもそもがたぶんリアルタイムの面白さだったのではないかと、パフォーマンスをやるようになってから僕はすごく思って。

──　インタラクティブの意味を再解釈されたんですね。

石橋　インタラクティブアートって、その双方向性ではなくて、たぶんリアルタイムで何か処理がされて、すぐに反映されるというところに、快を感じているのかなと。

真鍋　だからお客さんではなくてもよいということですよね。

石橋　そう。誰かがやっているところを見ていても、同じようにリアルタイムで起きていることであれば、自分でやるのと、ダンサーさんがやっているのと、実はそんなに差異はないのではないかという気もしています。いわゆるインタラクティブアートと言われる、自分が動いたら何かが動くというようなことは、本当に自分がやっているから面白いのかどうか、そこは結構どうなんだろうな、と思う部分があるんです。自分がやっている／参加しているから面白いと思っているのか、それともその仕組み自体を楽しんでいるのか、そういう面もあると思います。

社 会 状 況 に 対 す る 批 評 を ど の よ う に 視 覚 化 し て い く の か

──　いまの社会状況に対する批評の視覚化についておうかがいします。例えばスクエアプッシャーのミュージックビデオ「Terminal Slam」(2020)[→pp.002-003, 054-055]では、広告に対して感覚麻痺的になっているのではないかという問題意識から、広告をパーソナライズするという試みをされていますが。

真鍋　あの作品は、架空のMR（複合現実）グラスを用いて街中から広告を排除するというコンセプトで制作しています。ウェブやオンラインの広告については、かなりの個人情報が抜かれていたり、トラッキングされていて、そういったことがずっと問題になっています。ヨーロッパではEU一般データ保護規則（GDPR）のように、そうしたトラッキングが徐々に法律で規制されはじめていますが、一方で、現実世界もそのうちにMRのグラスをして歩くようになっていくと、いまオンラインで起きているようなことがリアルスペースでもどんどん起きていくだろう、と。MRグラスをして街中を歩いた際に、自分が何に興味を持っているのかということが、抜き取られて広告利用されていく。それが「Terminal Slam」で最初に思いついたことでした。何年後になるかはわからないですが、MRグラスをかけて街中を歩いて、すべてが自分の都合のいいように現実世界が書き換えられていく、ということになるかもしれない。実際、いまブラウザで起きていること、SNSやフェイスブックで見ている情報というのは完全にパーソナライズされていると思いますが、ARやMRのグラスなどが使われだすと、リアルスペースもそのようになっていくはずです。そうなったときに、やはりマネタイズの仕組みとしては、広告がどんどん個人に向けて打たれていくようになる。例えば渋谷を歩いていても自分の興味に近いお店だけがフォーカスされたり、便利になる一方で、行動がデータ化され広告利用されていくと思うんです。そこで一つ考えられるのが、その反対、カウンターとして、広告をすべてシャットアウトするような機能かなと。それで、そういうグラスができたときに街がどのように見えるかということを想定して作ったのが「Terminal Slam」のビデオです。想定なのでまだ実装自体はできていないんですけど、正確に何年後かというのは難しいですが、おそらく3、4年後には実際にそういうグラスが作られるのではないかなと思います。

—— そういう複合現実的な世界を、私たちは10年先、20年先という近未来の話だと思いながら見ているので、それをその近さで感じ取っている温度感というものに驚かされます。

真鍋　ARクラウドと言われる技術も出てきています。いまのARは基本的に近いものに対してCGを合成したりということがメインなのですが、サンフランシスコでは街全体が全部3Dデータ化されていて、その3Dデータの特徴点なども取られているので、例えばiPhoneをかざしたときに、GPS情報とカメラなどのセンサーからの情報を用いて特定のランドマークに合わせてCGを合成するということもできる状態になっています。例えばグラスをかけて建物を見たときに建物の広告を変えるということは、サンフランシスコの中だけで言えばできるようになっているんです。ただ渋谷はそういう風になりつつはあるけどまだ完全にはなっていない。プラットフォームとデバイスの両方を含めて、あとはハードウェアの問題もありますが、それらが揃うのもそんなに遠い未来の話でもないのかなという感じです。

—— これを見て、実際に広告に関わっている人たちからリアクションはありましたか？ つまり、映像にしても、いわゆるフラットな媒体にしても、これまでの広告のあり方というのはもう時代遅れであるという意識を彼らは持ったりしたんでしょうか。

真鍋　COVID-19で中止になってしまいましたけど、スクエアプッシャーのツアーのプロ

モーションとして、そういうARのアプリを作ろうという話はありました。MRグラスは
まだ実現できないのですが、例えば、iPhoneで広告を見ると、ここの広告が全
部スクエアプッシャーに書き換えられる、というようなことはもうできる。ツアーのライ
ブ会場のそばの街の風景と3Dデータがあれば、GPSのデータと3Dの情報との
ハイブリッドでできてしまうんです。

　　まずはアプリでやって、最終的にはMRグラスをかけた状態でみんなが街
中を歩く状態になると面白いかなと。そうなると現実の世界だけを見て生活して
いる人はいなくなると思うんです。ファッション的にイケてなかったとしても、実際に
便利になるわけで、やはり便利さは勝つと思うので。そうなってくるとかなり面白いと
思います。でもこういうシステムになっても、結局広告が一番マネタイズがしやすい
ので、グーグルやフェイスブックが8−9割広告であるのと同じように、MRのグラス
ができたときもトラッキングをして個人情報を抜いて……、とまた同じようなことに
なるのではないかな、とか。そういうことも少し予想しつつ、ビデオを作っていました。

従 来 的 な 資 本 主 義 の 枠 か ら 逸 脱 す る

―― マネタイズという点では、いわゆる従来的な資本主義の枠から逸脱していくような方法
については何かお考えですか?

真鍋　いまも知らないところでデータを抜かれまくっているわけですが、やはり個人の情報
は自分でちゃんと管理する必要もある。これは自分が作っているシステムではな
いのですが、今回の展示で協力してもらおうと思っているデータサイン（DataSign）
という会社があって、そこがデータ銀行という、銀行のように自分の意志でデータを
出したり出さなかったりできるシステムを考えているんです。それが本当にできるよ
うになって、自分で個人情報を管理できる仕組みができていくと、いまのグーグル
やフェイスブックが支配しているような状態は変わってくるのではないかなと思いま
す。僕はそのデータサインの太田（祐一）さんという方の話を聞いて共感したので
すが、データサインは同時に、ウェブサイトにアクセスしたときにどれだけの情報が
いろいろなところに流れているかということを可視化するツールも作っています。

　　ちょうど今日の朝話していたのですが、某メディアのウェブサイトにアクセス
しただけで、105個のサービスに対して905回の通信が行われていて、そのデータ
が主に広告ターゲッティングのために利用されている。これはどこのウェブサイトで
も、例えば慈善団体のウェブサイトでも、裏ではそうやって個人情報を抜いてい
たりするんですよ。

―― そうなんですか。それは倫理的に問題にはならないんでしょうか?

真鍋　慈善団体がそうやって個人情報を裏で取って、ターゲッティングして、募金をして
もらうような仕組みを作っているというのが、データを見るとわかるんです。いまのイ
ンターネット広告のエコシステムは完全に壊れているので、崩壊し始めているとは
思いますが、なかなかいますぐには変わっていかないとも思っていて。ただ、その問
題をきちんとわかるかたちで、展示や作品を通じて、啓発や警告まではいかない

ですけど、肌で感じてもらう、気づいてもらうということはできるかなと、考えています。

啓発や学習の可能性について
———————

—— 啓発という話では、『DIS Magazine』で知られるアーティストコレクティブ・DISのメンバーの一人、ローレン・ボイルを2年前に日本に講義に招聘したときに、new enlightment、つまり新しい啓発のやり方というのがいま非常に重要だということを言っていました。根本的に何か考え方を切り替えさせなくてはいけない、と。

真鍋　本当にデータドリブンというか、データありきになっていますね。先日〔編注：2021年1月6日〕アメリカの議会が襲撃された事件がありましたが、あのときにパーラーというトランプ支持派の人たちが使っているSNSのアプリがあって、みんな何も警戒せずにガンガン動画を撮影して、そのパーラー上でシェアしていました。でもそれが結局、アマゾンがサーバーを使わせないとか、グーグルもアップルもアプリを停止するような状態になって結局はシャットダウンされてしまった。ただ、そのデータが全部、ハッカーに抜かれていて公開されたんですね。動画の本体ではなく、いつどこで撮影されたかという時間や位置情報といったメタデータや、その人のスマホやパソコンのメタデータなど、すべて残った状態になっていた。結局そういったデータから、議会襲撃に参加した人の個人情報が公開されてしまう事態になりました。

—— いろいろな意味で明らかなエビデンスになっていくわけですよね。

真鍋　ハッカーやアクティヴィストの手によって収集されたデータから、社会を揺るがす大きな事件の真実を暴けてしまうのが面白いし、同時に恐ろしい時代でもあると思います。それがデータになっている状態であれば、自分たちが扱えるメディアになり、我々もそれを作品に使うこともできる。そこが面白いところかなと感じています。

　　　現在のようにオンライン、リモートがメインになって、ブラウザやアプリ経由でコミュニケーションをとるようになったことで、どうしてもGAFAのような大きなITの会社にデータを渡さざるをえなくなった状況があります。ただそのエコシステム自体が正しいかどうかということは、疑問としてはあるわけです。そのひとつとして、個人情報の取り扱いに関して、そこに何か新しいシステムを作る余地があるのではないか。それをテーマに作れたら何かの打開策になるのではないかと、そんなことを考えています。

　　　また、広告ドリブンのインターネットの世界を救う可能性があるNFTが、この先どうなっていくのかということも気になります。現在は取引の金額にフォーカスされていることが多く、壮大なピラミッドスキーム（ネズミ講）だという人もいますが、ブロックチェーンが持つ永続性や非中央集権的な仕組みを考えると、サスティナブルな新しいシステムが誕生するのではという期待もあり、作品制作を通じて実証実験をしているところです。

———　　　　　　　　　　　　　　　　　　　———

［2020年12月18日／2021年1月15日、ライゾマティクス中目黒オフィス／恵比寿オフィスにて収録］

An interview with
Daito Manabe & Motoi Ishibashi

As interviewed by Yuko Hasegawa

The birth of a media art collective

—— As Rhizomatiks celebrates its 15th anniversary, I'd like to look back to the beginning. What was the initial catalyst for creating Rhizomatiks? How did Rhizomatiks take shape as a collective?

Manabe[1] We launched Rhizomatiks in 2006. This was back in the heyday of web-content creation. Most of the other founding members of Rhizomatiks, apart from myself, were working in Adobe Flash. Although [Motoi] Ishibashi[2] hadn't joined Rhizomatiks yet, he was already my most frequent collaborator on projects at the NTT Inter Communication Center (ICC) and the Yamaguchi Center for Arts and Media [YCAM] that were an earlier extension of our present work. Of course, budgets were tight, so all the while we were also taking on client assignments to offset the production costs of our other projects. We were commissioned to create interactive video for the entrance of shopping centers and installations for fashion brand events. That sort of thing. We had already found a balance. I don't think the line between our own projects and client commissions has changed all that much over the years. As Flash fell by the wayside, the members of our web team gradually transitioned toward exhibitions and installations in physical space.

—— You've said that the name Rhizomatiks came from the word "rhizome." Who came up with the name? Was it something that everyone discussed and decided upon as a team?

Manabe The name Rhizomatiks already existed by the time I was graduating from university, around 2000. I remember things slightly differently from [Seiichi] Saito[3], so he might tell you something else. As I remember it, the business cards I carried around as a student already read "Rhizomatiks." Saito was in the architecture department, while I was studying music and mathematics. Influenced by Xenakis, we wanted to find a creative outlet that melded architecture, music, and math. The two of us were already making music and video for fashion events from our university days.

But it was Saito who came up with the name. Since I was majoring in math, the idea was to incorporate the sound of "mathematics." Saito took the word "rhizome" from Deleuze and combined it with "-tics," a suffix that denotes a broader ideology and assertion of principles. Tweaking the spelling to "-tiks," we arrived at Rhizomatiks. The name was meant as a reminder of how we wanted to do something new, on

1   Daito Manabe
    Born in Tokyo in 1976.
    Artist, Interaction designer, Programmer, DJ. Graduated from Tokyo University of Science Faculty of Science Division I Department of Mathematics and the The Institute of Advanced Media Arts and Sciences (IAMAS). Launched Rhizomatiks in 2006. Since 2015, has served alongside Motoi Ishibashi as co-director of Rhizomatiks Research, the firm's division dedicated to exploring new possibilities in the realms of technical and artistic expression with a focus on R&D-intensive projects. Manabe's work in design, art, and entertainment takes a new approach to everyday materials and phenomenon. However, his end goal is not simply rich, high-definition realism by recognizing and recombining these familiar elemental building blocks. Rather, his practice is informed by careful observation to discover and elucidate the essential potentialities inherent to the human body, data, programming, computers, and other phenomena, thus probing the interrelationships and boundaries delineating the analog and digital, real and virtual.

2   Motoi Ishibashi
    Born in Shizuoka Prefecture in 1975. Engineer, Artist. Graduated from the Department of Control and Systems Engineering at Tokyo Institute of Technology and the The Institute of Advanced

a separate plane from the existing hierarchies and relationalities. That was the concept.

—— How many people were in the original Rhizomatiks team?

Manabe   At its conception, Rhizomatiks consisted of one team member and three "directors." Actually, all three of us had been classmates at the Tokyo University of Science. Although Saito was in the architecture department, we had been experimenting together with a mix of music, architecture, and math as students. [Hidenori] Chiba [4] was the third director. Chiba and I had been in the same cohort in the math department, and then worked together in the same company after graduating. Our fourth founding team member was [Satoshi] Horii [5]. I met Horii at the Institute of Advanced Media Arts and Sciences (IAMAS) in Gifu. He's a year or two younger than me, so we weren't in the same graduating class at IAMAS, but we still made some audiovisual performances and exhibitions together. I sort of roped in like-minded collaborators who were already in my orbit. That's the Rhizomatiks origin story.

—— From the outset, Rhizomatiks has been a creative collective, leveraging each member's strengths, skills, and knowledge across a rich spectrum of media and technology. You've taken a nonhierarchical approach. Rather than top-down directives, each member has a hand in architecture, audio, etc.

Manabe   The commercial world is extremely compartmentalized. Our clients on advertising projects are used to having a very clear division of labor: copywriter, art director, creative director. By contrast, media art defies labels. It's hard to say what someone's title is when each individual is wearing multiple hats. Collaboration has become the norm nowadays, but at the time, it was almost unheard of in Japan. I think it posed a truly new way of interacting, redefining interrelationships. For those of us from a media art background, it was a completely normal, natural way of doing things. But from the perspective of clients in the advertising and commercial world, it must have been a shock. If they were to ask for my title, they would expect a one-word answer. But it's like, "I write code, I create video, I make music..." I think that stance was still incredibly rare even in those days.

Media art as a conduit for sharing programming's latent potential

—— I think the way mathematics dovetailed seamlessly with creation suggests that writing code is, in a way, similar to composing a painting. How did you develop and expand technology's untapped potential for presentation and sharing with others?

Manabe   Our advertising work was the first to really reach a larger audience, thanks in large part to the emergence of YouTube. Before YouTube, I don't think larger society really understood the value of media art and interactive video. Of course, we had been handing out homemade DVDs with our work, like everyone else. But YouTube was a game-changer that affected our approach to commercial projects. Up to that point, I think agencies had been dropping wads of cash to make

Media Arts and Sciences (IAMAS). In addition to producing devices, he has been actively involved in a number of advertising projects, art productions, workshops, and music video productions. In the past, he has won the Ars Electronica Award of Distinction and the Japan Media Arts Festival Excellence Award. Since 2015, has served alongside Daito Manabe as co-director of Rhizomatiks Research, the firm's division dedicated to exploring new possibilities in the realms of technical and artistic expression with a focus on R&D-intensive projects.

3   Seiichi Saito
Born in Kanagawa in 1975. Creative director, Designer. Saito began his career in New York in 2000 after graduating from Columbia University with a Master of Science degree in Advanced Architectural Design (MSAAD). Since then, he has been active in creative work at the ArnellGroup, and returned to Japan upon being selected for the Echigo-Tsumari Art Triennial 2003. Launched Rhizomatiks Co., Ltd. in 2006. Since 2016, he serves as director of Rhizomatiks Architecture. Vice Chairman of Good Design Award 2018-21. Creative Adviser of 2020 Dubai Expo Japan pavilion. An expert for the Peoples's Living Lab Promotion Council for Expo 2025 Osaka, Kansai, Japan.

4   Hidenori Chiba
Born in Ibaraki Prefecture in 1976. Producer. Graduated from the Department of Science at Tokyo University of Science. Founding member of Rhizomatiks. As a producer and business manager, he has been involved in large-scale projects both in Japan and overseas. In addition to producing a number of projects, he has overseen the entire company and led the corporate management. In 2019, he established Flowplateaux with the aim of social implementation and sharing of the experience of R&D for expression and creation based on collaboration with companies.

5   Satoshi Horii
Born in Saitama Prefecture in 1978. Visual Artist, Programmer.

CG video for their commercials. YouTube made advertisers realize that there were other ways to make commercials, that they could just tap YouTube to generate what we now call "buzz" and "viral videos." This must have been around 2009 or 2010. If you look at the Cannes International Advertising Festival [precursor to the Cannes Lions International Festival of Creativity] around 2010–2011, you'll see that it was all interactive video. We were able to ride that wave right before it crested. From *Nike Music Shoe* to Intel's *Museum of Me*, projects that Rhizomatiks had been involved in at the planning and production stages cleaned up at Cannes. Media artists, not only Rhizomatiks, had a field day at Cannes from 2010 to 2013. But the ad industry has quick expiration dates. By 2014, the wave had already crested, and they were already on to the next trend.

—— Where did the industry look next?

Manabe Ads gradually began transitioning toward this concept of "social good." In a way, I think it signaled a return to film with an emphasis on storytelling. But I haven't been back to Cannes for five years, so my information is dated. Either way, my impression was that "the next big thing" has a short lifespan in that world.

—— I see.

Manabe Media art is inherently adaptable and highly applicable. For example, the thumb-scroll iPhone interface was developed by a media artist named Marcos Alonso. Apple's visualizer was created by Robert Hodgin. Media art offers an endless supply of elements that can readily be harnessed for deployment in wider society. This is something that's been gaining steam since around 2010. When we look back 20 or 30 years from now, we might remember the present as an era of heightened societal awareness in media art, as well as a threshold when people finally realized media art's economic viability, both of which in turn enticed the appetites of corporations such as Apple and Google.

Speaking of appetites, the present status quo is quite different from the past. Media artists had an altogether different relationship with Bell Laboratories in the era of E.A.T. (Experiments in Art and Technology), which was established in 1966, when cutting-edge technology was the exclusive purview of the military and state-led projects, and not the kind of thing that would reach the public. But technology is no longer a niche field; it's now available to everyone. We're seeing more and more open source. Of course, some artists still make work using technologies that require access to patents or substantial economic means. But they are becoming the exception rather than the norm. In the 2010s and 2020s, I think a majority of media artists have only been able to achieve their visions with the help of IT behemoths. Machine learning, which has been the flavor of the month over these past few years, is a prime example.

In some cases, media artists have worked directly for Google. In 2005, Aaron Koblin joined Google as the director of their newly formed data arts group. The same thing started happening at Apple, and now, even the acclaimed media artist Scott Sona Snibbe works at Facebook as their director of AR content.

While some artists chose to join the corporations, others have

He has been creating interactive and video works mainly by programming, and has been presenting his works and designs in various forms such as installation, live performance, VJing, and commercial projects. Since joining Rhizomatiks in 2006, he has been in charge of a variety of creative roles ranging from dynamic visual creation to system design and its implementation. His renowned prizes include the Grand Prize at the 16th Japan Media Arts Festival as well as the Silver Prize at the Cannes International Advertising Festival.

continued to work independently. Kyle McDonald and Memo Atken come to mind as people who have managed to maintain a comfortable distance from the tech giants. Both create work using machine learning on a project basis with companies, without having to join their rosters directly.

—— I think we could say the early 2000s were a time of optimism toward an economic worldview that embraced neoliberalism and globalization. Ultimately, it seems the economic fruits of media artists were tapped by this system, and over the past ten years or so, these media artists have been further absorbed into GAFA.

Manabe   At the end of the day, AI and machine learning require vast computational resources. It goes far beyond what's possible at the individual level, and necessitates the use of resources at the disposal of big players. And more often than not, the innovations coming out of these big tech companies do serve as a source of inspiration. Generally speaking, I think that's where media art, as a discipline, is at the moment.

On the other hand, some media artists have been sounding the alarm on NFT and blockchain from an environmental sustainability perspective. I think this reluctance to blindly accept new technologies is very in-character with the media artist's approach. The media artist is someone who takes a more measured and analytical bird's eye view, kicking the wheels of new technologies such as NFT to identify potential problems.

Debut on the entertainment stage and collaborations with Perfume

Manabe   The jump to entertainment industry projects came around 2006 or 2007, when bands such as U2 and Massive Attack began partnering with UVA (United Visual Artists), a London-based studio in the media art sphere. In 2008, I worked with Joel Gethin Lewis, head of UVA's live entertainment division. I learned a lot from him. The experience encouraged me to apply the kinds of performances we had been doing in theatres and art centers to a live Perfume concert. After having approached Perfume a number of times in the past, the ball was put into motion when MIKIKO, Perfume's choreographer, asked us to collaborate as technical advisors. The first project was Perfume's Tokyo Dome performance in 2010. I think the performance was the first of its kind in Japan on that scale, featuring a real-time interactive system and proprietary devices custom made for the event.

—— How was the reaction from Perfume and their fans?

Manabe   I think there was quite a positive reception. Of course, this was around the time when Twitter and social media were just beginning to gain an active following in Japan.

—— I saw one of your Perfume performances for the first time in New York in 2014. I was surprised by the response from New Yorkers. They seemed very struck by how the digital and physical had blended so seamlessly.

Manabe   Yes, we've put on many performances in North America, with both

Perfume and ELEVENPLAY. It seems the coexistence of machine/
technology and human has struck a chord. I've seen a handful of
reviews commenting on this aspect, too.

—— Digital mediums are capable of a certain speed and sharpness that
cannot be replicated by your average human or other organic element. I
think the seamless blend of this precision and the human form were quite
remarkable and eye-opening.

Manabe In all honesty, we were still figuring out how to take what we had
been doing on the small theatre stage and transpose it to the massive
Tokyo Dome. It was a big jump, and in retrospect, I'm sure there were
many things we could have done better. But I guess someone had to be
the first to make the leap into the brave unknown. It was a rewarding
project, at least for the sake of nudging the industry needle a little bit
further.

A new calculus:
art vs. entertainment ≤ experimental vs. non-experimental

Manabe I think there is a great deal of overlap between the art and
entertainment fields from a production perspective. Many of the
underlying processes are the same. Of course, the final output is
different. The target, form, concept, and context are different. But the
work can still be experimental. Especially in our collaborations with
Perfume, I feel that we are constantly breaking new ground through
unprecedented combinations of technology and physical expression.
A lot of the things we do with Perfume wouldn't be possible with
anyone else. They're very expressive artists who have provided us with
excellent data. As dancers, they have a balanced center of gravity and
their movements are executed in sharp synch. But even more than this,
it's their precision. They hit their marks, the position and angles of the
choreography, with extreme accuracy. This precision is what makes it
possible to seamlessly blend the virtual and real worlds. I appeared in
dialogue with Paris-based media artist Suguru Goto a few years ago,
and he was saying that there isn't anyone quite like Perfume even on
the international stage: "There hasn't been another opportunity or
even environment for this hybrid of stage performance and media art
to take root. People abroad are able to see Perfume's performances
as a pure art form unto itself." This palpable difference in reception
between Japanese and international audiences is something that I've
also felt from experience.

—— The entertainment industry inherently caters toward a mass audience.
Perhaps there is an onus to prepare performances that exceed their
expectations, provide a different category of spectacle. Perhaps this is what
defines "entertainment." On the one hand, there is an unspoken consensus
that performances for a mass audience will not rock the boat too much.
They cannot be shockingly dark or subversive. But then you still want to be
experimental. I think it comes down to seeing how far one can go to push the
envelope. Rather than lumping everything together under the easy banner of
"entertainment," I would propose that the work can be better understood in
terms of trying to create something distinct, an achievement of R&D within the

Manabe   Sure, I think this social quotient is one way to contextualize Perfume. In the past, we've asked their fans to submit content, and have incorporated this secondary creation back into video shown onstage during official Perfume performances. A lot of our projects have been built on fan participation. Looking back, I think these participation-based projects have constituted a sort of social experiment, the likes of which would only be possible with Perfume.

From screen to space: *particles*.

—— I'd like to revisit an earlier work which I think exemplifies how your interest in experimentation with hardware has been deployed in real-life spaces. With *'particles,'* you transposed a visual effect that people had only previously seen on a digital 2D screen, recreating the same sense of physics and speed in 3D in the real world. Could you talk about your motivation behind that project?

Manabe   We developed *particles* [→pp.004–005, 028–029] in 2011. Essentially, the projected featured a towering helical rail system, over which ran balls equipped with built-in full-color LEDs and transmitters. By regulating the balls' luminescence, we were able to create the effect of flickering orbs that appeared to float through the air in the dark room, leaving an illusory afterimage in their wake.

At the time, and I suppose even now, the ultimate goal of 3D imaging has been to create holograms visible to the naked eye. There are a variety of ways to go about making a hologram. You could use magnets for levitation, rendering images on transparent panels to artificially simulate 3D visuals. You could even use laser plasma, smoke and lasers, to actually produce images in 3D space. But for this project, we wanted to step away from these kinds of approaches, and probe other modes of expression in 3D space. The result was *particles*.

—— As true holograms are not yet a technological reality, you enlisted the illusion of levitation to achieve a similar effect.

Manabe   We didn't necessarily set out to build a device that would create any particular image or text. Our motivation was more to develop a new theoretical framework that could create a novel visual effect. Once you have a framework, the key question then becomes how to fully utilize the concept to achieve unique results. But I'll let Ishibashi talk about the challenges and innovations that went into this project.

Ishibashi   As Manabe said, the motivation was to produce some kind of image out of thin air. We ended up experimenting in our studio with a lot of different methods in the search for a viable technical approach. At first, we tried rolling the balls through clear tubes. The underlying concept is what was important. We reasoned that we might be able to create an image if we could control the luminescence of a given element as it passed through a certain point in space. In the case of *particles*, that element ended up being LED balls. In *particles*, we were able to arbitrarily control when the balls were activated, as well as their color. By designing a rail architecture tied to a remote-controlled system, we were able to achieve a 3D effect as the balls passed through the air.

We made a CG simulation to illustrate the concept. fig.1 [→p.168] By adjusting the trajectory of the balls and controlling the timing of their illumination, we reasoned that it would be possible to create a range of images. The project was first presented as an installation at YCAM. It was a very challenging undertaking, particularly in terms of budget.

The rails are set up in a figure-eight pattern and have a total of 16 sensors affixed on both sides. The mechanism allowed us to track the balls' progress through each tier of rail. Each time the ball passed a sensor, the system would calculate the amount of time it took for it to reach the next sensor. For example, let's say a ball passed sensor #3. The system would know how many seconds the ball took to travel from sensor #3 to sensor #4 the previous revolution, so could estimate its progress between the two sensors. Based on this predictive calculation, the system would then control the lighting of each ball, turning the LEDs on or off as needed.

6   Daito Manabe and Yuya Hanai "Stage Visual Direction with AR/VR Technologies," *The journal of the Institute of Electronics, Information and Communication Engineers*, Vol. 103, No.6, pp. 564–570, June 2020.

The importance of real-time

—— You've also been involved in a number of multidisciplinary collaborations in the art realm. When you're creating an art installation, do you have any particular criteria in mind?

Manabe   Fundamentally, I think there are two crucial considerations: How do we go about creating reality? How does this work become a viewer's own, on both a mental and physical level?

Ishibashi   For example, a purely mechanical piece will be received entirely differently when presented in the context of a theatre production. We have to be mindful of broader factors, everything from the technology's potential to how it fits into expectations of the world to come. Based on these variables, will the viewer perceive the work in a fundamentally positive light? I feel the presentation of technical ideas as artwork or onstage in theatrical performances offers significant merits from the perspective of technological development.

—— How much is this a matter of building tension in relation to time? A theatre is a shared space, everyone in the audience is breathing the same air as the performers onstage. This organic connection undoubtedly makes it easier to engage and identify with a work, finding relevance to oneself as a viewer. Compare this to experimental video, which tends to be more distant and leave the viewer behind, even if the viewer connects on some level with the conceptual conceit. But as you said, there's not that same personal investment. I think that's an extremely important distinction.

Manabe   It's easy to "cheat" when you're not working in real-time. With preproduced video, you have the luxury of using CG to create any effect you want. But there's something else to be gained in real spaces. That's why Rhizomatiks is committed to real-time.

—— You discussed how to convey actuality through real-time performances in your paper, "Stage Visual Direction with AR/VR Technologies." [6] As an example, I've always been baffled by how concerts in a stadium packed with tens of thousands of spectators will stream a live feed of the performance on jumbotrons. From the stands, the musicians look like ants on the stage, and most of the audience inevitably ends up watching the screen. What's the difference from watching from your couch at home? But, of course, there is a difference. For most people, the point is experiencing the performance once, in person, and seeing the performer with their own eyes.

Manabe　These shared experiences in real space are something that we've been deprived of by Covid. Granted, any number of substitutes have emerged over the pandemic to fill the void with remote, VR experiences. This kind of interactivity is actually something that Ishibashi has been working on since the early 2000s, albeit oriented toward audiences in an art museum setting, rather than theaters.

—— Interactive installations in museums?

Ishibashi　I've been involved in quite a lot of experiential projects, or let's say projects that invited visitor participation, both for exhibitions and commercial spaces. Ever since I started working on live performances, I've really come to realize that what makes interactivity interesting is probably the fact that it's happening in real-time.

—— You've come to locate new meaning in interactivity.

Ishibashi　People tend to assume the appeal of interactive art is its bidirectionality, the give and take between participant and performance. But I would argue that we derive more pleasure in the immediacy of the form and how input is processed in real-time for instantaneous feedback.

Manabe　And that means you don't need to be a direct participant to appreciate real-time performances.

Ishibashi　Right. If something is taking place in real-time, I feel there's not too much of a difference between being a spectator or a direct participant. The experience is similar whether you are simply watching a dancer or are dancing onstage yourself. There's this received notion that "interactive art" is interesting because you are the subject being acted upon, as an external stimulus prompts an action of your own in response. But I'm skeptical if that's really true. Is it interesting because you're the one doing it, because you're participating? Or is it because the underlying mechanism itself is enjoyable? I think there's something more nuanced at play.

Visualizing social critique

—— I'd like to talk about the role of social criticism in your work. For example, in 2020, you created a music video for the Squarepusher track "Terminal Slam" [→pp.002-003, 054-055]. Thematically, the video explores the idea that we've become desensitized to marketing, and imagines a world with more personalized ads.

Manabe　The concept was that you could use fictitious MR (mixed reality) glasses to silence all the ads in the city. Internet ads have been a longstanding privacy issue, entailing flagrant tracking and the harvesting of a concerning amount of personal data. Europe has gradually started cracking down on these privacy breaches, as evinced by the GDPR: General Data Protection Regulation. But if people start wearing MR glasses, the sort of things that have been happening online are bound to start pervading our waking lives in the real world. Advertisers will be able to track your eye movements to learn what catches your attention when you're moving about town with the glasses on, and use this data to better target ads to your interests. This was what planted the seed for "Terminal Slam."

At some point in the future, MR glasses might end up being used to overwrite reality altogether. What you see through the glasses will not be reality, but a personal utopia, tailored specifically to you. The information we see on Facebook and other social media is already being thoroughly personalized. What's already happening in our browsers could make the leap to real space once we start using AR and MR glasses. When that happens, ads will become even more oriented toward individuals as the logical outgrowth of the monetization machine. You could be walking down the street in Shibuya and only those shops you're interested in will be in clear focus, the rest will be blurred out.

On the other hand, this same principle could be harnessed to create a real-world ad blocker, capable of blurring out ads in the cityscape. The "Terminal Slam" music video explores this premise, and tries to imagine what the future city might look like through MR glasses. Of course, it's just a thought experiment at this stage, and the idea hasn't been implemented yet for real. But if I had to make a rough guess, I think similar glasses might be possible in three- or four-years' time.

—— Watching the music video, I imagined it taking place 10 or 20 years in the future. It's surprising to hear that world can be expected on a much more immediate horizon.

Manabe We've already started to see technologies on what's called the "AR Cloud." Up to this point, AR has predominately been used to synthesize CG over things that are right in front of us, in close proximity. But already in San Francisco, they've been making 3D data of the entire city, and analyzing the dataset's defining features. For example, you can now simply hold up your iPhone to apply CG over specific landmarks, using GPS data and input from the camera's sensors. Technically, it's already possible to manipulate billboards and other advertisements in San Francisco with MR glasses. Shibuya is slowly heading in that direction, but it's not quite fully there yet. Although there are still hurdles to solve with the platforms, devices, and the hardware itself, the technology will likely come together in the not-so-distant future.

—— After releasing the music video, was there any reaction from the advertising industry? I wonder if it made them realize that video and other 2D ads are already becoming a thing of the past.

Manabe There had been talk of creating an AR app to promote a Squarepusher tour. But the tour was canceled due to Covid-19. The MR glasses are out of reach, but it would be possible to write an app that replaced all the ads on an iPhone with Squarepusher ads. As long as we had pictures and 3D data of the cities along their concert tour route, we could already create a hybrid combining GPS data and 3D data.

The first step is to try it out with an app. But as an end goal, I think it could be interesting to have everyone walking around the city wearing MR glasses. Everyone would be able to live in two worlds, even those pragmatists who only lived in reality before. As an accessory, the glasses' design might not be very fashionable at first, but they would definitely be convenient, and I think convenience always wins. I'd be curious to see what would happen. But even in such a system, ads would still be the easiest thing to monetize. No different from how Google and Facebook are 80-90% about the ads, I think MR glasses would end being another conduit for companies to track and harvest your personal data. Anyway, this element of prophesy was in the back of my mind when making the music video.

Breaking the mold of conventional capitalism

—— Monetization is synonymous with capitalism. Do you have any thoughts on what technology means for the future of capitalism? Do you see any alternatives to the conventional capitalistic framework?

Manabe   Companies are still having a field day trawling our data without our knowledge. I think it's imperative that we each do more to protect our own personal data. For the present exhibition, I was interested in partnering with a company called DataSign, which has essentially been developing a banking system for data. Similar to a bank account, your data will be stored in a locked account that will require your consent to make "withdrawals." If this system is brought to fruition, it could be a gamechanger. If people are given a way to manage their own personal data, I think it would help loosen Google and Facebook's stranglehold. I've been impressed by DataSign's founder, Yuichi Ota. I was actually just talking with him this morning. He said that the company is also building tools that will help users see where all their data is leaking in the background whenever they access a page online. Let's say you navigate to a certain product's website. That certain product's website will then send 905 requests to external sites and 105 other services, where your data will primarily be used for targeted advertising. This applies to pretty much all websites. Even if you're innocently browsing some charity's website, you should know that site is leeching your data in the background.

—— That seems like an ethical paradox for charities.

Manabe   Yes. If you follow the data trail, you'll see that even charitable organizations have put systems in place to collect your personal data in order to better target you for donations. The internet advertisting ecosystem is broken. We're just starting to see it collapse; I don't think this is something that's going to be fixed anytime soon. Still, it's important to educate people about these problems. I don't mean to sound like a doomsayer. I just hope our exhibitions and projects can be a more tangible, compelling way to help people to notice what's at stake.

—— When artist Lauren Boyle, a member of artist collective DIS known for *DIS Magazine*, came to Japan two years ago for the lecture at GA of Tokyo University of Arts, she emphasized the importance of a "new enlightenment." She said it will be necessary to fundamentally retool peoples' mindsets.

Manabe Everything has become data-driven; data is king. Just the other day [January 6th, 2021], a mob stormed the U.S. Capitol Building. Trump supporters embraced a social media app called Parler, uploading videos of the riot without hesitation. This led to Amazon booting Parler from its web hosting servers. Google and Apple also banned the app from their stores. Although Parler was ultimately shut down, hackers managed to grab all of the data before it went offline. They got everything. Not only the videos uploaded by rioters, but all the metadata, showing the exact location and time where the videos were filmed. The app had even stored metadata from each user's computers and smartphones. As a result of this data haul, the identities of people who participated in the Capitol riot were made public.

—— For better or worse, data becomes irrefutable evidence.

Manabe I think we live in an exciting but also terrifying age. Data collected by hackers and activists has the power to expose the truth behind monumental, history-changing events. Of course, this makes things particularly interesting for us at Rhizomatiks. Data is our medium, so we can remotivate the data from these incidents as art.

Now more than ever, we're living remotely online. Browsers and apps have become our primary communication tools, so there's no way to avoid giving up our data to massive IT companies like GAFA. But we can still question the validity of this ecosystem. Particularly in regard to our personal data, we can ask whether it's high time to make a new system. By creating work that explores these themes, I think that we can help pave the way for future breakthroughs.

I've been watching NFT closely for a while now. I think NFT could potentially be what saves us from an ad-driven cyber world. Although dialogue has tended to focus on NFT's applications in cryptocurrency — with some people even calling it a massive pyramid scheme — I think the immutability and decentralization of blockchain might herald the creation of a new and more sustainable system. For our part, we will continue to create work in the hopes that it may serve as proof of concept to make a difference.

—   —

December 18th, 2020 and January 15th, 2021
Rhizomatiks Nakameguro Office/Ebisu Office

ライゾマティクス──
システムを内破するマルチプレックス

長谷川祐子

ライゾマティクス(以下ライゾマと略)は2006年に結成以来、技術と表現の新しい可能性を追求してきた、東京を拠点として活動するクリエイターのコレクティブである。名称はドゥルーズとガタリのリゾーム概念[1]からとられており、網状に展開する地下茎(リゾーム)のように、彼らの表現活動は、「メディアアート」からデータの視覚デザインなどの研究開発建築、デザイン、広告やエンターテインメントなどのビジネスなど多方向に散逸している。その表現は、ハイパーな美学と最先端のテクノロジーの革新的な流用と最適化により、社会的に大きなインパクトを与えてきた。メディアテクノロジーを用いるアーティストがコンセプト、アイデアは自分で構想し、ハードウェアやエンジニアリングは専門家と協働することが多いのに対し、ライゾマは、アイデア、ハード・ソフト開発からオペレーションにいたるまでチームが一貫して行う。メンバーはアーティスト、プログラマーやエンジニア、デザイナー、建築のリサーチャーなどを含むフルスタック集団である。企業の研究開発、大きなイベントの演出システムの開発を通して、広告なエンターテイメントビジネスの情報や大型予算を自らのR&D(研究開発)に活用し、確実に自らの表現言語(システム)を進化させてきた。

「人新世」とよばれる人間が地球の環境圏の大半をコントロールする時代に、「自然」や「環境」といった言葉が見直しを迫られている。そして人新世を招いた要因であり、これと並びデフォルトとなってしまったのが「資本新世」である。[2]
　ガタリは3つのエコロジーとして自然環境、社会環境、精神環境を掲げ、4番目として「情報のエコロジー」に言及している。この4つめのエコロジーを「資本新世」を舞台に検証し、可視化、意味化しようとするのがライゾマの活動である。私たちをとりまく環境が高度に情報化され、そこからさまざまな新しい問題が派生している。例えば、嘘と偽情報(私たちのニュースエコシステムの脆弱性を明らかにする)に対するバイアスが組み込まれた権威主義(複雑な質問に対する単純な答えを提供する)への転換、そして私たちの飽くなきエネルギー消費量(Googleの検索ごとに、1秒のスクリーンタイムが地球温暖化と資源枯渇の一因となっている)等々。そんな中、私たちはハイパーオブジェクトであるメガデータにアクセスし、理解することがますます難しくなっている。
　ライゾマは活動の総体において、資本主義の内部構造に入り込み、intra-action(Karen Barad)[3]に関わっている。それは資本主義を支え、ともに発展してきたテクノロジーとシステムとの「もつれあった」関わりを意味する。通常アー

1　ジル・ドゥルーズとフェリックス・ガタリが共著『千のプラトー』で展開した「リゾーム」概念に由来する。絶対的な軸を中心に、リニアに、二項対立で成立する従来型の西洋的思考に対して、新たな思考の構造を多様な動きが網状に広がるイメージへの転換として「地下茎」と表現した。この名のもとにライゾマは、中心も始まりも終わりもなく、アイデアや技術、経験が、ジャンル横断的に関わる創造活動をめざした。

2　「人新世」は、資本主義などの人間の営みがあまりに大きく自然を変えてしまい、後戻りができなくなった時代を指す。この概念は、人間と自然は分割不可能であり、共存や関係性を示す「エコロジー」のなかから、もはや「自然」だけを取り出すことはできないという認識をもたらした。「資本新世」は、資本主義の展開において、資本主義が経済のみならず権力のシステムであり、文化の在り方でもあることを指す。

3　カレン・バラードは、先立つ分離、分断、すなわち個体というものを前提としている「相互作用(interaction)」に対して、分断を前提とせず、そもそも「もつれあって」いる存在しているという相互的な構成を前におく「内的作用(intra-action)」を提唱した。
Karen Barad, *Meeting the Universe Halfway: Quantum Physics And the Entanglement of Matter And Meaning*, Duke University Press, 2007.

ティストはコンセプトを形にするために手段・技術を選ぶ(目的→手段)。ライゾマの活動においては、目的→手段だけでなく、手段→目的という、テクノロジー(手段)からアイデアやコンセプトが導かれるという、双方向性のプロセスが複合的に発生している。それはかつての単純なars(アルス)+techne(テクネ)の一体関係ではない。テクノロジーはシステムを形成しており、今私たちが直面している多くの問題がテクノロジーと結びついているため、システムの機能やシステム間の相互関連や、なぜそのように動いているのかという、システムへのリテラシーが重要になる。ライゾマが翻訳、変容、増強、暴露、脱構築しようとしているのは、このシステム全体なのであり、従来的な「メディアアート」の領域の中に彼らを位置付けがたいのはそれゆえである。ライゾマの美学は「新しい美学」(ブライドル)に属するものであり、彼らの表現を「美学」として語る試みに対する、的外れな批判は芸術関係者における技術的リテラシーの弱さに一因があるといえる。

—

テクノロジー・システムを背景とした「新しい美学」については未だ生成途上といってよいが、自身がアーティストでもあるジェームズ・ブライドルの「The New Aesthetic and its Politics(新しい美学とそのポリティクス)」における説明は参照点の一つとなるだろう。彼は新しい美学は、ネットワーク自体の構造や性質を、批評の形で再現しているとする。[4]

—

> これらはすべて断片であり、進行中のプロセスの瞬間的な表現にすぎないのだ。それぞれの画像は、ハードコードされたものであれ、想像上のものであれ、はるかに大きなシステムの他の側面へのリンクである。すべてのウェブページ、すべてのエッセイ、そしてそこに書かれたり引用されたりするテキストの一行一行が、他の言葉、思考、アイデアへのリンクであるように。[5]

—

> 新しい美学は表層的なものではなく、美しさや表層の質感には関係していません。それはネットワーク技術の政治性に深くかかわり、それらを探索し、カタログ化し、分類し、接続し、調査しようとしています。それは多くの場合、読み出すことしかできない(read only)支離滅裂さと判読不可能性に見えますが、新しい美学は、ネットワークそれ自身の接続性と影響力の、深いレベルでの一貫性と多重性をはっきりと伝えています。(久保田晃弘訳)[6]

—

アーティストでありメディア研究者の久保田晃弘は「新しい美学」を人間の営為性につなげて、次のように語る。「新しい美学とはいわば見えない(けれど確かにそこにある)ものの美学であり、技術がどんなにみえなくなったとしても、それは人間が作ったものである以上、常に人間とその美学が潜んでいる。その美学を科学技術と人文学の双方の知識や経験を総動員して思索し、そこにある隠れた意味を顕在化させることが21世紀を生きるための必要不可欠なサバイバル技術である」。[7]

—

「ライゾマティクス_マルティプレックス」と題された本展は、美術館におけるライゾ

4 James Bridle, "The New Aesthetic and its Politics," in *You Are Here: Art After the Internet*, ed. Omar Kholeif, Cornerhouse & SPACE, 2014, pp. 20-27.

5 Ibid., p. 23.(筆者による訳)

6 Ibid., p. 25. 和訳は、ジェームズ・ブライドル『ニュー・ダーク・エイジ——テクノロジーと未来についての10の考察』(久保田晃弘監訳、NTT出版、2018年)所収の「監訳者解説」(pp. 328-329)より引用。

7 前掲書, p. 329.

マの初めての大型個展であり、今までの彼らの領域横断的な創造活動のアーカイヴが網羅されるとともに、現在にクリティカルにシンクロする新作プロジェクトを含む。新型コロナ感染によって世界がオンライン化を求められ、コミュニケーションについての新しい可能性が問われる現在、多くのプロジェクトや技術提案を現在進行形で実践しているライゾマの、大きなシステムへのリンクを前提とした「新しい美学」を見せる展覧会となっている。[8]

　本展では、実際のインスタレーションを仮想空間に取り込むことで、ヴァーチャリティとフィジカリティの境界、断絶と連動を再提案しつつ、それをオンライン、オフラインのハイブリッドで別のコンテンツデザインとして見せた。ネットワークの中での個人データの循環を検証したり、次世代の社会インフラとなるブロックチェーン、ノン・ファンジブル・トークン(NFT)によって構築されたNFTアートの是非を問う、クリティカルプラットフォームの設置など、デジタルとネットワーク社会の中での新しい人間性や倫理を追求している。

—

　メディアアートはもともとオープンソースや相互作用をその要素としており、アーティストの著作権やオリジナリティと同じくらい、伝達性やインターフェイスが重要となる。インターネットやAI(人工知能)が、個人主義、人間中心主義の人間活動の基盤に大きなゆさぶりをかけ、アートや文化的創造行為も大きな変化をむかえている現在、テクノロジー・システム・アートとでも呼べる新たなジャンルが生まれつつあるのではないだろうか。

—

　システムに入っていくメディアアーティストは、ハッカーであり、ハッカーは本来リバタリアンである。すべてのアーティストと同様に、彼らはどのような権力にも組織にも属さない。ハックしてきたデータを視覚化する、データ・ヴィジュアライゼーションは、希望と絶望の両方を見せる、現代アートの象徴的な役割の一つを果たすといえる。それが、抵抗のポストモダニズム——現代アートの批判的方法としての弁証法(ヘーゲル的な演繹法をもとにした思考法)——と異なる点は、創造過程にある複合性である。プログラミングは目的となる事象を具体化させ、理論的に公式やパターンをつくっていく数学的な演繹法と、解のない問題に対してさまざまな仮説をもって実験検証していく帰納法の組み合わせによっている。

　これに加えてデータはオブジェクトであるというOOO(Object orient ontology[オブジェクト指向存在論])が、実存的な力学をもって存在する。したがって、私たちはこれ(作品)を実際に活用したり、自分の身体感覚とシンクロさせたりして自らの知や感性の拡大変容にむけてコミットしなくてはならない。ここにナラティブやメタファーという感情や倫理に働きかける要素が必要となる。それをエレガントに、緻密に実装したのがライゾマといってよい。ライゾマは、テクノロジー・システムやデジタル情報を、正確にハックし、有機的に感情をまじえて加工し、増幅、可視化を通して共感できるリアリティのレベルにこれを落とし込み、観客を新たなエモーションや、身体ごとデータに触れるような、体験的エンゲイジメントの領域に連れていくことを試みる。

8　ライゾマはソーシャルディスタンシング時代の共有空間の在り方を模索する公開実験を、動画共有サービス「Twitch」を用いた《Staying TOKYO》で行った。関心のある人に自分の顔の映像を近づけると声がより聞こえるようになる、実際のパーティー空間と同様の体験ができるなど、数々の新たな試みが披露された。

一つはデジタル世代の身体感覚や想像力を増幅させることによる、彼らの生の祝福である。それはメディアテクノロジーによる身体感覚や感情の増幅であり、むしろそれが身体の一部となっていることにより、パーツを強化していくような作業に近い。真鍋をはじめとしてライゾマのスタッフがまず自分たちの身体で開発デバイスの実験をしてみるところから始まる、それは遊びであり、楽しい挑戦として動機づけられている。

　Perfumeの舞台演出は、パフォーマンスの身体表現とデジタルのセノグラフィーを一体化させる。彼女らの身体にハイパーな光のアウラや、スピード感のあるデジタル映像のプロジェクションを精密に接続することによって、その身体はポストヒューマンのシンボル性を帯びる。彼女らの動きが巨大な空間に投影された映像、光とシンクロすることで、身体がプロジェクション光（機械）を操作しているのか、プロジェクション光（機械）が身体を操作しているのか、主客を不明瞭にしてしまう、ポエティックでセンシャルな関係がそこにはあり、背後にはインターネットのクラウドが風景として広がっている。振付家のMIKIKOとの出会いをきっかけに2010年から10年にわたり継続されている女性パフォーマーたちとのコラボレーションは、サイバーフェミニズムの観点から分析することができる。映像や舞台での彼女たちの“ありよう”の自在な視覚的変容と神出鬼没の空間移動は、その多元性（multiplicity）、ノマド性（nomadicity）、連結性（connectivity）においてサイバーフェミニズムの特徴を表象している。デジタル領域における実践の家父長性な（patriarchal）アジェンダに対して、これを柔らかくフレキシブルなものにしていくフェミニズムのドライブ。ライゾマと彼女たちのコラボレーションは、身体にテック効果をアップロードする、その手つきの柔らかな繊細さと相互信頼にある。

　ドローンやキューブなどのロボット、光／映像、音と生身のダンスパフォーマンスを高い精度でシンクロさせて制御できる背後には、ライゾマ独自のきわめて人間的な手触りのあるメソッドがある。本展のハイライトのひとつは《Rhizomatiks × ELEVENPLAY "multiplex"》[→ pp.136-143] と題されたELEVENPLAYのダンサーの動きをモーションキャプチャでデータ化し、映像プロジェクションと動くロボットと共に構成したインスタレーションである。手前の部屋では舞台の動きにダンスとモーションデータが同期した映像が上映されている。奥の部屋にダンサーを撮影した舞台があり、そこでは装置（白いキューブ）が動き、映像プロジェクションが展開される様子が見られる。生身のダンサーとヴァーチャル空間との融合と並存、しかもその空間はリアルタイムにそこに存在するのだ。ライゾマは振付のMIKIKOと協働し、まず小さなキューブの模型をダンサーたちに動かしてもらい、彼女たちの身体ムーブメントの流れをキューブロボットの動きのプログラムに反映させる。そして舞台上を移動する撮影ロボットの動きもMIKIKOの視線の流れを参照している。ロボットと絡んで動くダンサーたちの身体が、ロボットの動きのプログラムと親和性をもつ。これをとらえるロボットカメラも、振付家の視点と重なることでなめらかな連携と自然な空気感が生まれる。人間のパフォーマーを排除した無人のステージにおいても、リアルタイム

のデータに基づき、壁と床のつながりがヴァーチャルな身体との関係においてわずかのギャップもないように、再調整され作り込まれている。二つの部屋の間に立つと両方を見ることができる。これはライゾマとしては初めての試みである。この二つの空間がつながっていることを理解したあとで、奥の部屋に戻ると、見る者は無人のロボット（キューブ）の周囲にダンサーの気配を感じることができる。これが真の意味でのヴァーチャル体験となる。

　　デジタル映像と生身の身体とロボットの組み合わせは、新たなテキストを書き出す媒体としての身体（ポストヒューマンのイリュージョン）の可能性を拡張する。ポストヒューマンの活動の舞台はテクノロジーのシステムの中、ネットワーク社会の中である。『攻殻機動隊』の草薙素子を例にあげるまでもなく、ネットワークの連鎖の中で与えられる記憶と人格−生の中をわたっていくメタファーの中で語られるからである。ビョークから依頼された「Mouth Mantra」(2015)のミュージックビデオで、歌う彼女のアイスランドのアイコンの口の「内側」に仮想現実の聴衆を入れた。そのように聴衆たちはどこにでも存在しうる。この場にいなくとも、ライゾマが開発した、コロナ時用の声援用のマスク[→p.046]やライブをリモートで楽しむ装置[→p.047]の先に彼らはいる。

2　data visualization

東日本大震災のとき、ライゾマがデザインの一部に関わり、ホンダとともに作成した震災発生直後の通行実績情報マップは、その的確な情報処理と美しい視覚デザインによって多くの人々の円滑な避難を補助した。ブラックボックスである金融の高頻度取引（High Frequency Trading）を示すアルゴリズムを開発し、東京株式市場のリアルタイムの取引状況を視覚化した《traders》(2013、東京都現代美術館)[→p.033]、ヴァーチャルに存在するビットコインの自動取引システムをライブで視覚化した《chains》(2013、カールスルーエ・アート・アンド・メディア・センター[ZKM]、ドイツ)[→pp.034-035]。ライゾマの創造は、data visualizationだけにとどまらない。《traders》ではリアルタイムの市場データと、独自に開発した仮想的に自動取引を行うソフトフェアによる売買のデータをあわせて視覚化した。《traders》では法規制があり実際の株の自動取引はできなかったが、《chains》においては、早期であったため、その時点ではビットコインには規制がなく、実際に開発したシステムで自動取引を行うとともにブロックチェーンの仕組みを可視化した。スクリーンの前のスイッチ操作により、観客は、自由でオープンなビットコインのトランザクションのダイナミズムと、ブロックチェーンの構造を切り替えて見ることができた。《chains》は、ブロックチェーンを学ぶための可視化と、自動売買システムを開発・展示した作品なのである。

　　ライゾマは見えないシステムを鮮やかな美学で可視化するだけでなく、その中に自らが開発したシステムによって、エンゲイジし、ハックしていくintra-activeな実践をそのコンセプトとしているのである。

—　　　　　　　　　　　　　—

続いてパリの「FUKAMI」展で展示した《invisible war》[fig.1]は、ネット空間

fig.1

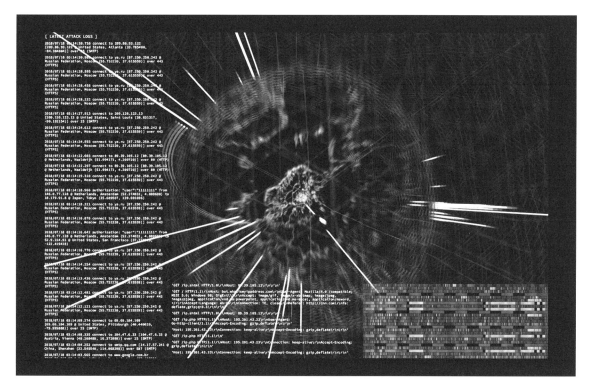

invisible war, 2018

のサイバー攻撃の状況を、環境の中の戦いとして可視化したものである。一般的な検索エンジンでは見つけられないディープウェブのさらに奥底に「ダークウェブ」が存在している。特殊なインターフェースを用いないとアクセスすることができない、知られざる空間が、サイバー犯罪の温床として、インターネットのみならず現実社会を大きく揺るがしている。真鍋はここで起こる「war」を可視化するために、ハニーポット（セキュリティの弱いWebサーバー）を囮として設定した。これを目標にサーバーをハッキングするために動員されたアクターは総当たり攻撃を開始、アクセスを取得すると、資産、ファイル、などを悪用しようとする。これに対して情報セキュリティ（InfoSec）とコンピュータセキュリティでは、ハニーポットを使用して脆弱性を公開し、防御を強化して、将来の不正アクセスを防止しようとする。このネット空間での戦いをライブでストリーミングした。

　　真鍋の卓抜なプログラミングとハッキングの技術は、我々をとりまく環境で起こっている見えない嵐（戦争）を正確かつ啓示的に視覚化する。リアルタイムでとらえるシンクロニシティと細部の仕上げの緊密さ。彼はしばしば目を閉じて音に集中する「行」によって感覚を鍛える。身体、関係、センサーによって生成する美意識−テクロノジーによって容易になだれ込む情報以外の情報を拾うセンサリングの訓練である。

　　「すべての事象はつながっている、これを手に触れるように可視化したい」
　　（真鍋）

日本において歴史的にある幽霊や鬼神、精霊などの概念の一つの機能は、セ

ンサーの感度をあげよという警告ではないだろうか。生き延びたいのであれば、目に見えず、耳に聞こえず、匂いも触感もない「それ」（ここにハイパーオブジェクトも含まれる）を、感知できるように感覚をとぎすますこと。

　私たちの周囲の世界の技術的複雑さが増すにつれて、それに対する私たちの理解は減じ、感覚は衰えていく。自動取引から、フィルター・バブルの中に私たちを閉じ込めるソーシャルメディア・アルゴリズム、不適切な人工知能の活用、検証不可能な情報環境、これに抵抗し、理解と感覚をチャージするのが批評精神とシステムの中でのintra-activeな実践である。

3　批　評　性

デジタルクリエイションにおいても同様だ。誰でもが同じ機能をもったデバイスやテクノロジーを簡単に手に入れることができる時代において、オリジナリティはいかにして可能になるのだろうか。真鍋は常に、新しく公開されたデバイスやアプリをいち早く試し、これをさらに独自に開発してきた。例えば、2008年に彼は《Face Visualizer》[→ p.018]（電極を顔面に固定することにより、筋肉の作動を通じて音楽作品を「視覚化」する）を実験開発し、2011年に機械学習技術を用いて顔の特徴点を解析し、それを使って顔のパーツに合わせて映像を投影、合成するソフトウェアを開発した。これは最新世代のiPhoneを保護するFace IDと同じタイプのアルゴリズムを利用していた。しかし技術開発は誰かによって必ず追いつかれてしまう。その意味でコンセプトの強度は重要になる。

—　　　　　　　　　　　　　　　　　　　　　　—

批判精神とオルタナティブな思考を維持することは、この変化の速い時代において容易ではない。観察、記録と視覚化、これによって現実を暴くという批評行為が成立していたとして、事件現場にいた当事者がたまたまとらえた一つの（証拠）映像（それは一瞬で世界に共有される）にかなうものはない。ドローンや、多くの探知装置も活躍するがそこで捉えられた画像もネットワークにアップロードされるときに改ざんされる危険がある。

　真鍋がスクエアプッシャーとコラボレーションをしたミュージックビデオ「Terminal Slam」[→ pp.002-003, 054-055] では、近い将来登場するであろうMixed Realityのデバイス（グラス）を通して都市の広告を消滅させ、全く異なった位相に変容させるラディカルでアナーキーなヴィジョンが提示される（それが広告なのかサインボードなのかを区別することはできなかったため、仕分けはライゾマの手作業となった）。が、広告を無化すること、あるいはすべて自分好みの広告に入れ替えてしまえることは一つの変革の裏表である。資本主義による情報の偽装、パッケージを引き剥がすこと、あるいは自分のコントロール下におくこと……。

　そして今回の展示作品の一つ《Trojan Horse》は、私たちの日常において、検索ネットにアクセスする行為によっていかに多くの個人情報が流出しているかを見せるものである。皮肉なことに「集合知」のコンセプトの上につくられているウィキペディアへのアクセスは全くどこからも情報が抜き取られていない。これは知へのアクセスが「資本主義」の埒外にあることを示している。

また真鍋のAIに関するリサーチはどこまで機械学習とコラボできるのか、その境界をプッシュすると同時に、エンコーディングとデコーディングによって、脳への入力とプログラム入力を有機的に構造化しようとする意図が見える。情報学専門の京都大学、神谷之康教授は、「ブレイン・デコーディング」によってヒトの脳活動パターンを深層ニューラルネットワーク（DNN）などのAIモデルの信号に変換することで、（見たり、想像したりしている）任意の物体を脳活動から解読する[9]。私たちはAI／機械の環世界を知ることはできない。だがこのブレイン・デコーディングによって、プロセスを一部共有することはできる。真鍋は、《dissonant imaginary》[→ pp.038-039]でこの技術を用いて音楽を聞いた際に頭の中に浮かんだイメージを予測し、映像に変換した。AIがパターンの相同性を照合しようとし続ける——残像のような不確かなイメージがハイスピードで次々と変化していく。音と映像の関連性、未来の音楽はイメージを頭に描くだけで生まれてくるのではないか？ 真鍋の探求は、脳の構造や機能のアナロジーとして、テクノロジーのブラックボックスをできるだけ透明にしていこうとする過程にみえる。

R&Dの展示セクションで明確に感じられたのは、リサーチ途上のデータやシステムの断片を視覚化してそのまま見せること、現在のXXにただ光をあてることが一つの批評行為になるという点だった。一歩先んじて見せる——システムの中に完全に組み込まれてしまう前に、それを引っ張り出し提示する。引っ張り出された断片を見て私たち各々が何に気づくのか、ライゾマは解釈を見る者に委ねる。そしてリサーチに続くデベロップメントにおいて、データや技術は活用、応用され、新しいデバイスや視覚表現を生む。

結び

この展覧会にはコンセプチュアルなレベルでのハイライトが二つあった。それは喫緊な問題との関わりゆえといってもよいだろう。ひとつは最初の部屋の、NFT化されたデジタルアートのオークション、OpenSeaの3日間のイベントデータの可視化「"Gold Rush" - Visualization + Sonification of OpenSea activity」である。

デジタルアートの画像データを暗号化することで、複製不可能という価値を付与する、そのことによって、今まで複製可能性を前提としていたデジタルアートの市場が変化していく。2021年初めから、数ヵ月の間に多くの人々がこの市場に参加した。クリスティーズも参加し、数億という落札価格作品も現れた。実際のOpenSeaの静的な画面のレイアウトとは全く異なり、多次元に展開される画像の息もつかせぬ速さで展開する取引が、嵐のように、漣のように画面をめぐる画像の大群によって示される。画面左手にイベントのプレイバックのテキストログが表示され、「created」「cancelled」「bid entered」「successful」「tranfer」「approve」といった取引の動きが示される。イベントのプレイバック再生にあわせてそれに紐づいた作品が表示される——取引が成立した作品の画像が一瞬拡大され、OpenSeaの海の中に消え去ってしまう。取引される画像データの分析にはディープラーニングの技術CNNが用いられており、高い

9　神谷ラボは、真鍋と多くのコラボを行う他、リーベンタインギャラリーで開催されたピエール・ユイグの個展「UUmwelt」の制作にも協力している。https://kamitani-lab.ist.i.kyoto-u.ac.jp/tagged/art

精度で高次元の画像を次元削減し、特徴量を2次元にマッピングする。画像の類似度、関連度を可視化することで、OpenSea上で行われている取引の傾向を人間の知覚で観察することができるようになっている、と真鍋は語る。

　　誰が顧客（コレクター）か、画像の鑑賞者かも定まらない未知の市場、従来のアート市場の価値体系の危機、暗号化にかかる膨大な電力消費へのエコロジカルな批判——すべてが不確定のままに膨大な情報と欲望が動いている。メディアアートの歴史家であるティナ・ライアンは、「NFTの構造そのものが、コンピュータやインターネットを使って美的なモノの定義を拡大してきた何世代にもわたるアーティストたちの遺産を無効にしてしまった」と言う。さらにライアンは、NFTは分散したり、インタラクティブだったり、偶発的だったり、刹那的だったりするデジタルプロジェクトの厄介な現実より、安定した単一の芸術作品という理想を優遇しており、非物質的なものに価値を見いだしてきた現代芸術の歴史と真逆の方向にドライブする、と批判する[10]。「永遠に単一の資産」たらんとするデジタルアートの転身、その固定した姿を、ライゾマは分散、偶発、刹那的な仮想空間の現象論のなかに描く。まさに今生成しつつある現実に目をむけよ、とライゾマは言う。半歩先の未来から警鐘を鳴らす。そして彼らは独自のOpenSeaプラットフォームのあり方をすでに考えている。

　　最後のエピローグの部屋は20台のモニターがミニマルに横一列に並ぶ。ブルース・ナウマンやハルン・ファロッキを思わせるドライな展示でありながら、そのモニターには各展示室のバックグラウンド、ソフトウェア、コーディングなどがすべて暴露されていた。

　　監視カメラの映像に今まで会場を歩いてきた自分の姿を見る。しかしそれはモザイク化され、ぼかされているために認識できないようになっている。プライバシーを暴くシステムが逆にこれを守るシステムに転換されている。テクノロジー・システムの多層性、複雑さを身体的な意識にループバックした見事なエピローグであった。テクノロジーのエコシステムは、企業や科学者、ほかエージェントが各々開発したプログラミング言語やハードウェアがアクターとなって複雑に影響し合いながら進化発展していく。その生態系の中で、重要な要となる（keystone）種を探り当てていくことと、同じ種の背後にある負の要素、脆弱性に対するセンシングは表裏である。

　　芸術家としてのハッカーの立ち位置がここにある。

10　Tina Rivers Ryan "Token Gesture," *Art Forum*, May 2021. https://www.artforum.com/print/202105/token-gesture-85475

Rhizomatiks: a multiplex that deconstructs the system from within

Yuko Hasegawa

Since its formation in 2006, Rhizomatiks has been a Tokyo-based collective of creators who pursue new possibilities in technology and artistic expression. The name of the group is taken from Gilles Deleuze and Félix Guattari's concept of the rhizome.[1] Just like an underground root (rhizome) that unfurls in a reticulated fashion, their practice disperses itself in multiple directions to encompass "media art," research and development such as the visual design of data, architecture, design, as well as business ventures such as advertising and entertainment. Their practice is distinct from other designers, and has made a significant impact on society through their hyperbolic aesthetic and innovative deployments and optimizations of cutting-edge technology. In contrast to artists working with media technology who often create their own concepts and collaborate with specialists in hardware and engineering, Rhizomatiks is a full-stack team that performs all these tasks in an integrated way, from ideation and hardware/software development to operations. Its members include artists, programmers and engineers, designers, and architectural researchers. Through research and development undertaken for corporations and the development of production systems for large-scale events, they have been able to utilize information and large budgets from the advertising and entertainment businesses for their own R&D, steadily evolving an expressive language (system) of their own.

In the Anthropocene, an era in which humans control most of the Earth's environment, the terms "nature" and "environment" demand to be reexamined. The "Capitalocene" is the factor that gave rise to the Anthropocene and became the default along with it. According to Guattari, the mental, the social, and the environmental constitute three ecologies, while the fourth is the "ecology of information."[2] The attempt to verify, visualize and bestow meaning onto this fourth ecology against the backdrop of this Capitalocene is at the core of Rhizomatiks' practice. The environment that surrounds us is becoming highly informatized, giving rise to a variety of new problems, including the shift towards authoritarianism (providing simple answers to complex questions) with a built-in bias against lies and disinformation (revealing the fragility of our news ecosystem), and our insatiable energy consumption (for every Google search, one second of screen time contributes to global warming and resource depletion). It has become increasingly difficult for us to access and make sense of the mega-data that are these hyperobjects.

In the totality of its activities, Rhizomatiks has infiltrated the

1 Derived from the concept of the "rhizome" as developed by Gilles Deleuze and Félix Guattari in their book *A Thousand Plateaus*. Deleuze and Guattari used the term to describe a new structure of thought that shifts towards the image of a web of diverse movements, as opposed to the conventional Western way of thinking based on binary oppositions around an absolute axis. With this name, Rhizomatiks sought to develop a creative practice in which ideas, techniques, and experiences would be able to relate to each other in a cross-disciplinary fashion without a center, beginning, or end.

2 The Anthropocene refers to an era when human activity, including capitalism, have so drastically altered nature that there is no turning back. This concept brought about the realization that human beings and nature are indivisible from each other, and that we can no longer only take the "nature" out of the notion of ecology that demonstrates coexistence and relationships. The "Capitalocene" refers to the development of capitalism not only in terms of economies, but also systems of power and authority and forms of culture.

internal structure of capitalism and transformed into a form of "intra-action" (Karen Barad), [3] which entails an engagement with the technology and systems that have supported capitalism and developed alongside it. Normally, artists choose means and technologies in order to give form to their concepts (objective → means). In Rhizomatiks' practice, there is a complex bi-directional process that does not only involve objective → means, but also a certain means → objective mechanism where ideas and concepts are derived from the technology (means). This is not the simple ars+techne fusion relationship of the past. Technologies produce systems, and since many of the problems we face today are linked to technology, it is important to be literate about systems, their functions, the interrelationships between systems, and why they work the way they do. It is these entire systems that Rhizomatiks seek to translate, transform, augment, expose, and deconstruct, which makes it difficult to place them within the realm of conventional "media art." Rhizomatiks' aesthetics belong to the "new aesthetics" (James Bridle), and the misguided criticism of their attempts to talk about their practice in terms of aesthetics is partly due to the technical illiteracy of those in the art world.

—

While this "new aesthetic" based on technological systems is still a nascent one, a key point of reference can perhaps be found in the essay "The New Aesthetic and its Politics" by James Bridle, an artist himself. According to Bridle, the new aesthetic reproduces the structure and nature of the network itself in the form of a critique. [4]

> All of these are snippets, they are only momentary representations of ongoing processes—as indeed the New Aesthetic is intended to be. Each image is a link, hardcoded or imaginative, to other aspects of a far greater system, just as every web page and every essay, and every line of text written or quoted therein, is a link to other words, thoughts, and ideas. [5]

> The New Aesthetic is not superficial. It is not concerned with beauty or surface texture. It is deeply engaged with the politics and politicization of networked technology, and seeks to explore, catalogue, categorize, connect, and interrogate these things. Where many seem to read only incoherence and illegibility, the New Aesthetic articulates the deep coherence and multiplicity of connections and influences of the network itself. [6]

Akihiro Kubota, an artist and media researcher, draws a connection between the "new aesthetic" and human agency. He asserts that "the new aesthetic is the aesthetics of what is invisible, so to speak (but certainly there). No matter how invisible technology has become, insofar as it has been created by human beings, it will always harbor a hidden human presence and a sense of its aesthetic. I believe that one of the essential survival techniques for living in the 21st century is to be able to contemplate this aesthetic by mobilizing the knowledge and experience of both science and technology and the humanities, and to bring their hidden meanings to light." [7]

—

3   In contrast to "interaction," which presupposes a state of separation and fragmentation based on the individual, Karen Barad proposed the notion of "intra-action," which is not premised on fragmentation, but rather the mutual constitution of an "entangled" existence. Karen Barad, *Meeting the Universe Halfway: Quantum Physics And the Entanglement of Matter And Meaning*, Duke University Press, 2007.

4   Bridle, James. "The New Aesthetic and its Politics," *You Are Here — Art After the Internet. Cornerhouse*, 2014, pp.20–27.

5   Bridle, "The New Aesthetic and its Politics," p. 23.

6   James Bridle, *New Dark Age: Technology and the End of the Future*, translated by Akihiro Kubota, NTT Publishing, 2018, pp. 328–329.

7   Akihiro Kubota, ibid., "Notes from the Translator," p. 329.

This exhibition, titled "Rhizomatiks, Multiplex," is the first major solo exhibition of the collective's work at a museum, and includes a comprehensive archive of their cross-disciplinary creative activities to date, as well as new projects synchronized with the present moment in a critical manner. At a time when the world is being forced to go online by COVID-19 and new possibilities for communication are being examined, Rhizomatiks are currently working on numerous projects and technological proposals, and this exhibition seeks to showcase a "new aesthetic" based on links to larger systems. [8]

By incorporating an actual installation into virtual space, we made a renewed proposition regarding the boundary between the virtual and the physical and disconnection and engagement, showcasing it as another form of content design in a hybrid online-offline format. This attempt represents the pursuit of a new kind of humanity and ethics in a digital, networked society. For example, we examined how personal data circulates within networks, and set up a creative platform to question the pros and cons of NFT art built with the blockchains and non-fungible tokens (NFTs) that will make up the next generation of social infrastructure.

—

Media art was originally based on the idea of open source and interaction, and the notions of transferability and interfaces are as important as the artist's copyright and originality. The internet and AI are disrupting the individualism and anthropocentrism of human endeavor in a major way, while art and creative cultural activities are also currently facing significant shifts. It is in this context that a new genre that might perhaps best be termed "technology system art" is emerging.

—

The media artist who sneaks into the system is a hacker, and the hacker is libertarian by nature, without being beholden to any authority or organization. In a certain sense, data visualization, which gives hacked data a visual form, is symbolic of the role of contemporary art in showing us both hope and despair. What makes it different from the dialectical method (a way of thinking based on the Hegelian method of deduction) as a critical method of contemporary art and a postmodernism of resistance is the complexity to be found in the creative process. Programming combines the mathematical deduction method, where the desired outcome is given concrete form and theoretical formulas and patterns are created, and the inductive method, in which various hypotheses are tested on problems without a solution. Programming, in particular, is generated by this mixture.

In addition, OOO (object-oriented ontology), which holds that data is an object, comes into play with a certain existential dynamic. As such, we have to commit ourselves to the expansion and transformation of our own information and sensibilities by actually deploying these objects (artworks) and synchronizing them with our bodily sensations. This is where we will require narratives and metaphors, elements that can operate on and trigger our emotions and ethics. It is Rhizomatiks that has pulled off an exemplary implementation of these elements in a way that is both elegant and meticulous. By accurately hacking and processing these technological

8   Rhizomatiks conducted an open experiment at Staying TOKYO using the video sharing service Twitch to explore the nature of shared spaces in the age of social distancing. A number of new experiments were showcased, such as the ability to hear voices better by bringing the image of one's face closer to the person of interest, and an experience similar to that of an actual party space.

systems and digital information while incorporating organic emotions into the mix, thereby amplifying and visualizing them to a level of empathetic reality, Rhizomatiks seek to lead their audiences towards a new realm of emotion and experiential engagement that allows them to touch the data with their bodies.

1. Amplifying the reality of bodily sensations

The first of these hacks consists in celebrating their lives through the amplification of the bodily sensations and imagination of the digital generation. This amplification of physical sensation and the emotions through media technology is akin to the process of strengthening parts of the body by making these elements part of it — a playful and fun challenge motivated by the fact that Manabe and the rest of the staff at Rhizomatiks start by experimenting with the devices that they develop on their own bodies.

Perfume's stage direction integrates the bodily expression of performance with a kind of digital scenography that precisely connects their bodies with a hyperbolic aura of light and projections of digital imagery with a sense of velocity to them, imbuing them with a sort of posthuman symbolism. As their movements become synchronized with the images and light projected in the huge space, a poetic and sensuous relationship emerges that renders the subject ambiguous: is it the body that is manipulating the projected light (machine), or the projected light (machine) that is manipulating the body? In the background, the cloud of the internet unfolds as a kind of landscape. Rhizomatiks' ongoing ten-year collaboration with female performers, which began in 2010 after an encounter with the choreographer MIKIKO, can also be analyzed from the perspective of cyberfeminism. The freewheeling visual transformations and phantasmal spatial movements that dictate how these women appear on video and onstage are manifestations of the distinct characteristics of cyberfeminism in their multiplicity, nomadicity, and connectivity. Here we can see a certain feminist drive to make this soft and flexible in relation to the patriarchal agenda of artistic practices in the digital realm. The collaboration between Rhizomatiks and these women lies in the soft, supple delicacy of their hands that uploads technical effects to the body.

What allows Rhizomatiks to control drones, cubes, and other robots, light/video, and sound to synchronize them with live dance performances with an extremely high degree of precision is their unique method with its exceedingly human sense of touch. One of the highlights of this exhibition is an installation titled *Rhizomatiks × ELEVENPLAY "multiplex"* [→pp. 136–143], which consists of motion-captured data of the movements of ELEVENPLAY dancers, video projections and moving robots.

In the front room, a video of dance and motion data synchronized with the movements onstage is projected. In the back room, there is a stage on which the dancers are filmed, where the equipment (a white cube) moves and the video projection unfolds. The fusion and coexistence of the live dancers and the virtual space, and the space itself, is there live, in the present. Working with choreographer MIKIKO, Rhizomatiks first had the dancers move a small model of a cube, reflecting the flow of their body movements onto the movement program of the cube robot. The actions of the filming robots moving on the stage also take their cue from the drifting of MIKIKO's gaze. The bodies of the dancers moving in tandem with the robot have an affinity with the movement program of the robot. The robot camera that captures all of this also overlaps with the choreographer's perspective, creating a sense of smooth coordination and a natural atmosphere. Even on an unmanned stage stripped of human performers, the connections between the walls and the floor have been readjusted based on real-time data so that there is not even the slightest gap in relation to the virtual body.

If you stand in between the two rooms, you can see both of these things. This is the first time that Rhizomatiks have attempted this. After viewers understand the connection between the two spaces and return to the room at the back, they can feel the presence of the dancers around the unmanned robot (cube), which is a virtual experience in the truest sense.

This combination of digital images, bodies of flesh and blood, and robots expands the possibilities of the body as a medium for the writing of new texts (the illusion of the posthuman). The stage on which posthuman activity will unfold is to be found within the system of technology, within the network society, because this narrative is being told in terms of the metaphor of traversing the memories and personality-life that one is given within this concatenation of networks — a situation not unlike, needless to say, that of Motoko Kusanagi in *Ghost in the Shell*. In the music video for *Mouth Mantra* (2015), commissioned from Björk, a virtual reality audience has been placed "inside" the mouth of the Icelandic icon as she sings. As such, the audience could be anywhere. Even if they are not present here and now, they are in front of the masks for cheering [→p.046] and devices for enjoying live performances remotely [→p.047] during the COVID-19 pandemic developed by Rhizomatiks.

2. data visualization

In the wake of the Great East Japan Earthquake, Rhizomatiks worked with Honda and took on some of the design work involved in creating a traffic information map that assisted in the smooth evacuation of many people in the immediate aftermath of the disaster through its accurate information processing and beautiful visual design. They developed an algorithm to show the workings of high frequency trading, which is a black box in finance, and developed *traders* (2013, Museum of Contemporary Art, Tokyo) [→p.033] , which visualizes real-time trading conditions on the Tokyo stock market, and *chains* (2013, Center for Art and Media [ZKM]) [→pp.034–035], a live visualization of the automated trading system of bitcoin that exists virtually.

Rhizomatiks' creations are not limited to data visualization. In *traders*, they visualized real-time market data as well as data from a virtual automated trading software that they developed themselves. While it was not possible to perform the actual automated trading of stocks in traders due to legal restrictions, *chains* was created at an earlier stage when there were no restrictions on bitcoin, making it possible to perform automatic trades with the system they developed and visualize the structure of blockchains. With a flick of the switch in front of the screen, the audience was able to toggle between the dynamism of free and open bitcoin transactions and the structure of the blockchain. *chains* is a work that generated visualizations for learning about blockchains, in addition to developing and exhibiting an automatic trading system.

The concept behind Rhizomatiks' work, then, is not only to visualize invisible systems with a brilliant and vivid aesthetic, but also to deploy their own systems to engage in and hack into them as an intra-active practice.

—   —

invisible war, fig.1 [→p.189] which was exhibited in Paris, visualized the situation surrounding cyber attacks on the space of the Internet in terms of a battle within a particular environment. The "dark web" exists at a level even deeper than that of the Deep Web, which cannot be found by ordinary search engines. This uncharted space, which can only be accessed through a special interface, is a hotbed of cybercrime that has shaken up not only the internet but also the real world. In order to visualize the wars that erupt here, Manabe set up a honeypot (a web server with weak security) as a decoy. Actors mobilized to hack the server will launch brute force attacks to gain access and exploit assets, files, and so on. In response, InfoSec and computer security will use honeypots to expose vulnerabilities and strengthen defenses to try to prevent future unauthorized access. This battle in the space of the internet was streamed live.

—   —

Manabe's superb programming and hacking skills are unparalleled in terms of their aesthetic, which consists in visualizing the invisible storms (wars) taking place in our environment in a way that is both precise and revelatory. The sense of proximity in the finish of the details is astounding. He often trains and sharpens his senses with "lines'" that involve him closing his eyes and concentrating on the sound. This is an exercise in sensing, in picking up information other than that which is readily available through the aesthetic-technology generated by the body, relationships, and sensors.

As Manabe has it, "all events are connected, and I want to visualize this in a way that you can touch." One of the functions of the historical concepts of ghosts, demons, and spirits in Japan is to warn us to sharpen the sensitivity of our sensors. If we want to survive, we must hone our senses to be able to perceive "them" (in this case, hyperobjects as well), which we cannot ordinarily see, hear, smell, or touch.

As the technological complexity of the world around us increases, our understanding and sense of it diminishes, from automated trading and social media algorithms that trap us in filter bubbles, to the inappropriate use of artificial intelligence and information environments that cannot be verified. A critical spirit and an intra-active practice that functions within the system resists this, recharging both our understanding and our senses.

9   In addition to pursuing numerous
collaborations with Manabe,
Kamitani Lab also supported the
production of Pierre Huyghe's
solo exhibition *UUmwelt* at the
Serpentine Gallery. https://
kamitani-lab.ist.i.kyoto-u.ac.jp/
tagged/art

The same is true for digital creation. In an age where everyone has easy access to devices and technology with the same functions, how is originality possible? Manabe has always been one of the first to try out newly released devices and applications, and then build on them in his own way. In 2008, for example, he experimented with *Face Visualizer* [→p.018], which "visualizes" a musical piece through muscle activation by attaching electrodes to the face, while in 2011, he developed a software that uses machine learning technology to analyze the distinctive attributes of faces to project and synthesize images synchronized to these parts of the face. These programs made use of the same type of algorithm found in the Face ID that protects the latest generation of iPhones. Technological development, however, is always going to be overtaken by someone else. In this sense, the strength of the concept becomes important.

—

Maintaining a critical spirit and alternative mindset in this fast-changing era is no easy task. Even if one manages to pull off the critical act of observation, recording, and visualization, thus exposing reality, nothing can compare to a single image (piece of evidence) captured by someone who happened to be present at the scene of a crime, which can be instantly shared with the world. Drones and many other detection devices can also be deployed, but even the images captured there risk being tampered with when they are uploaded to the network.

In "Terminal Slam," [→pp.002-003, 054-055] Manabe's music video collaboration with Squarepusher, he presents a radical and anarchic vision of urban advertising that disappears, transforming into a completely different phase through mixed reality devices (glasses) that may well appear in the near future (as it was not possible to distinguish whether it was an advertisement or a signboard, the sorting was done manually by Rhizomatiks). This, however, basically neutralized the advertising function. On the flip side, this means that one would be able to replace all of them with ads that conform to one's own taste..

The dissimulation of information by capitalism: ripping off packages, or keeping them under one's control.

One of the works in this exhibition, *Trojan Horse*, shows how much personal information gets leaked through the act of performing internet searches in our daily lives. Ironically, access to Wikipedia, which is built on the concept of "collective knowledge," does not extract information from anywhere at all. This shows that access to knowledge lies outside the purview of "capitalism."

Manabe's research on AI also pushes the boundaries of how far we can collaborate with machine learning. At the same time, his intent to structure the input to the brain and the program input through an organic process of encoding and decoding is evident. Professor Yukiyasu Kamitani of Kyoto University, an expert in informatics, uses a "brain decoding" technique to decode arbitrary objects (seen or imagined) from brain activity by converting such activity patterns into signals for AI models such as deep neural networks (DNNs). [9] While we cannot know the umwelt of AI/machines, we can share in some of its processes. In *dissonant imaginary* [→pp.038-039], Manabe used this technology to predict the images that would come into his mind while listening to music, and converted them into video. Vague, unstable images kept changing one after another at high speed, like a series of afterimages, as the AI sought to verify the similarities in the patterns. Might the relationship between sound and image, and the music of the future, be created simply by picturing images in our minds? Manabe's explorations into the visualization of dreams and creation of images of sounds he hears seem to be a process of making the black box of technology as transparent as possible, in terms of an analogy to the structure and function of the brain.

What seemed clear in the R&D section of the exhibition was that the weightiest critique is to show ongoing footage from the research process and fragments from the system by visualizing them as they are, and to simply highlight whatever is currently unfolding. Rhizomatiks shows this to us a little bit in advance: in other words, pulling it out of the system before it has been completely incorporated within it. What each viewer notices when we look at these extracted fragments is something that is left up to us. Their research is followed by development, where data and technology are used and applied to create new devices and visual representations.

Conclusion

There were two highlights in this exhibition on a conceptual level, which were surely the result of their involvement in some of the most pressing and urgent issues. One was the auction of digital art that had been tokenized and turned into NFTs that happened in the first gallery, and the other was *"Gold Rush"- Visualization + Sonification of OpenSea Activity*, which visualized data from a three-day event on OpenSea.

By encrypting the image data of digital art, we give it the value of non-replicability, which will go on to change the market for digital art, which up until now has been based on the premise of reproducibility. In the first few months of 2021, many people participated in this market, including Christie's, and bids for works in the tens of millions appeared. In stark contrast to the static layout of the actual screen on OpenSea, the breathlessly fast-moving transactions of images unfolding in multiple dimensions is shown by a swarm of images that circle the screen like a rippling storm. A text log of the playback of the event appears on the left of the screen, displaying movements in transactions such as created, cancelled, bid entered, successful, transferred, and approved. As the playback progresses, the works associated with it are displayed — the image of the work being traded is momentarily enlarged, before disappearing again into the "sea" of OpenSea. The analysis of this data on the traded images is performed using CNN, a deep learning technology that reduces the dimensionality of high-dimensional images recognized with a high degree of accuracy, and maps their features onto two dimensions. By visualizing the degree of similarity and relevance of the images, Manabe explains that it is now possible to observe trends regarding the transactions taking place on OpenSea through human perception.

An unknown market where it is not clear who the customer

(collector) or viewer of the image is, a crisis in the value system of the traditional art market, and an ecological critique of the enormous quantities of power consumed by encryption - all of these are driven by a massive amount of information and desire, in a state of complete uncertainty. According to media art historian Tina Rivers Ryan, the structure of NFTs themselves has invalidated the legacy of generations of artists who have used computers and the internet to expand the definition of aesthetic objects. The NFT privileges the ideal of a single, stable work of art over the messy reality of digital projects that are dispersed, interactive, contingent, and ephemeral. Ryan criticizes NFTs for driving in the opposite direction of the history of contemporary art, which has found value in the immaterial. [10] In their phenomenology of the dispersed, contingent, and ephemeral virtual space, Rhizomatiks depict the transformation of digital art into a "single asset, forever" and its fixed form. Look at the facts that are being generated right now, they say. Rhizomatiks sound the alarm from half a step into the future. And they are already thinking about what their own unique take on an OpenSea platform might look like.

The final "epilogue" gallery consists of 20 monitors lined up in a minimalist, horizontal row. While it was a rather austere exhibition reminiscent of Bruce Nauman or Harun Farocki, it also revealed all the background, software, and coding behind each exhibition gallery.

In the surveillance camera footage, I saw myself walking through the exhibition galleries. It was blurred so that it was unrecognizable, however. A system intended to compromise privacy has been transformed into a system that protects it. It was a brilliant epilogue that looped the multilayeredness and complexity of technological systems back into our physical consciousness. Technology ecosystems evolve and develop through complex interactions between programming languages and hardware developed by companies, scientists, and other agents that function as actors. Exploring the keystone species within these ecosystems and sensing the negative elements and vulnerabilities associated with these same species are two sides of the same coin.

And this is where the hacker-as-artist comes into play.

10   Tina Rivers Ryan, "Token Gesture," *Artforum*, May 2021 https://www.artforum.com/print/202105/token-gesture-85475

後ライゾマティクス――個展によせて

森山朋絵

はじめに

ライゾマティクスの個展が、東京都現代美術館で開幕した――この展覧会が
いま成立した意味を、私たちは考えねばならない。世界がコロナ禍という特異
点を迎えた2020年半ばに企画は本格化し、結成15周年かつ公立館初の大
規模個展であることに加え、本展キュレーター[1]による当館最後の企画展となっ
た。そして筆者は、1980年代末から現在まで、公立館におけるアート＆テクノロ
ジー展に課題を含め長く取り組んできた学芸員として、本展を実装する機会を
得た。500を超える大量のデバイスを要塞のように展示室に設置し、各種の限
定条件を乗りこえ、デジタルツインコンピューティング／並行世界的に、オンライン／
フィジカル双方の会場を成立させる――それが今回のミッションである。2021
年1月、会社組織「ライゾマティクス」が発展的に改組される[2]と同時に個展準
備も爆発的に加速し、またたく間に3月20日の初日を迎えた。

ライゾマティクスの成立と展開

ライゾマティクスはよく「新しい領域」の「新しいアーティスト」だと紹介される。果
たしてそうだろうか？ この領域の企画展を開催するたび、私たちは「最先端のテ
クノロジーを駆使」という決まり文句に辟易する。メディアアートは新旧のテクノロ
ジーを「思いがけない方法」で用い、表現のプラットフォームとするが、それはデジ
タルテクノロジーには限らない。[3] ライゾマティクスの成立と展開について考えると
き、メディアアートが持つ、過去から現在まで続くアルケオロジカルな拡がりが想
起される。真鍋は大学で数学、石橋は工学を修めたのち岐阜県立国際情報
科学芸術アカデミー[IAMAS]に学んだ。同校では開学当時から初代学長・坂
根厳夫のもと、国内外で活躍するメディアアーティストらが教鞭を執り、レジデン
ス作家としても結集していた（ソムラー＆ミニョーノ、スコット・S・スニッブ、岩井俊雄ほか多数）。
温故知新／不易流行というメディアアートの教えに沿い、彼らは工学系論文と同
じく先行研究に努め、真鍋はそれらをアーカイブとしてネットにも上げている。例
えば、ビジュアライゼーションは「クリミア戦役死者の実態を可視化したナイチン
ゲール」に遡るとか、ゼロ年代初頭のACM SIGGRAPHで毎年見かけたモー
ションキャプチャは、19世紀のマレやマイブリッジよりギルブレス夫妻による「クロ
ノサイクルグラフ」[4]に近いとか、誰かが示唆したとする。すると真鍋は瞬時にそ

1　長谷川祐子、2021年3月末まで東京都現代
美術館参事、現・金沢21世紀美術館館長。

2　2021年1月末に株式会社アブストラクトエ
ンジンに社名変更、チーム「ライゾマティクス」
「パノラマティクス」を設置し、株式会社フロ
ウプラトウを設立。

3　「『メディアアート（media art）』とは、主に複製
芸術時代以降のメディア（コンピューターやエレク
トロニクス機器等）を用い、双方向性、参加体
験性等を特徴として表現される芸術領域で
ある」。それに対し「『メディア芸術』とは、メディ
アアート、アニメーション、マンガ、ゲーム、映
画等、複製技術や先端技術等を用いた総
合的な芸術である」。森山朋絵／国立メディ
ア芸術総合センター（仮称）設立準備委員
会「国立メディア芸術総合センター（仮称）基
本計画」、2009年8月、p. 2

4　Frank B.Gilbreth and Lillian M.Gilbreth,
*Applied motion study; a collection of
papers on the efficient method to industrial
preparedness*, Sturgis & Walton Company,
1917. 及び、坪内和夫（早稲田大学理工学部）
「人間工学の方法論 VI：人間作業動作の
分析法 III」3.3クロノサイクルグラフ、『人間
工学』第2巻3号、1965年、pp. 25-26

れを「これですか」と探り当ててアーカイブする。つまり、彼らは変異遺伝子的に異界から侵入した表現者ではない。芸術と技術が不可分であったルネサンス以前からあった、自らの表現をプラットフォームごと創出しようと開発を重ねる、シンプルかつダイレクトな普遍的方法論の実装者なのである。結果としてそれが、少し先をスペキュラティブに見ているという評価につながる。そのような世界線に立って本展を見るとき、研究機関的な集合体として彼らが持つ、理学部／工学部的な面──その両面を見ることが重要であり、「デバイスアート」や「ロマンスエンジニアリング」[5]という言葉を生み出した日本において、とりわけエンジニアリングと実装の術を注視すべきことに思い至る。さらに、そこに美学芸術学的な面を付加するのが従来型のキュレーターの役割だったということになるだろう。

幾 つ か の 作 品 に 関 す る ノ ー ト

メディアアートにとっては再現も新作も同じであることから、本展はほぼ全新作となった。ライゾマティクスは最後の瞬間までデフラグ／最適化を繰り返し、初日以降もOngoingに一部を更新した。それはネガティブでも驚きでもない。彼らは工学系研究室と同様、研究成果をシェアしフィードバックし先へ進むメンバーの集合体だからである。ゆえに、プロローグの映像マッピングと体験デバイスカウンターに続く部屋には、約600の過去作品のビジュアルクロニクルと、作家が最も興味を持つ最新作とが同時に並んだ。一方《NFTs and CryptoArt-Experiment》では、作品売買のパラダイムシフトが"Gold Rush"として可視化されている。「現代美術」的にはクラシックな複製芸術論が思い浮かぶが、このプラットフォームの価値はその変異スピードにある。むしろコミュニケーションサービスPIXIVに溢れる作品群やミクシィ、エア学会としてのニコニコ学会β、ビットコイン取引、それらを取りまく多様なSNSに集うコミュニティの勃興期の活況が想起される。

また《Rhizomatiks × ELEVENPLAY "multiplex"》とその前室を往来することによって、体験者は現実とAR（拡張現実）の境界を往来する。個展直前の《border 2021》公演では、MIKIKO率いるELEVENPLAYが爆音とともにパフォーマンスしつつ、AR世界にいる体験者の肩に素早く触れ、現実世界へ引き戻した。優れたAR表現の極北、生命／非生命の境界、生死の境界を超えるような一つの到達点がそこにはあった。今作では、健気に動く人工物ロボティクスCubeの上に初めてダンサーが乗る。OmniホイールがM・デュシャンの《埃の培養》(撮影｜マン・レイ)を思わせる轍をたどるにつれ、研ぎ澄まされた映像と音が「人と機械」の境界を曖昧にし、存在しない「肉体の気配」が生まれる。何より凄いのは、これらが約10分ごとに実空間で正確に再現され続けることである。

ARにも100年の歴史がある。90年代半ば、人工現実感(VR)の先進国たる日本で、筆者は設立されたばかりのVRの学会に誘われ、理事やIVRC審査員を長く務め、IEEEに投稿し、その趨勢を間近に見た。[6]「電脳コイル」や《セカイカメラ》、近年では本展で展示中の《Pokémon GO AR》デバイスを含め、舘暲や廣瀬通孝ら初代研究者が「3度目のVR元年」と呼ぶ活

5　岩田洋夫(筑波大学)「『デバイスアート』とはメカトロ技術や素材技術を駆使しテクノロジーの本質を見せる芸術様式を指す」。(独)科学技術振興機構 戦略的創造研究推進事業(CREST)「デバイスアートにおける表現系科学技術の創成」(プロジェクトメンバー：安藤英由樹、稲見昌彦、岩田洋夫、草原真知子、クワクボリョウタ、児玉幸子、土佐信道、八谷和彦、前田太郎、矢野博明)、2009年
土佐信道「ロマンスとエンジニアリングがあれば、人は空を飛べる」。明和電機10周年「ROMANCE＊ENGINEERING展」渋谷パルコパート3・SQUARE7、2002年

6　日本バーチャルリアリティ学会(1996設立)及び国際学生対抗バーチャルリアリティコンテスト(1993年創設)。IEEE(アイ・トリプル・イー、Institute of Electrical and Electronics Engineers)は、米国に本部を置き世界最大規模の電気情報工学分野の学術研究団体、技術標準化機関。
Tomoe Moriyama, "Curating Digital Media—Next Generation of Japanese Media Art & Exhibition," *Proceeding of IV '06*, IEEE Computer Society, London, 2006, pp. 664–670.

況を経て、社会のメタバース化は進んだ。図らずも疫病によってXRは劇的に普及したが、成果を早期に見せていたのはSIGGRAPH（全米電算機学会）'93のTomorrow's Reality（M・クルーガー、J・ショー、S・フィッシャーら）や、SIGGRAPH 2000のエム・アール・システム研究所（通商産業省／キヤノン）のデモである。水飛沫を上げて掌の上で跳ねるイルカには「座標精度の正確さ」があった。時を経て、ライゾマティクスの異常なレジストレーション精度が《multiplex》をより優れた表現にした。その作品世界には、論文「A Taxonomy of Mixed Reality Visual Displays」（ポール・ミルグラム／岸野文郎、1994年）にいう4つの複合現実世界「Virtual-Reality Continuum」[7]がシームレスに共存する。

　1990年代には八谷和彦や松村泰三が見えざる赤外線を作品に応用したが、複数のライゾマティクス作品で「不可視なものの可視化」が重要な役割を果たしている。[8] 不可視光である赤外線を利用したモーションキャプチャシステム──その構造は、屋外のサンクンガーデンで衛星群を指しつつ自律的に活動する"コロ助"《RTK Laser Robotiks Experiment》や、後述する《particles 2021》のサーキットを巡る球デバイス（今回は自発光せず、不可視の赤外線LEDを内蔵）と通底している。かつて「ミッション［宇宙×芸術］」展（東京都現代美術館、2014年）[9]でも衛星による地上への描画を試行したが、今作で準天頂衛星「みちびき」やGPS、各国の衛星に向けて屋外でレーザーを放つロボティクス"コロ助"は、衛星からの監視ではなく、自らが指し示す複数の衛星との信号送受信から、RTK-GNSSの手法を用い、自らの位置を高精度で算出し動いている。

　展示のクライマックスにはマッシブなエンジニアリング作品を──と設置されたのが《particles 2021》である。真鍋・石橋やライゾマティクスはArs Electronicaとも縁が深い。2003年から約10年間Prix Ars Electronica審査員を務めるうち、筆者は真鍋ら多くのメディアアーティストや石黒浩ら研究者とともにArs Electronica新センターの開館式典に招かれた。^{fig.1}リンツ市が欧州文化都市となった2009年元旦、真鍋はセンター開館記念イベントとして、建物を覆う大型壁面ディスプレイを駆使した最初のビジュアルサウンドイベントを、ドナウ河畔で敢行したのである。その帰国後、筆者は同フェスティバル30周年にあわせた日本の受賞者特集展「サイバーアーツジャパン」（東京都現代美術館、2010年）[10]を企画し、真鍋の《Electric stimulus to face》の16人バージョン

7　Paul Milgram (University of Toronto)／Fumio Kishino (Osaka University), "A Taxonomy of Mixed Reality Visual Displays," *IEICE Transactions on Information and Systems* vol. E77-D, no. 12(12), 1994, pp. 1321-1329にいう、現実世界(Real Environment)／現実にバーチャルが混入した世界(Augmented Reality)／バーチャルに少し現実が混入した世界(Augmented Virtuality)／完全にバーチャルな世界(Virtual Environment)。

8　八谷和彦《見ることは信じること》(1996年)ほか一連の作品群が「メディアラボ第2期展示『魔法かもしれない』」(日本科学未来館、2008年)及び「魔法かもしれない」(SKIPシティ彩の国ビジュアルプラザ、2011年)で展示された。

9　「ミッション［宇宙×芸術］」展(東京都現代美術館、2014年)にて多摩美術大学／東京大学《ARTSAT：衛星芸術プロジェクト》(2010年-)を展示し、世界で初めて運用中の芸術衛星INVADERからのデータを用いたメディアインスタレーションを実現、INVADERは会期終了直後の9月2日に大気圏に再突入し消滅した。

10　文化庁メディア芸術祭協賛事業「サイバーアーツジャパン─アルスエレクトロニカの30年」(東京都現代美術館、2010年)にて、日本からの受賞者約200作品(2009年まで)から20組と、過去の全受賞者クロニクルを展示。渡邉英徳《Ars Electronica Archive in Second Life》により、国立新美術館で開催中の文化庁メディア芸術祭受賞作品展会場とリアルタイムに展示空間が連携した。

fig.1

Prix Ars Electronica 2009審査員メンバー、白いジャケットの真鍋大度（Digital Musics）から右に2人置いて筆者（Interactive Art）、左に2人置いてCasey Reas（Processing 開発者の1人、Hybrid Art）ほか、創始者レオポルドセーダー、芸術監督シュトッカーの姿もある

Members of the Prix Ars Electronica 2009 jury. Daito Manabe (Digital Musics) in the white jacket, to the right, the author, Tomoe Moriyama (Interactive Art), and Casey Reas (one of the developers of Processing, Hybrid Art) on the left. The founder, Leopoldseder and the artistic director, Stocker, are also there.

を展示、筋電を使ったイベントも実施することができた。^{fig.2} リンツから芸術監督G・シュトッカーと先頃惜しくも逝去したArs Electronica創始者H・レオポルドゼーダーも来館したが、彼らは日本のメディアアート環境への理解が深く、日本の若手には「『アート&テクノロジーと社会』を常に意識せよ」と助言していた。それを体現するライゾマティクスへの彼らの信頼は、センター／グランプリ／フェスティバル／フューチャーラボを通じて、いつも非常に厚かった。^{fig.3}

　最初の《particles》が登場した2011年のグランプリ審査は、東日本大震災直後の静かな空気の中、リンツで進められた。GALAでの喜ばしい受賞発表と、筆者が現地でモデレーターを務めた受賞者シンポジウムでの対話が思い出される。彼らは当初Hybrid Art部門を目指したが、Interactive Art部門で受賞した。Hybrid Artは2000年代半ばに新設され、横断的というよりも複合的な表現や技術を顕彰する部門である。当初よりE・カッツらバイオアートの受賞が多く、バイオアート部門的な解釈もあったが、ライゾマティクス的には本展タイトルにも通底する、本来の複合的な表現として《particles》を呈示したと思われる。^{fig.4}

　一方、2010年前後には3D計測技術やハードウェア制御技術の向上と並行して「新しい3次元空間装置の開発」というミッションが全世界的に探求

fig.2

Cyber Arts Japan – Ars Electronica 30 Years for Art and Media Technology

(February 02 – March 03, 2010, Museum of Contemporary Art Tokyo)

Japan has close bonds with Ars Electronica because of the numerous Japanese artists who have related with Prix, Festival or Center exhibition. Through many art works and events, the exhibition will explore new possibilities of expression in current Japanese Art scene.

www.mot-art-museum.jp/exhibition/cyberarts/

ウェブサイト「ARS ELECTRONICA EXPORT "CyberArts Japan"」(東京都現代美術館、2010年)より、真鍋大度パフォーマンス風景［参考図版］(*freeze!–2009 International MedTech Art Show*, National Taiwan Museum of Fine Arts, Taiwan)

Daito Manabe performance scene from website: ARS ELECTRONICA EXPORT, "CyberArts Japan" (Museum of Contemporary Art Tokyo, 2010) [reference Image], (*freeze!–2009 International MedTech Art Show*, National Taiwan Museum of Fine Arts, Taiwan)

fig.3

Festival Ars Electronica 2010 の企画展「Repair Yourself」にて、《fade out》の蓄光スクリーンにレーザープロジェクターで次第に描画され消えていく筆者の肖像。Tabakfabrik Linz(リンツ)、2010年

Portrait of the author, gradually drawn and disappearing by laser projector on the luminescent screen of *fade out* at the exhibition "Repair Yourself," Festival Ars Electronica 2010, Tabakfabrik Linz (Linz), 2010.

fig.4

受賞者トーク「Prix Forum V—Interactive Art」
配信中の石橋、真鍋、筆者（司会）ほか受賞者、
Festival Ars Electronica 2011、ブルックナーハウ
ス（リンツ）、2011年9月5日
Ishibashi, Manabe, the author (moderator)
and other award-winners during the delivery
of the award-winner talk "Prix Forum V–
Interactive Art," Festival Ars Electronica
2011, Brucknerhaus, Linz, September 5, 2011.

されていた。実現手法は多様で、国内ではプラズマが用いられ、海外ではArs Electrocnia FuturelabがLED搭載ドローンによる《Spaxels》を発表した。[11]《particles》はそのさなかに山口情報芸術センター［YCAM］で成立し、文化庁メディア芸術祭で受賞後、国立新美術館で披露され、LenovoのTVCFにも登場した。インタラクションに加え、自発光する球がレールを巡る状況音と光の粒子で空間の奥行がより感じられた最初の《particles》は、世界が当時盛んに取り組んだ「人類の夢」への彼らなりの答えだったのである。

　　本展の《particles 2021》は、真鍋らによる「音響彫刻」として生まれ変わり、新たな生命を吹き込まれた。動く球を正確に射抜く半導体レーザー光のパラメータと球の位置情報により、音が生まれる。その音響合成手法はグラニューラーシンセシスであり、球の位置の高低で音程や音像が決まるが、的確な音像の成立じたい至難の業であろう。しかしその音色は、真鍋・石橋がともに過去のレファレンスに挙げる岩井俊雄作品《映像装置としてのピアノ》[12]（1995年）においても、MIDIピアノがランダムに生む不協和音が不思議な調和を持っていたことを想起させる。展示室では、作家本人も名づけ得ない、デヴィッド・リンチ的なストロボ光とカッティング音のシーンに人々は釘づけになり、輝く巨大な構造体を見上げる。《particles 2021》は時に地鳴りのように震え、鳴動する彫刻として屹立している。

後 ライゾマティクス

来場者は最後に、エピローグにある多数のモニターを通して、カメラが捉えた自分の姿が「非生命」認識され実写に戻るのを目にする。逆に、陳列されたアンリアレイジの服は「生命」認識され、ぼかされてしまう。また、たとえコロナ禍にともなう休館下にも、ミラーワールドたるオンライン会場が本領を発揮する。展示支援システムの持つ課題[13]に彼らが応えてくれた「体験デバイス」は、専ら順路や位置情報のみを可視化しているが、観客の生体データから鑑賞体験の質を評価できる日も遠からず訪れるかもしれない。

11　斎藤英雄（慶應義塾大学）「『自由空間に3次元コンテンツを描き出す技術』研究終了報告書」、戦略的創造研究推進事業CREST研究領域「デジタルメディア作品の制作を支援する基盤技術」、2012年。またアルスエレクトロニカ・フューチャーラボはドローンを用いた《Spaxels》（2012年–）以降インテルと協働し《Drone100》（2015年）で世界記録を樹立した。
https://ars.electronica.art/center/de/drone-100/

12　岩井俊雄は《映像装置としてのピアノ》（ZKM、1995年）のあと坂本龍一との共作「現代音楽を楽しもう——XII 坂本龍一×岩井俊雄 MUSIC PLAYS IMAGES×IMAGES PLAY MUSIC」（水戸芸術館ACM劇場、1996年）を発表、同作でPrix Electronica 1997 Interactive Art部門のグランプリ受賞。さらに《MPI×IPM（Music Plays Images×Images Play Music）》（恵比寿ザ・ガーデンホール、1997年）で公演。真鍋は岩井の《TENORI-ON》ほかにも言及している。

13　森山朋絵「アートミュージアムにおける展示支援の現状と課題・2017」、『東京都現代美術館研究紀要 2016』、2017年、pp 115–122

私たちは、ライゾマティクス以後の世界線を想う。ライゾマティクス展へ至る道には、過去からの無数の試みが連なっている。ダイナミックプロジェクションを用いたPerfumeのステージは、動く対象に人力で投影する「写し絵」を想起させ、メッシュスクリーンを駆使した演出は、エティエンヌ・ガスパール・ロベルトソンによる「ファンタスマゴリア」[14]の空間エフェクトに通底する。オーケストラルヒットはヤニス・クセナキスに、グレインに分解されたマイクロサウンドはデニス・ガボールに遡るように、《particles 2021》もまた、遠い未来に誰かの手で、バシェの音響彫刻[15]のように復元される日が来るだろう。

かつて「エレクトロニカリー・ユアーズ」展(東京都写真美術館、1998年)図録の序文で、英国ナショナルポートレートギャラリーのチャールズ・S・スミス館長は「いずれ工学の学位を持つ学芸員を美術館に迎える日が来る」と予見した。[16]今世紀に入り、技術的な基礎論文に加えてアートへの応用論文も業績として認められはじめ、理学・工学系から芸術領域への進出が増え、プログラミング教育も2020年に義務教育化された。「エンジニアリングの美をわかる人がいると信じて」「ブレストより手を動かすのが大事」で「実験データを作品にする」作家の活動は続く。現代美術領域は、ここ何十年も「技術が先に立つアート」に不寛容であった。しかし1995年には既に東京都写真美術館が「ヴァーチャル・リアリティも体感」と紹介され、今やメディアアート/メディア芸術は必修化された。fig.5 [17]つまり本展は、現代美術領域においても「テクノロジーはコンセプトになりうる」[18]ことがついに成立した瞬間だったのである。

現代美術はまだ、1960年代の壮大な伏線回収中かもしれない。しかし過去を内包する前衛として、二つの大戦をはさみ約30年ごとにマヴォ/実験工房/ダムタイプ/ライゾマティクスと続くコレクティブの次世代は、既に生まれている。かつて筆者らがゲストキュレーターを務めた「ネクスト―メディアアートの新世代」展(NTTインターコミュニケーション・センター[ICC]、2004年)に、真鍋は「新世代」として登場した。また石橋は《G-display》(1999年)や、名和晃平との工学系協働をいち早く実装していた。[19]やがて彼らはER(エモーショナルリアリティ)やクロスモーダルな五感の共有さえ課題とし、解を見つけていくだろう。再び社会はオリンピックから万博へと向かい、ムーンショット型研究開発やアルテミス計画が発動する――しかし、まだ「人間とテクノロジー」[20]という命題は終わらない。

14 *Étienne-Gaspard Robertson, Mémoires récréatifs, scientifiques et anecdotique (Recreational, Scientific and anecdotal memories)*, vol. 1, 2の口絵、1831年

15 ベルナール・バシェ/フランソワ・バシェが1969年に武満徹の招聘で制作、大阪万博EXPO '70で展示後に解体された。大阪府、京都市立芸術大学、東京藝術大学が復元を進め5点を「音と造形のレゾナンス―バシェ音響彫刻と岡本太郎の共振」展(川崎市岡本太郎美術館、2020年)にて展示。

16 チャールズ・S・スミス「序」、J・ライハート/森山朋絵ほか共著『エレクトロニカリー・ユアーズ』、東京都写真美術館、1998年、p. 10より「だんだんと電子的なコレクションが増えるよう私たちは念願しています。いずれ工学の学位を持つ学芸員を美術館に迎える日が来るでしょうし、また新しい空間は防音にしなければならないでしょう。私たちはさらに展示室がこうした変化を反映して発展するものと理解しています」

17 「ヴァーチャル・リアリティも体感 東京都写真美術館」(特集:アート驚く日本の美術館'95)、『太陽』1995年4月号、平凡社。森山朋絵「理事巻頭言 バーチャルリアリティ後の世界」、『日本バーチャルリアリティ学会誌』第26巻1号、2021年、pp. 4-5、及び、文部科学省「(旧)中学校学習指導要領」、2002年

18 『日曜美術館「ライゾマティクス まだ見ぬ世界へ」』(NHK Eテレ、2021年4月4日放送)にて、長谷川祐子らのコメントより。

19 森山朋絵「まだ遠く、暗い道の果てに」、『ネクスト:メディアアートの新世代』、NTT出版、2004年、pp. 28-29。また石橋は《G-Display》を「フューチャー・デザイン・シンポジウム」(ICC、1999年)で発表した10年後、2009年に名和晃平/DGN石橋素・藤元明のプロジェクト「HUMMING」を立ち上げ「iida EXIBITION 2010 SUMMER」(表参道ヒルズ space O、2010年)にて、名和コンセプトモデルの映像イメージ・送信システム部分を担当。

20 「特集:人間とテクノロジー」(『美術手帖』1969年5月増刊号、美術出版社)には「別冊付録1|テクノロジーと芸術の歴史的展開」と併せてG・ケペッシュ、N・シェフェール、J・ライハート、山口勝弘、幸村真佐男らが論考を掲載した。内閣府が主導する「ムーンショット型研究開発制度」は「人が身体、脳、空間、時間の制約から解放された社会を実現」することを目指す(稲見昌彦「はじめに」、『自在化身体論』、NTS、2021年、p. 5)。アルテミス計画はNASAが2024年までに展開するアポロ計画以来の有人月着陸プロジェクト。

fig.5

故・池田満寿夫が東京都写真美術館でソムラー&ミニョノーのVR作品《Trans Plant》を体験する姿が掲載された特集、「ヴァーチャル・リアリティも体感 東京都写真美術館」、『太陽』1995年4月号表紙、平凡社
Artist Masuo Ikeda, experiencing Sommerer & Mignonneau's VR work *Trans Plant* at the Tokyo Metropolitan Museum of Photography, from "Experiencing Virtual Reality: Tokyo Metropolitan Museum of Photography," *THE SUN* No.406, April 1995, Heibon-sha, cover.

Post-Rhizomatiks: on their solo exhibition

Tomoe Moriyama

Introduction

A solo exhibition by Rhizomatiks has opened at the Museum of Contemporary Art, Tokyo. It seems imperative for us to consider the significance of this exhibition taking place at the current moment. The planning for this project began in earnest in mid-2020, at a time when the world was confronted by the singular event that was COVID-19. In addition to marking the 15th anniversary of the group's formation and being their first large-scale solo exhibition at a public museum, it was also the last exhibition at the museum organized by its curator.[1] I was given the opportunity to stage this exhibition, in my capacity as a curator who has worked on art and technology exhibitions at public museums for a long time, from the late 1980s up until the present. The mission this time around was to install a profuse, fortress-like array of more than 500 devices in the exhibition galleries, overcome a variety of limiting factors, and create both online and physical venues in a way that would recall a digital twin computing environment, or parallel worlds. In January 2021, the corporate organization Rhizomatiks was restructured [2] as part of its ongoing evolution, and preparations for the exhibition kicked into a higher, explosive gear. In the blink of an eye, opening day on March 20 was upon us.

The establishment of Rhizomatiks and its development

Rhizomatiks are often referred to as a "new artist" working in a "new domain." But is that really the case? Each time an exhibition in this field is organized, we recoil from the cliché of how it "uses the latest technology." Media art uses both new and old technologies in "unexpected ways" as platforms for expression, but these are not limited to digital ones. [3] When we think about the formation and evolution of Rhizomatiks, we are reminded of how the domain of media art has expanded from the past to the present. Manabe studied mathematics at university, while Ishibashi studied engineering before attending the International Academy of Media Arts and Sciences (IAMAS) in Ogaki, Gifu Prefecture. Ever since this school opened, media artists active both in Japan and abroad have taught at the school and gathered there as artists-in-residence, including Christa Sommerer and Laurent Mignonneau, Scott Snibbe, Toshio Iwai, and many others, under the leadership of its first president, Itsuo Sakane. In line with how media art teaches how to "learn from the past while forging ahead into the future," these artists devoted themselves to prior research, just

1   Yuko Hasegawa, Artistic Director of the Museum of Contemporary Art Tokyo (until the end of March 2021), currently Director of the 21st Century Museum of Contemporary Art, Kanazawa.

2   In the end of Jan. 2021, they have changed the name of the company to Abstract Engine and established two teams within it: Rhizomatiks and Panoramatiks, also they established Flowplateaux as an associated company.

3   "The term 'media art' refers to the field of art characterized by interactivity and participatory experiences that relies primarily on media (computers, electronic devices, and so on) from the age of reproducible art and after. 'Media arts,' on the other hand, is a comprehensive and integrated art form that deploys media art, animation, comics, games, movies, and other reproductive and advanced technologies." Tomoe Moriyama / National Media Arts Center (tentative name) Establishment Preparation Committee, "National Media Arts Center (tentative name) Basic Plan," August 2009, p 2.

as they would with an engineering thesis, which Manabe posted on the internet as a kind of archive. The idea of visualization, for instance, dates back to the nightingale who visualized the actual situation concerning casualties during the Crimean War and submitted it to Queen Victoria, while motion capture, which was seen every year at ACM SIGGRAPH (Association for Computing Machinery's Special Interest Group on Computer Graphics) in the early 2000s, is more related to the "chronocyclegraph" [4] by Frank Gilbreth and his wife than to Marey and Muybridge in the 19th century. Manabe would then instantly search for and archive these things, saying "is this it?" In other words, these artists were not some kind of genetic mutant invaders from another world. Rather, they were the implementers of simple, direct, and universal methodologies that have existed since before the Renaissance, when art and technology were inseparable from each other, and which were being developed to create platforms for their own artistic practices. The result is a reputation for looking a little ahead of them, in a speculative manner. In viewing the current exhibition from this sort of global perspective, it is vital to look at both sides—the science and engineering aspect that Rhizomatiks have as a collective that resembles a research institution, as well as the art of how they engineer and implement their projects, particularly in Japan where the terms "device art" and "romance engineering" [5] have been coined. In addition, it would be the role of the conventional curator to add a further aesthetic and academic layer to their practice.

Notes on a few of the artworks

Since reproductions and new works are basically the same thing in media art, this exhibition consisted almost entirely of new works. Rhizomatiks performed a repeated process of defragmentation and optimization up until the very last moment, and some parts were updated on an ongoing basis even after the first day of the exhibition. This is neither negative nor surprising, because they are a collective who share their research results, give and receive feedback, and make progress, just like an engineering laboratory. As such, in the room following the prologue video mapping and hands-on device counter, a visual chronicle of about 600 past works and the latest works that the artists are most personally interested in were displayed simultaneously. *NFTs and CryptoArt-Experiment*, on the other hand, visualized a paradigm shift in the buying and selling of artworks as "Gold Rush". In terms of contemporary art, this work recalls the classic theory of reproducible art. While the value of this platform may lie in the speed with which it mutates, it is more reminiscent of the boom surrounding the explosion of various communities centered on communication services like PIXIV, with its profusion of artworks, Mixi, Nico Nico Gakkai Beta as an Fictional society, Bitcoin, and blockchain trading, as well as the various social media platforms associated with them.

Also, by moving back and forth between *Rhizomatiks × ELEVENPLAY "multiplex"* and the room in front of it, the person partaking in the experience traverses the boundary between reality and augmented reality (AR). Just before this solo exhibition, ELEVENPLAY, led by MIKIKO, gave an aurally explosive performance

4   Frank B. Gilbreth and Lillian M. Gilbreth, *Applied motion study; a collection of papers on the efficient method to industrial preparedness*, Sturgis & Walton Company, 1917. Kazuo Tsubouchi, Waseda University, 3.3 Chronocyclegraph, "Methodology of ergonomics VI: work study, its application to ergonomics III," *The Japanese Journal of Ergonomics* Vol. 2, No. 3, 1965, pp25–26.

5   "Device Art is a new form of art that displays the essence of technology through the use of new materials and mechatronic devices.," by "Expressive Science and Technology for Device Art Project" (Collaborators: Hideyuki Ando, Masahiko Inami, Hiroo Iwata, Machiko Kusahara, Ryota Kuwakubo, Sachiko Kodama, Novmichi Tosa, Kazuhiko Hachiya, Taro Maeda, and Hiroaki Yano), which was funded by Core Research for Evolutional Science and Technology (CREST) of Japan Science and Technology Agency, 2009.
And by Novmichi Tosa, "With romance and engineering, one can fly." From Maywa Denki 10th Anniversary, "ROMANCE*ENGINEERING Exhibition," Shibuya Parco Part 3, SQUARE 7, 2002.

called *border 2021*. Sometimes the dancers were briefly brushing the shoulders of the audience in the AR world, and pulling them back to the real world. This was a pinnacle of advanced AR artistic expression, a high point that transcended the boundaries between life and non-life, and the border separating life and death. In this work, a dancer rides for the first time on the Cube, an artificial robot that moves briskly with a sense of vitality. As the Omni wheel follows the ruts, reminiscent of Duchamp's *Cultivation of Dust* (Photo | Man Ray), the sharpened images and sounds blur the boundary between man and machine, creating the "presence of a body" that does not exist. The most amazing thing is that all these phenomena are continuously reproduced with precision in real space every 10 minutes or so.

Augmented reality, too, has a hundred years of history behind it. During the mid-1990s, in Japan, a leading country in the field of virtual reality (VR), I was invited to join a newly established international association for VR, and began working with them. [6] I served as a council member, board member, and Interverse Virtual Reality Challenge (IVRC) judge for a long time, contributing the paper to the Institute of Electrical and Electronics Engineers (IEEE) and watching trends closely. The transformation of society into a metaverse has progressed by way of "Dennou Coil," *Sekai Camera*, and more recently, the *Pokémon GO* phenomenon, which its device is currently on display in this exhibition, in what the original researchers, including Susumu Tachi and Michitaka Hirose, called "the third first year of VR." Although XR was dramatically popularized by the epidemic, I saw the early results were shown on in "Tomorrow's Reality" (M. Kruger, J. Shaw, S. Fisher, et al.) at SIGGRAPH '93 and the MR Systems Laboratory (Ministry of International Trade and Industry/Canon)'s demonstration at SIGGRAPH 2000. Over time, Rhizomatiks' extraordinary precision of registration has made *multiplex* an even better expression. In the world of these works, the four virtual reality continuums described in the article "A Taxonomy of Mixed Reality Visual Displays" (Paul Milgram and Fumio Kishino, 1994) [7] exist seamlessly alongside each other.

In the 1990s, Kazuhiko Hachiya and Taizo Matsumura deployed invisible infrared light in their works. This notion of visualizing the invisible has gone on to play an important role in several works by Rhizomatiks. [8] A motion capture system that makes use of invisible infrared rays—this is a structure similar to that found in "Korosuke (*RTK Laser Robotiks Experiment*)," which operates autonomously while pointing to a group of satellites in a sunken garden, and the spherical device that tours the circuit in *particles 2021* (this time, it does not emit light, but contains built-in, invisible infrared LEDs). Previously, at the "mission [Space × Art]" exhibition (Museum of Contemporary Art Tokyo, 2014) [9], we tried drawing on the ground using satellites, and in this work, the robot "Korosuke" emits lasers outdoors that target the Quasi-Zenith Satellite "Michibiki," GPS, and satellites belonging to various countries. In this work, Korosuke moves by using the RTK-GNSS method to calculate its own position with a high degree of accuracy by transmitting and receiving signals from multiple satellites indicated by itself, instead of being monitored by satellites.

For the climax of the exhibition, *particles 2021* was installed as

6   Virtual Reality Society of Japan (established in 1996) and International collegiate Virtual Reality Contest / Interverse Virtual Reality Challenge (established in 1993). IEEE (Institute of Electrical and Electronics Engineers) is the world's largest scale academic research organization and technical standardization body in the field of electrical and information engineering, headquartered in the United States.
Tomoe Moriyama, "Curating Digital Media—Next Generation of Japanese Media Art & Exhibition," *Proceeding of IV '06*, IEEE Computer Society, London, 2006, pp. 664–670.

7   There are Real Environment / Augmented Reality, a world where reality is mixed with virtual / Augmented Virtuality, a world where virtual is mixed with a little reality / Virtual Environment, a completely virtual world.
Paul Milgram, University of Toronto / Fumio Kishino, Osaka University, "A Taxonomy of Mixed Reality Visual Displays," *IEICE Transactions on Information and Systems* vol. E77-D, no. 12 (12), 1994, pp. 1321–1329.

8   Kazuhiko Hachiya, *Seeing is believing*, 1996, and a series of other works were exhibited in the "Media Lab Phase 2 Exhibition 'It Could Be Magic,'" 2008 at National Museum of Emerging Science and Innovation (MIRAIKAN, Tokyo) and "It Could Be Magic", 2011 at SKIP City Sai-no-kuni Visual Plaza.

9   We exhibited *ARTSAT: Satellite Art Project* (2010–) by Tama Art University / The University of Tokyo, at the "mission [SPACE×ART]–beyond Cosmologies" exhibition held at the Museum of Contemporary Art Tokyo, in 2014. It was the world's first media installation deploying data from an operating satellite. INVADER deorbited and reentered the Earth's atmosphere for disintegration on September 2, 2014.

a massive work of engineering. Manabe, Ishibashi, and Rhizomatiks have a close relationship with Ars Electronica, and while serving as a member of the Prix Ars Electronica jury for about 10 years starting in 2003, I was invited to attend the opening ceremony of the new Ars Electronica Center with Manabe and many other media artists and researchers, including Hiroshi Ishiguro. fig.1 [→p.204] On New Year's Day 2009, the day Linz became European Capital of Culture, Manabe staged the first visual sound event by the Danube River, using a large wall display that covered the entire building to celebrate the opening of the Center. After seeing this event, I returned to Japan and organized "CyberArts Japan" (Museum of Contemporary Art Tokyo, 2010) [10], an exhibition featuring Japanese award winners to coincide with the 30th anniversary of the festival, and exhibited a 16-person version of *Electric stimulus to face*, which made Manabe internationally famous. fig.2 [→p.205] A myoelectric event was also held. Artistic director Gerfried Stocker and festival founder Hannes Leopoldseder also came from Linz to visit the festival. Leopoldseder, who sadly passed away recently, had a deep understanding of Japan's media art environment and advised young Japanese artists to "always be aware of 'art, technology and society.'" The trust that they placed in Rhizomatiks to put this into practice was always very strong, through the Center, Grand Prix, Festival, and Futurelab. fig.3 [→p.205]

The Grand Prix jury for 2011, when the first version of *particles* appeared, convened in Linz in the quiet atmosphere immediately following the Great East Japan Earthquake. I remember the joyful announcement of the awards at GALA ceremony and the conversations at the winners' symposium that I moderated there. While Rhizomatiks had initially aimed for the Hybrid Art category, which was established in the mid-2000s to honor practices and techniques that are composite rather than cross-disciplinary, they were given the award of distinction in the Interactive Art category. From the very beginning, many bio-artists such as Eduardo Kac won the award, and some saw the category as something akin to bio-art. As far as Rhizomatiks was concerned, however, they had presented *particles* as an essentially composite work that also resonates with the title of the present exhibition. fig.4 [→p.206]

Meanwhile, around 2010, along with the improvement of 3D measurement and hardware control technologies, the mission of "developing a new 3D spatial device" was being explored in the world, and a diverse range of techniques was deployed to achieve this. In Japan, plasma was used, while outside the country the Ars Electronica Futurelab presented *Spaxels*, which made use of LED-equipped drones. [11] *particles* was created at the Yamaguchi Center for Arts and Media (YCAM) in the midst of this, and after winning an award at the Japan Media Arts Festival, it was presented at the National Art Center, Tokyo, in addition to appearing in a Lenovo TV commercial. In addition to the interactive element, the first version of *particles*, in which the depth of the space was enhanced by the sound and light particles of a light-emitting ball traveling on rails, was Rhizomatiks' own answer to the "dream of humanity" that the world was feverishly pursuing at the time.

For this exhibition, *particles 2021* was reborn as an "acoustic sculpture" that Manabe and others worked on, acquiring a new

10 Sanctioned Event of the Japan Media Arts Festival "Cyber Arts Japan—Ars Electronica 30 Years for Art and Media Technology" (Museum of Contemporary Art Tokyo, 2010), showcased some 200 award-winning works by 20 groups of artists from Japan (up until 2009), as well as a chronicle of all past award winners. Hidenori Watanave's *Ars Electronica Archive in Second Life* linked the exhibition space with the venue for the exhibition of award-winning works from the Japan Media Arts Festival that was being held at the National Art Center, Tokyo in real time.

11 Hideo Saito, Keio University, "Technology to Display 3D Contents into Free Space, Research Completion Report," Competitive Funding for Team-Based Basic Researches, funded by Core Research for Evolutional Science and Technology (CREST) of Japan Science and Technology Agency, 2012
Ars Electronica Futurelab has been collaborating with Intel since *Spaxels* (2012–), which used drones, and set a world record with *Drone100* (2015). https://ars.electronica.art/center/de/drone-100/

lease of life. The position of the sphere, based on the parameters of a semiconductor laser beam that accurately shoots through a moving sphere, produce sounds. While the sound is synthesized through granular synthesis, and the pitch of the sound or sound image is determined by the position of the sphere, the actual construction of a precise sound image is exceedingly difficult. The timbre of the sound, however, reminds us of the mysterious harmony of the dissonant tones randomly produced by the MIDI piano in Toshio Iwai's *Piano — as image media* [12] (1995), which both Manabe and Ishibashi cite as a past reference. In the gallery, people found themselves glued to the scene of David Lynch-like strobe lights and cutting sounds that the artists themselves could not put a name to, looking up at the giant, shining structure. *particles 2021* stands tall as a sculpture that sometimes shudders and rumbles like the earth.

Post-Rhizomatiks

At the end of the exhibition, visitors see their own image captured by the camera through the numerous monitors in the epilogue section recognized as "non-life," and returned to the world of live action. The *Anrealage* clothes on display, on the other hand, are perceived as "life," and become blurred out. In addition, even when the museum is closed due to COVID-19, the mirror world of the online venue comes into its own. And the "experiential device" they have developed in response to the challenges posed by exhibition support systems [13] visualizes only the exhibition route and location information, but the day when the quality of the viewing experience can be evaluated from the biological data of the audience may not be that far off.

We contemplate a world line after Rhizomatiks. The road that has led up to this exhibition is lined with countless past attempts. Perfume's stage, which makes use of dynamic projection, recalls the phenomenon of "Utsushi-e" as Japanese Magic Lanterns, in which human power is used to project images onto moving objects, while the staging, which makes full use of mesh screens, is similar to the spatial effects seen in Étienne-Gaspard Robert's phantasmagoria theater [14]. Just as orchestral hits can be traced back to Iannis Xenakis, and microsounds decomposed into grains can be traced back to Dennis Gabor, *particles 2021* will one day be restored by someone in the distant future, just like François & Bernard Baschet's sound sculptures were [15].

In the foreword to the catalogue of the exhibition "electronically Yours" (Tokyo Metropolitan Museum of Photography, 1998), Charles S. Smith, director of the National Portrait Gallery in the UK, predicted that "We realize that in years to come museums may have curators with engineering degrees." [16] In addition to basic technical theses, theses on the applications of engineering in the field of art have begun to be recognized as achievements starting this century, more and more people from the fields of science and engineering have entered the field of art, and studying programming has become a compulsory part of education in 2020. Believing that there are people who understand the beauty of engineering, and that "moving my hands is more important than brainstorming," in order to "turn experimental data into works

12 After *Piano — as image media* (ZKM, 1995), Toshio Iwai and Ryuichi Sakamoto collaborated on "Let's Enjoy Contemporary Music XII: Ryuichi Sakamoto × Toshio Iwai, MUSIC PLAYS IMAGES × IMAGES PLAY MUSIC" (ACM Theatre, Art Tower Mito, 1996). It won the Golden Nica, Grand Prix in the Interactive Art category at Prix Ars Electronica 1997. Iwai also performed at *MPI × IPM (Music Plays Images × Images Play Music)* (The Garden Hall, Yebisu, Tokyo, 1997). Manabe has also referred to Iwai's *TENORI-ON* and other works.

13 Tomoe Moriyama, "Exhibition Support System Use in Art Museums: Update and Issues 2017," *Annual Report 2016 / Bulletin No.19*, Museum of Contemporary Art Tokyo, 2017, pp. 115–122

14 Frontispiece of Étienne-Gaspard Robertson, *Mémoires récréatifs, scientifiques et anecdotique (Recreational, Scientific and anecdotal memories)* vol. 1 & 2, 1831

15 Created by Bernard and François Baschet at the invitation of Toru Takemitsu in 1969, these sound sculptures were dismantled after being exhibited at Expo '70 in Osaka. The Osaka Prefectural Government, Kyoto City University of Arts, and Tokyo University of the Arts are restoring these works, and five of them will be shown at the exhibition "Resonance of Sound and Form: Baschet's Acoustic Sculptures and Taro Okamoto's Resonance" (Taro Okamoto Museum of Art, Kawasaki City, 2020).

16 "We hope that gradually our electronic collection will grow. We realize that in years to come museums may have curators with engineering degrees, that new spaces will have to be sound proofed, and that the galleries will develop to reflect these changes.," Charles Saumarez Smith, Director, National Portrait Gallery, quoted from "Preface" of *electronically yours* (ed. Jasia Reichardt / Tomoe Moriyama), Tokyo Metropolitan Museum of Photography, 1998, p. 11.

of art," Rhizomatiks' practice continues to develop. For decades, the contemporary art world has been rather intolerant of "technology-first art." Media-conscious media art/media art, however, has already become a compulsory subject in schools. fig.5 [→p.207] [17] In other words, this exhibition represents the moment when the idea that "technology can be conceptualized" [18] finally came to be established in the field of contemporary art as well.

Contemporary art may still be in the process of absorbing and rehabilitating the grand foreshadowing that occurred during the 1960s. The next generation of collectives following in the wake of Mavo, Experimental Workshop, Dumb Type, and Rhizomatiks, however, which comes along about every 30 years between the two World Wars as an avant-garde that encompasses the past, has already emerged. Manabe featured as part of the "new generation" at the exhibition "Next: The New Generation of Media Art" (NTT Intercommunication Center [ICC], 2004), for which the author and others served as guest curators. Ishibashi also realized earlier, his implementation as *G-display* (1999) and other collaborative engineering projects with artists like Kohei Nawa. [19] Even ER (emotional reality) and the cross-modal sharing of the five senses promise to be issues that they will find solutions to in the future. Japanese society is once again going from the Olympics onwards to the World Expo, while The Moonshot Research and Development Program or the Artemis program of NASA will launch...but the proposition of "humans and technology" [20] has not yet faded from view.

17 "Experiencing Virtual Reality: Tokyo Metropolitan Museum of Photography," from Special Feature: Art Surprises Japanese Art Museums '95, *THE SUN* No.406, April 1995, Heibon-sha. Tomoe Moriyama, "Director's Preface: The World after Virtual Reality," *Journal of the Virtual Reality Society of Japan* vol.26, No.1, March 2021, pp. 4–5. Ministry of Education, Culture, Sports, Science and Technology, "Courses of Study for (Former) Junior High School," 2002.

18 Comments by Yuko Hasegawa and others, from NHK Educational TV show "Nichiyo Bijutsukan (NHK Sunday Museum)—Rhizomatiks: To the unknown world," Broadcast on April 4, 2021.

19 Tomoe Moriyama,"Down the long, Dark Road Ahead," in *n_ext: New Generation of Media Artists,* NTT Intercommunication Center [ICC], NTT publishing, 2004, pp. 28–29 Ten years after Ishibashi presenting *G-Display* at "Future Design Symposium" (ICC, 1999), in 2009, Kohei Nawa, DGN Motoi Ishibashi / Akira Fujimoto launched a project called "HUMMING." At the "iida EXHIBITION 2010 SUMMER" (Omotesando Hills, Space O, 2010), Ishibashi was in charge of system design / programming for Nawa's conceptual model.

20 "Feature: Humans and Technology," *Bijutsu Techo,* May 1969 Special Issue, Bijutsu-Shuppan-sha. In addition to "Appendix 1 (separate volume): The Historical Development of Technology and Art," G. Kepes, N. Schöffer, J. Reicherdt, Katsuhiro Yamaguchi, Masao Komura, and others have published important essays in this issue. The Moonshot Research and Development Program, led by the Cabinet Office, aims to "Realization of a society in which human beings can be free from limitations of body, brain, space, and time"(Masahiko Inami, "Introduction," co-auteur *Theory of Jizai-Body*, NTS, 2021, p. 5). And the Artemis program is NASA's manned moon landing project since the Apollo program, which will be deployed by 2024.

ライゾマティクス年譜
1996–2021

編｜ライゾマティクス／森山朋絵

Rhizomatiks Chronicle
1996–2021

Ed. Rhizomatiks / Tomoe Moriyama

凡例　本年譜には、ライゾマティクスとしての活動及び個々のメンバーの歩みを、主要な創作活動を中心に記載した。

Notes　This chronology focuses on the activities of Rhizomatiks, the history of individual members, and their major creative activities.

1996
- 東京理科大学で真鍋大度、齋藤精一、千葉秀憲が出会う

1999
- 石橋素が東京工業大学制御システム工学科を卒業後、岐阜県立国際情報科学芸術アカデミー（IAMAS）に入学
- 石橋がNTTインターコミュニケーションセンター［ICC］にて、当時画期的だった加速度センサーを用いた《G-Display》を展示

2000
- 真鍋が東京理科大学理学部数学科を卒業。大手電機メーカーに入社
- 齋藤が東京理科大学理工学部建築学科を卒業。ニューヨークのコロンビア大学へ留学し建築デザインを学ぶ一方、アーティストとして活動を始める

2001
- 石橋がインタラクティブ映像など手がけるコマーシャルワークを展開。後にDGNとして起業し、真鍋も参加することになる
- 真鍋が千葉に誘われてベンチャー企業に転職、半年ほど勤務する
- 齋藤がニューヨークの広告代理店にて働き始める。インタラクティブなプロジェクトへの取り組みも行い、第49回ベネチア・ビエンナーレなどにも出展

2002
- 真鍋がIAMASに入学

2003
- 堀井哲史がIAMASに入学
- 齋藤とダートマス大学大学院に交換留学中の真鍋が、作品《Rhizomatiks》を共同制作してダートマスカレッジで展示。そのタイトルが後の会社名となる
- 齋藤が越後妻有トリエンナーレにて光る風船をモチーフとした屋外のインスタレーション《**Reboot Project 1 GINGA》を展示。プログラミングやサウンドとして真鍋も関わる
- 石橋が東京藝術大学先端芸術表現科の非常勤講師に着任

2004
- 真鍋、IAMASに卒業制作《Chair the Difference》を提出
- 真鍋が東京藝術大学の非常勤講師に着任、サーバ管理とメディアアート講義を担当。石橋ら講師陣と、クライアントワーク含むインタラクティブ映像などの仕事を手がける
- 真鍋がNTTインターコミュニケーションセンター［ICC］（東京）の「ネクスト：メディア・アートの新世代」展で澤井妙治、城一裕と連名で《"riot please"--/a....ha...++》を展示
- 山口情報芸術センター［YCAM］でのモノクロームサーカス＋藤本隆行による公演《Refined Colors》に真鍋が参加。海外での発表も行う
- 広島そごうのエントランスに設置したカメラセンシングによるインタラクティブ映像オブジェ《Motion Mirror ver.01.02.03》をDGNとして石橋・真鍋が手がける。表現方法の違う3コンテンツを企画・制作
- パソナ東京ショールームのラウンジスペースに設置されたインタラクティブオブジェを石橋（《Chasquare》）、真鍋（《Ripple》）がそれぞれ手がける。どちらも天井のカメラによって人の動きを解析し、リアルタイムで映像を生成している

2005
- FENDI NY店舗にて石橋がインタラクティブシステムを制作
- YCAM(山口)にて内橋和久＋UAインスタレーティブ・コンサートによる《path》に真鍋が携わる。舞台上のミュージシャンが、照明や映像まで自在にコントロールできるシステムを開発し、空間全体が即興的／有機的に変化していくコンサートとなった
- 2005年アジアビューティエキスポでのSHISEIDO Professionalブース内において鏡とカメラセンシングを組み合わせたインタラクティブ映像《Motion Mirror ver.04.05.06》を企画・制作
- ラポルテ青山やリステア銀座店のオープニングパーティーにて、空間内を動き回る人の持つカメラの映像がスクリーン前の人の動きに合わせて再構築されるインタラクティブ映像《View Face》を発表
- アーティスト集団「C-DEPOT」による展示「EXHIBITION C-DEPOT 2005 face」(スパイラルガーデン、東京)にDGNとして石橋らが参加。くしゃみをテーマとした作品《ENGAGE》を発表
- カルティエ銀座店・心斎橋店で行われた腕時計「TANK」のローンチパーティーにて、腕時計のデザインとブランドの歴史を表現したインタラクティブ映像《Advance the hands on the clock》を石橋・真鍋が制作
- リステア神戸店オープン記念パーティーにおいて、旅をテーマに、地球儀型のインターフェースとそれに応じたインタラクティブ映像による作品《Touch a Glove》を石橋、真鍋、齋藤らが制作
- Designworks表参道店オープニングパーティーにて、石橋らがエントランスの演出を担当。床に投影された映像や音楽が来場者に応じて変化する《Flock U》という作品として展示された

2006
- カラーキネティクス・ジャパン社 設立5周年記念パーティーにてRFIDタグを内蔵したカードによって音楽と映像を制御できる実験的作品《RFIDライトシーケンサー》を発表。後にICCにて展示された
- 川口隆夫によるダンス公演《Table Mind》に携わる。この年に初演が開かれると、2011年にはアップデートして再演された
- 銀座ソニービルのリニューアルに際し、1階と地下1階を結ぶ、踏むと音と光を発する階段《メロディステップ》の開発に携わる
- スコットランドのウィスキーブランドGLENMORANGIEのローンチパーティーにおいて、その歴史と特徴を水をメインモチーフとし映像で表現。会場全体の映像や音響の演出も手がけた
- 化粧品ブランドMIU COSMETICSの設立記念パーティーにて、シンクロナイズドスイミングの演出を担当。加速度センサーを内蔵した防水加工のワイヤレスデバイスを用いて、リアルタイムにLEDを制御、調光している
- 「株式会社ライゾマティクス」設立(7月25日)
- ウェブサイトからインタラクティブデザインまで幅広く手がけるクリエイター集団として起起。当初は齋藤、千葉、真鍋、IAMAS出身の堀井哲史の4人でスタートし、黒瀧節也はサテライトメンバーとして参画
- 石橋が国立科学博物館で開かれた「ふしぎ大陸南極展2006」にて、ペンギンやオーロラをインタラクティブに体感できる演出を展示した
- 2006年3月就航の航空会社スターフライヤー社のデザイン、

コンセプト、その完成までのヒストリーを紹介する展覧会「And Beyond」展において、インタラクティブショーケースのデザイン、制作を行った
- 大阪府枚方市にある遊園地「ひらかたパーク」にて開催された「劇場版 どうぶつの森 わくわくヴィレッジ」にて、インタラクティブなアトラクションを5点制作・発表した

2007
- 中浜大輔がライゾマティクスに入社。齋藤と清水啓太郎が出会う
- 真鍋、石橋、齋藤らが北九州イノベーションギャラリー(福岡)で《Sonic Floor》を発表
- 真鍋と石橋がICCキッズ・プログラム 2007「サウンド×イメージ——音を見て、映像を聞こう」展にて、《Proce55ing Life》を発表
- 白井剛(AbsT)と川口隆夫(ダムタイプ)出演の舞台「true / 本当のこと」(YCAM)で、筋電センサーなどを用いた演出などを手がける。2007年の初演から海外を回るなどロングラン公演となった
- スコットランドのシングルモルトウイスキー「GLENMORANGIE」ローンチパーティーでのインタラクティブシステム《KALEIDO FEELING SCOPE》を制作
- 水戸芸術館現代美術ギャラリー(茨城)で行われた松井龍哉展「フラワーロボティクス」において、システムや音響などの制作・デザインを担当

2008
- SCAI THE BATH HOUSE(東京)にて行われた「アピチャッポン・ウィーラセタクン「Replicas」」にて、鑑賞者の位置に応じて音が変化するマルチチャンネルサウンドシステムを構築した
- ロッテリア@ミライカン 日本科学未来館店に設置されているライブラリの壁に、ホタルの明滅の同期現象(シンクロ)をテーマにしたLEDユニットの作品《sync-ing 001》を展示
- 東京ミッドタウンでHIROCOLEDGEの浴衣をメインとしたスペシャルショップのレセプションパーティーにて、高速回転でのレーザーの「歪み」を利用してシンボルマークを動かした《Moving symbol》を展示
- 東京藝術大学の特別講師を務めていた真鍋と、柳澤知明が出会う
- 真鍋と石橋がライゾマティクス主宰の研究機関「4nchor5la6(アンカーズラボ)」を設立。柳澤、アーティストの堀尾寛太も参加
- 真鍋が「TAICOCLUB Art Project Vol.3」の一環で、タレントの芹那出演の映像作品を手掛ける。映像は渋谷スクランブル交差点のSib.TVで一度だけ上映された
- 10月23日に真鍋が《electric stimulus to face》をYouTube動画として公開し、世界的に注目を集める(2021年初頭時点で再生回数は180万回を超える)
- 日本科学未来館5階の常設展示『こちら、宇宙ステーション／ISS』をDGN、ライゾマティクスなどが共同で制作
- 可聴域の音を用いた通信システムと、それに応じて光るキューブによる作品《Command line wave》を真鍋と石橋が発表。全国の美術館を巡回した「ようこそ魔法の美術館 親子で楽しむ光のアート」展に展示された
- 東京ビッグサイトで行われたイベント、「TOKYO BEAUTY CONGRESS 2008」のメインステージにおいて、映像制作および映像制御システムの構築を担当

イーアスつくばにあるCYBERDYNE社の展示スペース「サイバーダインスタジオ」内にて、人体とロボット技術の歴史を紹介する作品《サイバニクス・アナトミア》を展示

2009

- 欧州文化都市2009の年始にあわせてリニューアル開館したアルスエレクトロニカ・センター(リンツ・オーストリア)の記念イベントを真鍋が手がけ、センターの外壁を覆う全面ディスプレイを用いた最初の作品となる
- 真鍋が「アルスエレクトロニカ・グランプリ」のデジタル・ミュージック部門の審査員を務める
- 木村浩康がライゾマティクスに入社。以降デザイナーとして、数多くの案件を手がける
- IVRC(国際学生対抗バーチャルリアリティコンテスト)2009にて、真鍋が東京大学のアルバロ・カシネリらとともに、描かれた線や近くにある三次元物体の輪郭を捉えて音を出す《scoreLight》を発表。第13回文化庁メディア芸術祭エンターテインメント部門優秀賞受賞
- 無線制御装置でコントロールするLEDを口内に入れるデバイスを、コンテンポラリー・ダンス作品《Cage》のために制作し《LED in my mouse》発表。以降、多数のバージョンが発表され、2011年にはラフォーレ原宿の「LAFORET GRAND BAZAR」のPR広告にも使われた
- 石橋、真鍋による《Pa++ern》を発表。Twitterから投稿して刺繍の模様をデザインするプログラミング言語を用い、遠隔操作でTシャツを製作・販売する作品として、インスタレーション版をBGALLERY(新宿ビームスジャパン、東京)で展示
- 「ICCキッズ・プログラム 2009プレイフル・ラーニングたのしむ∩まなぶ」展(ICC、東京)で《the Way Sensing GO +》展示。制作チームの代表を真鍋が務める
- 「TodaysArt Festival」(オランダ)にて、真鍋の《Face Visualizer, Copy》パフォーマンスを発表
- 《Face visualizer, instrument, and copy》発表。筋電位センサー、電気刺激装置、ソフトウェアで表情を他人の顔にコピーするプロジェクトとして世界各国のミュージック/アート/映像関連フェスティバルで招待上演
- 真鍋・石橋とダムタイプ藤本隆行が、連名で「Time Lapse Plant/偽加速器(prototype/試作)」展(BankART Studio NYK)を開催。《true/本当のこと》のワンシーンを体験型インスタレーションにした作品を展示

2010

- ライゾマティクス本社及びアンカーズラボが白金台に移転。石橋がライゾマに正式に参加。有國恵介がライゾマティクスに入社。デザイン制作チームが設立される
- 第2回恵比寿映像祭「歌をさがして」にて、前年の「Time Lapse Plant」展で展示したもののアップデート版となる作品《Time Lapse Plant》を展示
- 真鍋が「サイバーアーツジャパン－アルスエレクトロニカの30年」展(東京都現代美術館、東京)に参加、《Face visualizer, instrument and copy》を展示、石橋をゲストに講堂でレクチャーパフォーマンスを行った。
- NIKEとの共同開発プロジェクト《NIKE MUSICSHOE》を発

表。NIKEの新作「NIKE FREERUN+」を楽器に改造し、ブレイクビーツユニットHIFANAの演奏を収録。システムを真鍋、デバイスを柳澤知明が開発

- 真鍋、本間無量が、やくしまるえつこのシングル「ヴィーナスとジーザス」ミュージックビデオを制作
- 彫刻家の名和晃平とKDDIのiidaブランドとのコラボレーション《PixCell - PRISMOID》において、その携帯電話の画面をメールや赤外線通信に応じて変化させるシステムを石橋が構築した
- 真鍋＋石橋による《points》を「5番チューブ 再開発計画Vol.6」展(せんだいメディアテーク、宮城)で発表
- 真鍋＋石橋による《fade out》をアルスエレクトロニカ・フェスティバル2010で発表。蓄光シートに紫外線レーザーを照射し、その減光時間を利用して階調のある写実的なポートレイトを描き出す作品を展示
- Perfumeの映像・アートディレクションを担当する関和亮、演出振付家のMIKIKOに声をかけられ「結成10周年、メジャーデビュー5周年記念! Perfume LIVE@東京ドーム「1 2 3 4 5 6 7 8 9 10 11」」の演出に参加。「Perfumeの掟」の3Dスキャンデータ、システム開発、映像制作、風船LED、仕掛け風船などを担当

2011

- 真鍋＋石橋が美術館における初の大規模展示として《particles》を「particles」展(YCAM、山口)にて発表。
- 《particles》が「第15回文化庁メディア芸術祭アート部門」優秀賞を受賞、同受賞作品展(国立新美術館、東京)にて展示された
- やくしまるえつこのシングル「COSMOS vs ALIEN」リリースにあわせたスペシャルウェブサイト「COSMOS vs ALIENシューティング」を真鍋、堀井、堀が制作
- 「アルスエレクトロニカ・グランプリ」で《particles》がインタラクティブ部門準グランプリを受賞、アルスエレクトロニカ・センターにて3年間の常設展示となる。以降、同作品は「MEDIACITY SEOUL 2012」(韓国)、「Stereolux」(フランス)でも展示
- 3月12日、東日本大震災の翌日に、Hondaとの共同制作「CONNECTINGLIFELINES」発表。同作は「第10回東京インタラクティブ・アド・アワード」グランプリ、「第59回カンヌライオンズ国際クリエイティビティ・フェスティバル」の数部門で受賞、また「D&AD 2012」、「ワン・ショー・インタラクティブ2012」、「アドフェスト2012」など国内外で多数受賞した
- BOOM BOOM SATELLITES「BROKEN MIRROR」のミュージックビデオにおいて、2人のパフォーマンスに合わせて投影される映像がインタラクティブに切り替わるシステムの構築を手がけた
- Perfume「レーザービーム/微かなカオリ」ミュージックビデオのLEDライティング・デザインを担当
- Intel®によるFacebook連動キャンペーンサイト「The Museum of Me」公開。同作は「カンヌライオンズ2012」で3つの金賞を受賞した。さらに「CLIO Awards 2012インタラクティブ部門」で最高賞Grand CLIO、イギリスの「The Favorite Website Award (FWA)」で年間最優秀ウェブサイトに選出、ADFEST 2012サイバー部門最高賞、「第15回文化庁メディア芸術祭エンターテインメント部門」優秀賞など、国内外で多数受賞

- やくしまるえつこ「ルル」「ときめきハッカー」のミュージックビデオを手がける。工業用ロボットアームを作品に本格的に導入した
- やくしまるえつこのシングル『ルル/ときめきハッカー』リリースにあわせてウェブサイト「YAKUSHIMARU BODY HACK」を公開。やくしまるの脳波、心拍、眼電など生体データをリアルタイムで配信するバイオデータストリーミングコンテンツ
- 「Sonar Music Festival」(スペイン)にて、真鍋が《Face Visualizer, Copy》パフォーマンスを発表
- 真鍋、石橋による《16 Forms》を「KAITEKIのかたち」展(スパイラルホール、東京)で発表。MIKIKOが振り付けたポーズを3Dスキャナで撮影、そのポーズを元に3Dプリンターでフィギュアをつくり、ロボットアームに光源を持たせてアニメーションとした作品
- SONY新製品のタブレット発売に際し、ルーブ・ゴールドバーグ・マシンを使った映像作品《Two will》発表
- やくしまるえつこメトロオーケストラ「ノルニル」のミュージックビデオを、真鍋、石橋、本間が制作。アーティストひとりのみがいる空間で、全球パノラマカメラを搭載したロボットによる撮影を試みた (堀井がウェブ版を作成)
- やくしまるえつこメトロオーケストラ「少年よ我に返れ」のミュージックビデオのため、ロボットアームとプロジェクターによるインスタレーション《proportion》を制作
- MIKIKO率いるダンスカンパニーELEVENPLAYによる「dot.」(ラフォーレ原宿、東京)公演において、プログラムとテクニカルサポートを真鍋、石橋が担当
- 真鍋が《Slit Scan Sculpture》制作。60年代から使われる映像エフェクト「スリットスキャン」を3Dデータによる彫刻作品に応用した
- 「映像をめぐる冒険vol.4 見えない世界のみつめ方」展にて展示された鳴川肇《AuthaGraph World Map》の展示協力を石橋、柳澤が行う

2012
- 自社スタジオを白金高輪に構える
- DELLのゲーミングPC「ALIENWARE」シリーズのバイラルCM「EXTREME GAMER×LED×ALIENWARE」発表
- 真鍋、石橋による彫刻作品《line》発表。3Dスキャンとロボットアームによるベンディングマシンを用いた
- Perfumeの世界デビューを記念したウェブサイト「Perfume global site project #001」の企画・制作に携わる。7月に「Perfume global site project #002」、2013年6月に「Perfume global site project #003」を公開。第16回文化庁メディア芸術祭エンターテインメント部門大賞など、受賞多数
- 真鍋、石橋、柳澤、本間が、Perfume「Spring of Life」ミュージックビデオの衣装制作、ロボットアーム、インタラクションデザイン、3Dスキャンデータ制作などを担当
- 「MTV VIDEO MUSIC AWARDS JAPAN (MTV VMAJ) 2012」(幕張メッセ・幕張イベントホール、千葉)にて、Perfumeの衣装デバイス、ソフト制作を担当
- 「キリンチューハイ氷結 Presents Perfume 3rd Tour『JPN』」の3Dスキャンデータ制作、システム開発、映像制作を担当
- Perfume「氷結SUMMER NIGHT」(渋谷ヒカリエ、東京)にて、ホログラフィック演出、映像、インタラクティブシステム開発、3Dスキャンデータ制作を担当

- 渋谷ヒカリエ(東京)の円形大型LEDデジタルサイネージのコンテンツを制作
- GATORADE RUNのイベント(二子玉川ライズ、東京)で、トレッドミル上で走る体験者を囲んで敷き詰めたLEDによる映像と音がシンクロするマシン《FUN RACE MACHINE》を発表し、クリエイティブディレクション、プログラミング、装置設計を担当
- NIKEのウェアラブル・デバイス「Fuel」のロンドンでのプロモーションイベント「FuelFest」演出を担当
- 真鍋、石橋、本間が制作を担当したやくしまるえつこ「ロンリープラネット」のミュージックビデオを公開
- 「Perfume Global Compilation "LOVE THE WORLD"」(グローバル・コンピレーションアルバム)及び「Perfume WORLD TOUR 1st」の楽曲「Butterfly」の3Dスキャンデータ制作を担当
- 真鍋、石橋、齋藤、坂本によるインスタレーション作品《Physicalizing Data by Rhizomatiks》をTOKYO DESIGNERS WEEK 2012「コンテナ展」(東京)で発表。Perfumeの3人を3Dスキャンやモーションキャプチャーを使ってデータ化し、等身大の3DモデルにCG映像などを投影した
- TOTOとtotoによる「トートーとトトGREEN COLLABORATION PROJECT」の宣伝大使「S.G.T.K.」(スーパー・グレート・トイレ・キーパー)のテクニカルディレクション、プログラミング、デバイス制作を担当
- 真鍋、石橋がレーザー、鏡、モータを用いたインスタレーション作品《pulse vol.1》を(G/P Gallery、東京)にて発表。《pulse vol.2》を同年12月のイベント「electraglide2012」(幕張メッセ、千葉)で発表し、《pulse 3.0》を2013年1月のYCAM(山口)での個展で発表
- NYのアーティストFaltyDL「Straight & Arrow」のミュージックビデオを真鍋と関和亮が制作
- マザー牧場(千葉)のウィンターイルミネーション「キラキラウィンターファーム」公開。クリエイティブディレクション、企画、プログラミングを担当
- 「2012 NHK杯国際フィギュアスケート競技大会」エキシビション「東北からの"ありがとう"スケーティング」の演出を担当、現地のジュニアスケーターによる氷上演技と映像を同期させ、アイスリンクに映像を投影した
- 「もしスマートフォンで街をコントロールできたらどうなるか」をテーマとしたCMを制作、au by KDDIのCM「FULL CONTROL YOURCITY」としてオンエア開始。CM、ウェブサイト、スマホアプリ、ライブイベント連動のキャンペーンが行われた
- 「第63回紅白歌合戦」(NHK)におけるPerfume、嵐のステージ演出の技術サポートを担当

2013
- 清水啓太郎がライゾマティクスに入社
- ELEVENPLAYとの「shape」、「cube」、「ray」、ミュージックビデオ作品「MAHOROBA」、「Tantra」など、盛んに制作と発表を展開する
- やくしまるえつこ+真鍋大度+石橋素+菅野薫《LOVE＋1＋1》を「LOVE展:アートにみる愛のかたち—シャガールから草間彌生、初音ミクまで」(森美術館、東京)にて展示
- Perfume「未来のミュージアム」のミュージックビデオ、特設サイトを担当

- 2度目のPerfumeワールドツアーおよび「カンヌライオンズ国際クリエイティビティ・フェスティバル 2013」のパフォーマンスにてDynamic projection systemを用いた演出を披露。Perfumeの身体をリアルタイムトラッキングし、身体と衣裳のパーツをセンサーが認識、衣裳や身体の動きに同期した映像マッピングを行った
- 「Eyeo Festival」(ミネアポリス、アメリカ)にて、ベンジャミン・フライ、キャセイ・レアス、ゴラン・レヴィン、メモ・アクテン、ラファエル・ロサノ＝ヘメル、ヘザー・ドゥーイー・ハグボル、イワン・プピレフら登壇者とともに、真鍋が登壇して活動をプレゼンテーションした
- アイルトン・セナが樹立したF1世界最速ラップの走行データを解析し「あの日のセナの走り」を蘇らせるプロジェクト《Sound of Honda/Ayrton Senna 1989》を公開。「第17回文化庁メディア芸術祭エンターテインメント部門」大賞、「カンヌライオンズ2014」7部門15個の受賞に加え、「チタニウムライオン」グランプリなど受賞多数
- 千葉・幕張メッセで開催されたチャリティライブイベント「FREEDOMMUNE 0〈ZERO〉ONE THOUSAND 2013」にて、プロジェクションマッピングによりステージ全面を大型立体映像装置に変えるプロジェクトを行った
- 「Rhizomatiks inspired by Perfume」展(ICC、東京)開催。ライゾマティクスが開発し、Perfumeのプロジェクトで使用された衣裳やソフトウェア、ハードウェアが展示され、活況を呈した
- Perfumeの東京ドーム公演にて、観客の3Dスキャンデータから映像を制作。そこから派生した映像作品《3D scan data visualization》を制作、発表した
- 東京2020オリンピック・パラリンピック競技大会の東京開催決定にともない、招致プロジェクトの一環として、太田雄貴「Fencing Visualized Project」を展開
- 「うさぎスマッシュ展 世界に触れる方法(デザイン)」(東京都現代美術館、東京)で、東京証券取引所の株式データをリアルタイムにビジュアライズする《traders》を展示
- 齋藤が「建築家にならなかった建築家たち」展(EYE OF GYRE、東京)を企画・監修。建築を離れた建築家たちによるテクノロジーやアートを使った試みを紹介した
- 真鍋が「情熱大陸」(毎日放送)に出演
- 「第64回紅白歌合戦」(NHK)でPerfumeの演出を技術サポート

2014
- 真鍋、石橋によるインスタレーション《rate》を「Media/Art Kirchen-Reality Distorrion Field」(バンコク芸術文化センター、タイ)で発表
- 「真実の愛」がないとはずれないブラジャー「TRUE LOVE TESTER」を鴨井、清水が担当開発し、ランジェリーブランド「Ravijour」の10周年記念プロジェクトとして発表
- ドローンを用いた最初期のプロジェクトとして本間＋真鍋＋石橋が制作に携わったやくしまるえつこ「X次元へようこそ」のミュージックビデオ公開
- 「MEDIA AMBITION TOKYO 2014」(六本木ヒルズ、東京)で、INTERSECT BY LEXUS×Rhizomatiksによる「レクサスLFA」をモチーフに、六本木の眺望と重畳表示するインスタレーション《physical presence》を発表

- 齋藤、清水啓太郎を中心に、セブン・ドリーマーズ・ラボラトリーズ株式会社のブランド立ち上げに携わり、同社が開発したカーボン製のオーダーメイドのゴルフシャフト「オート・クチュール・デザイン・シリーズ」、および鼻に挿入するいびき対策デバイス「ナステント」のクリエイティブディレクションを手がけた。いずれも「2015年度グッドデザイン賞」を受賞
- 経済産業省のウェブコンテンツ「OPEN METI」を手がける。経済産業省が保有するビッグデータを、活用可能なオープンデータとして公開するプロジェクトとして展開
- SquarepusherとZ-MACHINESのコラボレーション楽曲「SAD ROBOT GOES FUNNY」のミュージックビデオを真鍋が制作
- 「Resonate Festival」(セルビア)で、メディアアーティストのカイル・マクドナルド、プロジェクションとダンスのオリジネイターであるクラウス・オーベルマイアーとともにレジデンス制作を行い《Transcranial》を発表
- 齋藤、中浜大輔、堀、佐藤、鴨井、武政、阿部がアイウェアブランドJINSの開発プロジェクトに協力、眼電位センサーと6軸センサーが内蔵されたアイウェア「JINSMEME」を発表、2015年11月から一般発売した
- 国立競技場リニューアルイベントの一環として、過去の有名スポーツ選手の記録を視覚化した《Reviving Legends》や、クラウドソーシングで競技場を3Dスキャンするプロジェクト《REMEMBER OUR STADIUM》を手がけた
- 真鍋が「プロフェッショナル仕事の流儀」(NHK)に出演
- ELEVENPLAYとの共作《fly》を山口情報芸術センター[YCAM]で制作し、カールステン・ニコライら参加の音楽フェスティバル「Sonar Music Festival」(スペイン)でも発表する
- 坂本龍一と真鍋のコラボレーション作品《センシング・ストリームズ─不可視、不可聴》を「札幌国際芸術祭2014」同年で「第18回文化庁メディア芸術祭アート部門」優秀賞受賞
- 中国各地の優秀なバスケットボール選手を選抜する「Nike Rise」キャンペーンの一環として、フルLEDとプレーヤーのトラッキングシステム「Nike Rise / House of Mamba」を備えたバスケットボールコートを上海で発表。齋藤がクリエイティブディレクターとして企画・制作に携わり、堀井、田中陽、登本悠介、原田克彦、本間、清水が参画
- ELEVENPLAYとの共作「Mosaic」をメキシコにて発表。「セルバンティーノ国際芸術祭」、「MUTEK Festival」を含む4都市5会場6公演を行った
- 「The Human Sized Synthesizer」公開。真鍋、齋藤、堀井、黒瀧龍也、清水らがRed Bull Music Academyと共同制作したヒューマンサイズの巨大シンセサイザー
- 東京駅開業100周年イベント「Tokyo Colors 2014」を展開。有國のもと企画、プロデュース、制作を行う
- Apple社のMac誕生30周年スペシャルサイトで「Appleに影響を与えたキーパーソンの一人」に真鍋が選出される
- Perfumeのアバターが生息するオープンワールドのウェブサイト「Perfume WORLD」を制作。Perfume 5th Tour 2014「ぐるんぐるん」の演出にも使用された
- 「第65回紅白歌合戦」(NHK)でPerfumeの演出を技術サポート。ドローンを用いて演出

2015

- ライゾマティクス本社・自社スタジオを恵比寿に移転。床面積400平方メートルの元倉庫をリノベーション
- 齋藤がクリエイティブディレクターとして関わるフルLEDバスケットボールコート「Zoom City Arena」を「NIKE NBA All star weekend」で発表。田中、本間、ベッカ・カワイチが参画
- 齋藤が「六本木アートナイト2015」(六本木ヒルズ、東京)のメディアアートディレクターを務める。巨大ミラーボール「アケボノ号」と800個の提灯LEDを搭載した「ハル号」を公開
- ELEVENPLAY×Rhizomatiks Researchのコラボレーション公演「ELEVENPLAY Dance Installation MOSAIC Ver.1.5」(スパイラルホール、東京)にて「fly−(2015 version)」を発表。トラッキング技術とドローンの制御技術を用いてオブジェクトを三次元的に配置する手法を披露した
- 齋藤が「2015年ミラノ国際博覧会」(イタリア)の日本館における「LIVE PERFORMANCE THEATER」のクリエイティブディレクションを担当し、堀井、田中、武政竜也、本間、清水が参画。同プロジェクトでミラノ万博展示デザイン部門金賞を受賞
- 真鍋がSquarepusher単独公演「Damogen Furies」(恵比寿ザ・ガーデンホール、東京)にオープニングアクトとして出演
- イラストレーターの貞本義行がデザインを務めたPerfumeの3Dアニメーションがキャラクターである、メルセデス・ベンツ新型Aクラスのプロモーションアプリ「Next Stage with YOU」の開発を担当
- 安川電機100周年記念式典にて「人とロボットの協調」をテーマに産業用ロボットが音楽に合わせて動くダンスパフォーマンス「YASKAWA×Rhizomatiks×ELEVENPLAY」を上演し、演出を担当
- 「ライゾマティクス グラフィックデザインの死角」展(ギンザ・グラフィック・ギャラリー、東京)開催。田中一光のポスター作品をビッグデータとして取り込み、解析して生成する作品を発表。木村、登本、堀井、田中、小島、本間、藤井、元木が参画した
- 「真駒内花火大会」(真駒内セキスイハイムスタジアム、北海道)にて花火のパフォーマンス「segments」を披露。演出を真鍋が、音楽を黒瀧が担当。Rhizomatiks Research＋MIKIKOによるLEDのライトスティックと花火、ダンサーのコラボレーションとして展開された
- ELEVENPLAY + Rhizomatiks Researchによるパフォーマンス「24 drones」公開。音楽を黒瀧が担当
- Rhizomatiks Research + ELEVENPLAYによる「border」(スパイラルホール、東京)プレビュー公演。翌年2月に内容・システムを大幅にアップデートした完全版をYCAM(山口)で上演した
- ELEVENPLAYの公演「right brain」「shadow」「24 drones」、Nosaj Thing「Cold Stares ft. Chance The Rapper + The O'My's」、ビョーク「Mouth Mantra」などのミュージックビデオ、HIPHOPの歌詞を自動生成する作品を手がけた
- 「NHKスペシャル NEXT WORLD 私たちの未来」(NHK)の放映にあわせ、ライゾマティクスが開発したAIを搭載し、サカナクション、アンリアレイジらも参加した特設ウェブサイト「SYMPHONY」を手がけた。また、本木雅弘主演映画を分析した《Cinema Analysis using IBM Watson™》のビジュアルなどを制作した

- CAPSULE「Another World」のMVにおいて、ドローンによる演出などに関するテクニカルディレクターを真鍋が務めた
- 米テキサスの音楽イベントSXSW2015におけるPerfumeのライブにて、リアルタイム3Dスキャンのデータと事前に取得したデータと組み合わせる「シームレスMR」を用いた生中継を行った
- Perfumeの海外展開用サイト「Perfume global site」にて、世界各国の言語に翻訳した歌詞をファンが投稿できるプロジェクト「Perfume Translyrics Project」を始動させた
- 「第66回紅白歌合戦」(NHK)でPerfumeの技術サポートを担当

2016

- 10周年を機に3部門Research/Architecture/Designを設立。統合した経営をライゾマティクスとして行う
- NYのアーティスト、マルコ・テンペストとRhizomatiks Researchのコラボレーションによる24台のドローンを使った映像作品として、Magic Lab + Rhizomatiks Research「24 Drone Flight」を公開
- インスタレーション《SPACE EXPERIMENT》を「MEDIA AMBITION TOKYO 2016」(六本木ヒルズ他、東京)で展示。佐藤、柳澤らが参画し、VRビデオゲーム「Rez Infinite」の共感覚的なコンセプトを体現するために制作した「Synesthesia Suit」を、水口哲也 + Rhizomatiks + Keio Media Design名義で発表した。「2016年度グッドデザイン賞」受賞
- パリ日本文化会館の新企画展シリーズ「トランスフィア(超域)」の第一弾として、真鍋大度+石橋素「創意のランドスケープ」展(パリ日本文化会館、フランス)を開催、《Deleted Reality》を発表
- 木村がNHKエンタープライズの8K：VR作品「Aoi −碧−サカナクション」のアートディレクションを手がける
- Rhizomatiks Architectureの有國、田中、細野が「北加賀屋アパートメントリノベーション計画」(大阪)に参加。
- 真鍋、石橋が「STRP Festival」(オランダ)にて《Rate》を発表
- 真鍋、花井、堀井、本間がLAのビートメーカーNosaj Thingのアメリカツアー「NO REALITY TOUR 2016」でコラボレーション、パフォーマンスを行う
- ELEVENPLAYが米NBCネットワークの公開オーディション番組「America's Got Talent(AGT)season11」に出演。Rhizomatiks Researchがテクノロジーサポートを行い24台のドローンとのライブパフォーマンスを披露
- 第31回オリンピック競技大会(2016/リオデジャネイロ)/リオ2016パラリンピック競技大会閉会式で、2020年東京オリンピック「フラッグハンドオーバーセレモニー」のAR演出、床面映像、LEDフレーム制作、LED衣装制作等を担当。真鍋、石橋、堀井、花井、登本、田中、本間、上條、原田、柳澤、坂本、田井、望月、西本、石川、浅井、毛利が参加した
- 真鍋+石橋《Rate》を「Scopitone Festival」(フランス)にて発表
- Rhizomatiks Architecture、渡辺綾子、ベッカ、山口望未らが、エルメスのメンズファッションショー「The Nature of Men」スペシャルナイトの演出を担当
- Rhizomatiks Researchが「のと里山空港アートナイト2016」(石川)にてミュージックビデオを制作。FaltyDLの楽曲提供により、空港滑走路を使った公開収録で撮影された
- Rhizomatiks Architectureがインスタレーション作品

《CURTAIN WALL THEATRE》を「Tokyo Midtown DESIGN TOUCH 2016」で展示

- 清水を中心にRhizomatiks Designが総合プロデュースを手がけた世界初の全自動衣類折りたたみ機「ランドロイド」（セブン・ドリーマーズ・ラボラトリーズ株式会社）を「ceatec 2016」で公開
- 目の錯覚を利用して、CGによる合成を行わずに同様の演出効果が得られる「ダイナミックVRディスプレイ」を開発。「MUSIC STATION ウルトラFES」（テレビ朝日系列）や「第67回紅白歌合戦」（NHK）のPerfume歌唱パートなどで披露した
- ZKM（カールスルーエ、ドイツ）で2016年3月から開催された「GLOBALE: New Sensorium」展にて、ビットコインの仕組みを利用したインスタレーション《chains》を発表
- Perfumeのアルバム「COSMIC EXPLORER」の発売にあわせて、楽曲の構成やメロディー、過去のアートワークを解析して作られたユーザー参加型ウェブサイトを制作した
- 日本全国および北米にて行われた「Perfume 6th Tour 2016 COSMIC EXPLORER」において、演出、衣装制作を手がけた。公演中にはロンドンとニューヨークにて「A Gallery Experience Supported by Rhizomatiks」も開催された

2017
- 「アート＋コム／ライゾマティクスリサーチ 光と動きの『ポエティクス／ストラクチャー』」展（ICC）にて、モーションキャプチャーと鏡を用いた新作《distortion》を展示
- FaltyDLの「Shock Therapy」のミュージックビデオのディレクションを担当。「のと里山空港」（石川県輪島市）でのアートイベントにて大型の空撮用ドローンによって公開収録された映像に、ARを用いて楽曲構造を視覚的に表現した
- ドイツ・ハノーバーにて行われたCeBIT 2017のオープニングアクトとして、森山未來やELEVENPLAYらによるパフォーマンスを手がけた
- 渋谷キャストの渋谷と青山を結ぶ1階貫通通路の常設インスタレーション《Axyz》を有國らが手がける。一過性のサイネージではなく、長くそこに残るような表現をつくり、人と空間の関わりを生み出すことを目指した
- ルイ・ヴィトンの期間限定ポップアップストア「LOUIS VUITTON in collaboration with FRAGMENT POP-UP STORE」にて、32枚のパネルスクリーンを設置した体感型デジタルインスタレーション《morphing》を展示
- イギリス・マンチェスターで開催された「Bluedot festival」にて、ラヴェル電波望遠鏡にプロジェクションするインスタレーション《Celestial Frequencies》を展示。望遠鏡のイメージと、リアルタイムで受信したデータのビジュアライズを組み合わせた作品となった
- 東京ミッドタウンにて行われたイベント「3776:the digital anatomy~富士山の解剖学~」にて、富士山に関する研究・観測データを視覚化し、芝生広場のモニュメント『江戸富士』にプロジェクションする演出を行った
- Rhizomatiks Designが制作を手がけた、ユーザーが投稿した日本の情景写真をクリエイティブコモンズライセンスでクラウド的に集めて広めるフォトアーカイブ「FIND/47」をリリース
- モーションキャプチャーとレーザープロジェクターによる立体

映像作品として、ELEVENPLAYとの共作インスタレーション「phosphere」をSónar Barcelonaで発表

- Rhizomatiks DesignがBunkamuraオーチャードホール（東京）にて上演されたヴェルディによるオペラ「オテロ」において、登場人物の感情や指揮者の動きなどをデータ化した演出を披露した
- NHK Eテレにて放送された子供向けバラエティ番組「オドモTV」のコーナー『オドモテック』を真鍋が担当。翌年にはレギュラー放送も開始された
- Rhizomatiks Researchが567台のプリンターを駆使した視覚効果を展開し、アメリカのロックバンド「OK Go」の新曲「Obsession」ミュージックビデオにテクニカルチームとして参加
- 「FUTURE-EXPERIMENT VOL.01 docomo × Perfume 距離をなくせ。」のライブ演出などを担当。3人が東京、ニューヨーク、ロンドンに分かれてパフォーマンスをし、中継映像をリアルタイムに合成、NTTドコモの5G通信技術によりタイムラグのない映像を実現した
- ライゾマティクス結成10周年記念展「Rhizomatiks 10」（スパイラルホール、東京）を開催。体験型ダンスパフォーマンス作品《border》を展覧会用にアレンジした作品《border installation ver.》などが発表された
- 能や狂言などの伝統芸能とテクノロジーの競演による舞台《FORM》を東京国際フォーラム（東京）にて開催。野村萬斎の総合演出のもと、真鍋が映像演出を行った
- Perfumeの「TOKYO GIRL」や「EVERYDAY」などのミュージックビデオの作中で、ライゾマティクスが独自に開発したオリジナルデバイスを用いた演出が展開された
- 「内村五輪宣言！～TOKYO2020 開幕1000日前スペシャル～」（NHK総合）のPerfume出演パートスペシャル企画として、ファンのツイートによってPerfumeの姿が完成する「Perfume Lighting Project」を発表した
- 「第68回紅白歌合戦」（NHK）でPerfumeの技術サポートを担当

2018
- AI、機械学習を活用したダンスパフォーマンス作品としてELEVENPLAY、アーティストのカイル・マクドナルドとの共作「discrete figures」を発表。「MUTEK Montréal」で世界初演後、スパイラル（東京）で日本初演し、以降も海外招聘多数
- Perfumeが過去に生み出してきたパフォーマンスを最新テクノロジーで「再構築－Reframe」することをテーマとした公演「Perfume×TECHNOLOGY presents Reframe」が開催され、今までの活動に基づく多様なデータを用いた演出が展開された
- ドルチェ＆ガッバーナの「Fall Winter 2018/19 Women's Fashion Show」にて、ランウェイ上に飛ばしたドローンが新作バッグを次々と披露する演出を手がける
- 齋藤とRhizomatiks Architectureが、最新技術のレーザーファイバーと映像で日本建築のスケールを原寸再現する《パワー・オブ・スケール》を「建築の日本展」（森美術館）で展示
- 真鍋が、京都大学神谷之康研究室／ATRとの共同プロジェクトとして脳活動と音／映像の関係性、クロスモーダル現象に関する作品《dissonant imaginary》に着手
- 真鍋と2bitがパリのロスチャイルド館にて開かれた「深みへ―日

本の美意識を求めて−」展にて、サイバー攻撃の様子をビジュアライズした作品《invisible war》を展示

- 「内村五輪宣言！〜TOKYO 2020開幕 2年前スペシャル〜」（NHK総合）にて、Perfumeの演出を担当。CGや合成を使わずに無数のレーザーとPerfumeのダンスが絡み合う光の演出を行った
- 真鍋が、国内美術館での初個展「真鍋大度∞ライゾマティクスリサーチ」展を鹿児島県霧島アートの森で開催。《Light Field Theater》や《discrete figures》のインスタレーションバージョンなど新作を展示した
- 檜山晃（ダイアログ・イン・ザ・ダーク）とRhizomatiks Research、アンリアレイジが、物体との距離を測定して振動する服を制作。服を通して空間を「みる」ことを目的とした作品《echo》を発表した
- 「Perfume 7th Tour 2018『FUTURE POP』」の演出を担当。横浜アリーナでのカウントダウンライブ中に「第69回紅白歌合戦」（NHK）への生中継および「【docomo×Perfume】FUTURE-EXPERIMENT VOL.04 その瞬間を共有せよ。」のイベントも行われた。翌年の海外ツアーにも同じく帯同した
- ジャニーズ事務所のアイドルグループ「嵐」の全国ツアー「ARASHI Anniversary Tour 5×20」の演出のテクニカルの監修、花道上のメンバートラッキングシステム、360カメラシステムを担当
- 聴覚で楽しむAR体験として、ポケモンの鳴き声を集め、遊ばせることもできる《Pokémon GO AR庭園》（六本木ヒルズ 毛利庭園、東京）を、森ビル／Niantic主催「INNOVATION TOKYO 2018」のARプロジェクトとして展開。集音器型のオリジナルデバイスも制作。真鍋、石橋、小幡、原田、望月が参加

2019
- ライゾマティクス社恵比寿オフィスをスタジオ機能に特化、経営・マネージメント・デザイン機能は中目黒オフィス（空間設計：スキーマ建築計画）に移転
- ZIP-FMで真鍋のレギュラー・ラジオ・プログラム『Leftfield』がスタート
- 「The Coachella Valley Music and Arts Festival 2019」（インディオ、カリフォルニア）に、J-POP女性グループとして初出演したPerfumeのライブにて、リアルタイムエフェクトを手がける
- 「LINE CUBE SHIBUYA（旧渋谷公会堂）」の柿落し公演「Perfume『Reframe 2019』」にて、Perfumeの映像、音声、振付、歌詞データを再構築したコンセプトライブのビジュアル・インフォメーションデザインを担当
- ヒップホップMC KOHHが「FUJI ROCK FESTIVAL '19」に出演した際の、ステージ映像演出を手がける
- 大丸心斎橋店本館のグランドオープンにあわせエスカレーターサイドに設置された巨大LEDモニター「D-WALL」のビジュアルプログラミング（田中）とスペースデザイン（元木）を担当
- SHIBUYA SKY（渋谷スクランブルスクエア屋上）のプロジェクトをRhizomatiks Designが担当。有國、清水、Rhizomatiks Researchのチームが大規模複合施設におけるディレクションとして手がける
- 齋藤が総合プロデュースする「Sense Island −感覚の島− 暗闇の美術島」（猿島、神奈川）で、夜の無人島を舞台にしたアートイベ

ントにRhizomatiks Architectureがアーティストとして参加

- 芸術文化都市東京の魅力を伝える「Tokyo Tokyo FESTIVALスペシャル13」のプロジェクトとして、増上寺（芝、東京）にて《Coded Field》を発表。位置測位技術（GNSS）を利用し、屋外で大型パブリックアートプロジェクトを展開
- 真鍋が「天皇陛下御即位をお祝いする国民祭典」の祝賀式典における奉祝曲の照明演出、ソフト開発、オペレーションを担当
- Dentsu Lab Tokyoと共同開発した《Fencing Visualized Project》の基幹技術である「Fencing tracking and visualization system」が、第72回全日本フェンシング選手権大会にて世界初の実戦導入となる
- 「ミラノデザインウィーク」（ミラノ、イタリア）のLEXUSブースにて、モーションキャプチャーでダンサーの動きがプログラムされたロボット、無数の光、そしてダンサー1名によるパフォーマンス「LEADING WITH LIGHT」を発表した
- COREDO室町テラスにオープンした猿田彦珈琲 誠品生活日本橋店での常設インスタレーション《DRIP WORDS -言葉の抽出-》において、モーショングラフィックスなどを手がけた
- 野村萬斎とゲストアーティストとが互いの専門分野を駆使して展開するパフォーマンス＆トーク「解体新書シリーズ」特別編「MANSAI◉解体新書 その参拾 特別編『5W1H』」に参加。人間の行動を数学的・身体的に捉えなおしたパフォーマンスを行った
- アメリカ・ワシントンDCにある革新的アートスペース「ARTECHOUSE DC」にて個展「Lucid Motion」を開催。大型のイマーシブディスプレイを用いた作品を発表した。真鍋、堀井、浅井、計良、細野、井上、石塚、渡部が参加
- ニューヨークのカルチャースペース「The Shed」にて、即興で制作発表されたArcaの新作パフォーマンスに真鍋がアーティストとして参加。筋電位センサー、喉頭マイクをArcaに取りつけ、多様なサウンドに変換した
- 「第70回紅白歌合戦」（NHK）でPerfumeの技術サポートを担当

2020
- PARCO MUSEUM TOKYO（渋谷、東京）にて「Rhizomatiks inspired by Perfume 2020」展を開催。フォトグラメトリデータ、デバイスやソフトウェア、リアルタイム顔認識などによる作品のセクションで構成
- 真鍋とPeleの清水憲一郎がSquarepusher「Terminal Slam」ミュージックビデオの監督を務め、「アルスエレクトロニカ・グランプリ」コンピュータアニメーション部門佳作賞受賞
- Perfumeの全国ドームツアー「Perfume 8th Tour 2020 "P Cubed" in Dome」の演出を担当。ベストアルバムによるツアーにちなんで、過去に使われた演出の規模を拡大した多くのアップデートが披露された
- 齋藤、真鍋が、実験的オンラインイベント「Staying TOKYO」を緊急事態宣言前にスタート。多様なトークゲスト（オラファー・エリアソンほか）を迎えオンラインイベントやオンラインパーティーを展開
- J-WAVE「INNOVATION WORLD ERA」スタート。ナビゲーターを務める4人のクリエイターの一人として真鍋が第一日曜日を担当
- 真鍋が、大学の同期で俳優のムロツヨシと、ヨーロッパ企画主

宰の上田誠とのユニット「非同期テック部」を結成。緊急事態宣言に伴う自粛期間の最中に、インスタライブやYouTube Liveで作品を発表、オムニバス映画「緊急事態宣言」(Amazon Prime Video)に参加

- エレクトロミュージックとデジタルアートの祭典「Mutek San Francisco」がバーチャル空間の中に構築した美術館に作品を発表するという形で、プロジェクト《Virtual Live at Mutek San Francisco》を展開
- カイル・マクドナルドと真鍋が、オンラインコミュニケーションツール「Social Distancing Communication Platform (SDCP)」のプロトタイプ開発に着手。後に「HEERE(ヒア)」と改称してサービススタート
- 花井、望月を中心に、音声認識するマスク型デバイス「Messaging Mask」を開発。ARやプロジェクションによるテキスト出力で、ささやき声でも共感を増幅させる機能を実現
- Rhizomatiks Designの佐藤が、安藤忠雄設計による図書文化施設「こども本の森 中之島」(中之島、大阪)の常設作品《本のかけら》の企画・演出を担当
- 実験的オンラインイベント「Staying TOKYO」が緊急事態宣言終了後に「PLAYING TOKYO」に変更。オフライン企画を交えて実施し、毎週金曜のオンライン配信を続行する
- パリコレ初のオンライン開催「21SS Men's Fashion show」にて、White Mountaineeringデジタル・ショーケースを真鍋が監督、Rhizomatiks Researchが演出を手がける
- 映画『Reframe THEATER EXPERIENCE with you』が全国劇場公開され、真鍋、石橋が副音声《Theater experiment with you》で参加
- エヴィクサー株式会社との協働により、自宅にいながらライブ配信と同期した演出を楽しめる《Home Sync Light》を開発
- Perfume初のオンラインフェス「"P.O.P" (Perfume Online Present) Festival」全体のウェブサイトや、ラストに展開された「Imaginary Museum "Time Warp"」のライブ演出、サイトや全体のデザインを担当
- 齋藤がプロデュースを務める奈良県奥大和(吉野町・天川村・曽爾村)の芸術祭「MIND TRAIL 奥大和 心のなかの美術館」が開催される
- 「Ryuichi Sakamoto: Playing the Piano 12122020」のオンラインライブ演出を担当。「MUSIC/SLASH」による高音質配信と併せて、坂本龍一による2020年最後のピアノコンサートとして開催。石井、計良、高松がCGを担当
- 「第71回紅白歌合戦」(NHK)でPerfumeの技術サポートを担当
- ELEVENPLAYの映像作品「S.P.A.C.E.」の演出を担当。ソーシャルディスタンスを保ちつつ踊るダンサーの動きを幾何学的に分解・再構築し、新たな身体表現を生み出した
- サカナクションや坂本龍一、菅野よう子、Nosaj Thing、DJ KRUSHらアーティストのオンラインライブ演出を担当。オンラインならではの演出やリアルタイムにこだわる演出を展開した
- アメリカを拠点に活躍する日本人ミュージシャン、カズ・マキノのソロ曲「Come Behind Me, So Good!」のミュージックビデオを担当。ダンサーのフォトグラメトリデータと地形の3Dスキャンデータを同一空間にシームレスに同居させる演出を行った

- バルセロナにて行われたSonarにてレクチャーパフォーマンス《morphechore》を発表。脳活動を解析し振付したダンスを行い、真鍋をアバターとした身体が徐々に崩壊していく様子を映像で展開した
- 「第71回紅白歌合戦」(NHK)でPerfumeの技術サポートを担当

2021
- 株式会社ライゾマティクスが「ライゾマティクス」と「パノラマティクス」の2つのチームを有する「株式会社アブストラクトエンジン」へ社名変更。関連会社として新たに株式会社フロウプラトウを設立
- 2015年の公演をよりアップデートさせ、会場での体験＋鑑賞とオフライン鑑賞が可能な「border 2021」(スパイラルホール、東京)を開催
- 国土交通省が主導する3D都市モデル整備・活用・オープンデータ化プロジェクト「Project PLATEAU」が始まる。パノラマティクス齋藤がクリエイティブディレクションを担当し、フロウプラトウから木村、丸野、阿部、宿院が参加。
- 「坂本龍一：観音听时」(木木芸術社区[M WOODS HUTONG]、北京)にて、坂本龍一＋真鍋大度《Sensing Streams 2021 – invisible, inaudible》を展示
- 個展「ライゾマティクス_マルティプレックス」(東京都現代美術館、東京)開催。CryptoArtにおける課題や今後のビジョンを問いかけるライゾマティクス独自のプラットフォーム「NFT-Experiment」をオープン。真鍋のディレクションのもと、ウェブサイトをフロウプラトウ木村、小山、塚本、武政が制作した

主要参考文献

編 | 森山朋絵/Rhizomatiks

Selected References

ed. Tomoe Moriyama / Rhizomatiks

凡例 | 「主要参考文献」は、主に作家より提供された資料をもとに作成し、概ね年代順に掲載した。

資料は以下のように大別される（1…単行本・学術論文・公演パンフレット・フェスティバル等の出版物、2…逐次刊行物、3…展覧会カタログ、4…ウェブサイト、5…TV/ラジオ番組）が、原則として下記の内容・掲載順で情報を表記し、それぞれの文末に媒体種別を記載した。

| 1–4…筆者、記事名、書籍・誌紙名、発行年、発行者、掲載頁
| 5…TV/ラジオ局名、コーナー名、番組名、放送月日

頁表記については原則として原典に従い、頁表記を特定できないものや不詳部分については記載していない。また、ウェブ上にある文献資料等については作家研究・作品や活動のアーカイブにあたる主要な記事にとどめ、本書発行日の時点で閲覧可能なもののみを掲載した。

Notes | This "Selected References" has been compiled mainly using reference materials kindly provided by the artists and was listed as far as possible in chronological order. It was classified as follows into 5 categories (1…books/academic paper/performance pamphlets/festival publications or brochure, 2…periodicals/incidental publications, 3…exhibition catalogs, 4…website, 5…TV/radio programs). The media type is indicated at the end of each sentence. And these categories include the following items of information:

| 1–4…author, title of article, name of periodical/publications, date and/or volume number, page
| 5…TV/radio station name, corner name, program name, broadcast date

As a rule, page citations follow the pagination of the original source text. Unclear items have been omitted. For the web resources, it was limited only the articles about their artworks or archive studies, also was limited only the pages which can be read at the time of the date of issue.

2001
- 『alter-X magazine vol. 03』、2001年5月1日

2004
- 真鍋大度《Chair the Difference》、『ネクスト：メディアアートの新世代』、NTT出版、2004年、p. 56
- 原久子「［展覧会レビュー］ヴォイス・パフォーマンス「ヴォイス プラントロン 2004 ライブ」」、『artscape』、2004年3月20日、ウェブサイト
- 「**Reboot Project 1 GINGA」、『大地の芸術祭──越後妻有アートトリエンナーレ2003』、現代企画室、2004年
- 「ネクスト：メディアアートの新世代」、『美術手帖』2004年4月号、美術出版社、p. 186
- 『季刊インターコミュニケーション』第3号、NTT出版、2004年、pp. 206–208
- 真鍋大度「Chair the Difference」、『IAMAS 2004 GRADUATION EXHIBITION CATALOGUE』、2004年
- 「ネクスト：メディア・アートの新世代 リーフレット」、NTTインターコミュニケーション・センター［ICC］、2004年

2005
- 「展覧会PREVIEW」、『美術の窓』2005年6月号、生活の友社
- 「PICKUP Exhibition」、『月刊ギャラリー』2005年6月号、ギャラリーステーション
- 「マチネタ！渋谷エリア」、『東京ウォーカー』2005年7月号、KADOKAWA
- 「［Art Flash News］path──インスタレーティブ・コンサート」、『artscape』、2005年7月1日、ウェブサイト
- 原久子「［展覧会レビュー］path──インタレーティブ・コンサート「内橋和久＋UA」」、『artscape』、2005年7月3日、ウェブサイト
- 『アート・トップ』vol. 205、芸術新聞社、2005年
- カラーキネティクス・ジャパン「And Beyond展」、『COLOR KINETICS JAPAN 事例一覧』、2005年8月19日、ウェブサイト
- 「「MACHINA」と「HEXAGON」、KDDIデザイニングスタジオで公開」、『ITmedia Mobile』、2005年11月7日、ウェブサイト
- 『東京芸術見本市2005 ガイドブック』、東京芸術見本市事務局、2005年

2006
- 「石橋素＋真鍋大度《RFID バマンのグループの七作品を体験するライトシーケンサー》」、『季刊インターコミュニケーション』、NTT出版、2006年、p. 210
- 『ふしぎ大陸南極展 2006』、朝日新聞社、2006年
- 「渋谷慶一郎＋池上高志／「filmachine（フィルマシン）」」、『MAPING SOUND INSTALATION』、山口情報芸術センター、2006年、ウェブサイト

2007
- 「true/本当のこと プレスリリース」、山口情報芸術センター、2007年7月
- Bruno Bossis「The breaking-continuity paradox in artificial vocality aesthetics」、『SMC'07, 4th Sound and Music Computing Conference』、2007年7月11日、pp. 255–258
- 『季刊インターコミュニケーション』第4号、NTT出版、2007年、p. 125

石橋素、真鍋大度「インタラクションの舞台裏 BEYOND THE BROWSER」、『Web Designing』2008年1月号、毎日コミュニケーションズ

2008

- 石橋素、真鍋大度「Miu cosmetics & NIKE6.0 RAMP GIG '08 スポーツとインタラクション」、『Web Designing』2008年6月号、毎日コミュニケーションズ
- Eliot Van Buskirk「Video: Music Makes Face Twitch」、『WIRED』、2008年10月27日、ウェブサイト
- Eliot Van Buskirk「日本人アーティストによる「音楽信号で顔の表情を動かす動画」」、『WIRED』、2008年10月28日、ウェブサイト
- kentaro「動画：音楽にあわせて表情を無理矢理変えるマシン」、『engadget日本版』、2008年10月28日、ウェブサイト
- 『BRUTUS』2008年12月1日号、マガジンハウス
- 「Webの可能性を拡げるデザイン 4nchor5 La6」、『Webデザインノート』no. 09、誠文堂新光社、2008年

2009

- 『Catalogue: Human Nature』、Ars Electronica Archive、2009年
- Alison Abbott「Science arts centre opens in a blaze of colour」、『nature』、2009年1月5日
- 川口隆夫（ダムタイプ）、坪池栄子「「アーティストインタビュー」日本のマルチメディア・パフォーマンスを支える照明アーティスト藤本隆行の世界」、国際交流基金Performing Arts Network Japan、2009年7月31日、ウェブサイト
- Eoin Smith「Turntable and Computer Composition」、『Proceedings of Sound, Sight, Space and Play 2009』、2009年5月6日、pp. 37–44
- 「口の中でLEDを光らせてみた場合」、『ギズモード・ジャパン』、2009年5月7日
- 真鍋大度「連載：Ideas come from everywhere」1. Hello, world!」、『CBCNET』、2009年5月27日、ウェブサイト
- mariko takei「4NCHOR5 LA6「The Way Sensing Go +」公開制作」、『SHIFT日本語版』、2009年6月18日、ウェブサイト
- 『Freeze! 2009 International MEDTECH Art Show』、2009年6月25日
- 「「true／本当のこと」東京公演リーフレット」、カラーキネティクス・ジャパン、2009年
- 「TOPICS STAGE「true／本当のこと」」、『装苑』2009年9月号、文化服装学院出版局
- 「Art Daito Manabe + Motoi Ishibashi「Pa++ern」」、『装苑』2009年9月号、文化服装学院出版局
- 「ライゾマティクスが語る空間デザイン」、『ケンプラッツ』、日経BP、2009年11月27日、ウェブサイト
- 「「EDITOR'S PIC」コラボレーター紹介」、『Designers'』vol.2、日経アーキテクチュア、2009年
- Alvaro Cassinelli, Yusaku Kuribara, Masatoshi Ishikawa, Ishikawa-Komuro Laboratory, University of Tokyo, Daito Manabe, Rhizomatiks「scoreLight: a laser-based synesthetic experience」、『SIGGRAPH ASIA 2009,

Digital Content Expo 2009 Symposium』、2009年12月

- Alvaro Cassinelli, Yusaku Kuribara, Masatoshi Ishikawa, Daito Manabe「scoreLight」、『SIGGRAPH ASIA '09: ACM SIGGRAPH ASIA 2009 Art Gallery & Emerging Technologies』、2009年12月、p. 15
- 「Time Lapse Plant／偽加速器 (prototype／試作) フライヤー」、BankART 1929、2009年

2010

- 「青山デザイン会議 (第131回) iPadで何ができる？：長谷川踏太、真鍋大度、伊藤正裕」、『ブレーン』2010年8月号、宣伝会議、pp. 66–75
- Daito Manabe, Motoi Ishibashi, Seiichi Saito「BodyHack workshop」、『TEI '10: Proceedings of the fourth international conference on Tangible, embedded, and embodied interaction』、2010年1月、pp. 345–348
- 真鍋大度「「連載：Ideas come from everywhere」第2回」、『CBCNET』、2010年2月17日、ウェブサイト
- 田所淳、比嘉了、久保田晃弘『Beyond Interaction——メディアアートのためのopenFrameworksプログラミング入門』、ビー・エヌ・エヌ新社、2010年
- 『映像作家100人 2010——JAPANESE MOTION GRAPHIC CREATORS 2010』、ビー・エヌ・エヌ新社、2010年
- A. Cassinelli, Y. Kuribara, A. Zerroug, M. Ishikawa Ishikawa - Komuro Laboratory, University of Tokyo, D. Manabe Rhizomatiks「scoreLight: playing with a human-sized laser pick-up」、『NIME2010』、2010年6月
- 「カレッタ汐留で女性書家・中塚翠涛さん作品展——デジタルアートも」、『新橋経済新聞』、2010年7月15日、ウェブサイト
- 「せんだいメディアテーク「5番チューブ再開発計画」、石橋素と真鍋大度による展示が9月18日から開催」、『CBCNET』、2010年8月20日、ウェブサイト
- Joyce Shintani, Metin Kara「Ars Electronica 2009: "Human Nature" in Linz, Austria」、『Computer Music Journal』vol. 34, no. 2, Summer 2010、pp. 90–93
- Douglas Repetto, Columbia University「Doing It Wrong」、『Frontiers of Engineering: Reports on "Leading-Edge Engineering from the 2010 Symposium"』、2010年、p. 50
- Takashi Ikegami「Studying a self-sustainable system by making a mind time machine」、『S3 '10: Workshop on Self-Sustaining Systems』、2010年、pp. 1–8
- 「岐阜 おおがきビエンナーレ 2010／温故地新 パンフレット」、IAMAS、2010年
- 「8組19人のクリエイティブ」、『Web Designing』2010年11月号、毎日コミュニケーションズ
- 「第14回文化庁メディア芸術祭 受賞作品集」、文化庁メディア芸術祭実行委員会、2010年

2011

- WTF NIKE TULIO「The Art Directors Annual 90」、AVA Publishing、2011年、p. 236
- 「SEOUL SQUARE MEDIA CANVAS 2011 K-J COLLABORATION PROJECT」、『SEOUL SQUARE

MEDIA CANVAS 2011 K-J COLLABORATION PROJECT」、2011年2月8日

- Saito Akiko「真鍋大度＋石橋素「particles」ができるまで。2年越しで実現した巨大インスタレーションとは?」、『CBCNET』、2011年5月3日、ウェブサイト
- 「やくしまるえつこ、特設サイトで個人情報だだ漏れ」、『音楽ナタリー』、2011年5月20日、ウェブサイト
- 「せんだいメディアテーク「いま、バリアとはなにか」」、2011年6月1日
- 「［特集・やくしまるえつこ］真鍋大度氏に訊く「生体データ」という手段」、『MARQUEE』vol. 85、マーキー・インコーポレイティド、2011年
- NHK「コネクトファイル」、2011年6月3日
- 「シングル「ルル／ときめきハッカー」をめぐる一連の共同作業、それぞれの制作意図とは?」、『SWITCH』2011年7月号、スイッチ・パブリッシング
- 「関和亮×真鍋大度 もぐもぐインタビュー「声を映像化したかった」」、『ガジェット通信』、2011年7月16日、ウェブサイト
- Matsui Design Studio「TASAKI Timeless Message〜氷の城〜」、Matsui Design Studio、2011年8月19日、ウェブサイト

2012
- 「［ディレクターズトークvol. 45］真鍋大度」、『ブレーン』、宣伝会議、2012年、pp. 79-81
- 神吉弘邦「［CROSS×TALK］テクノロジーとアートの境界面から人間について考える。暦本純一×真鍋大度」、『テレスコープ・マガジン』、2012年、ウェブサイト
- 「OPEN LAB「これからのモノ作りのカタチ」齋藤精一氏（rhizomatiks）」、『カタリストBA』、東急、2012年2月8日、ウェブサイト
- 「デザイン エクストリーム セミナー2012 Intel The Museum of Me」、『Shuffle』、2012年3月15日、ウェブサイト
- 「ブンブンサテライツ、4/24（火）14：00〜15：00にMV撮影現場をUst生中継」、『BARKS』、2012年4月23日、ウェブサイト
- 「SonarSound Tokyo 2012」、『EYESCREAM』2012年5月号
- Alvaro Cassinelli, Daito Manabe, Stéphane Perrin, Alexis Zerroug, Masatoshi Ishikawa「scoreLight & scoreBots」、『CHI EA '12: CHI '12 Extended Abstracts on Human Factors in Computing Systems May 2012』、2012年5月、pp. 1011-1014
- 内田伸一「最先端に辿り着くための迷走：真鍋大度インタビュー」、『CINRA.NET』、2012年5月14日、ウェブサイト
- 「テクノロジーとクリエイティビティが融合した作品を生み出す：石橋素」、『CBCNET』、2012年5月14日、ウェブサイト
- NHK「テクネ 映像の教室」、「プロジェクション」、2012年8月21日
- UNITED ARROWS LTD.「あなたを真似して動きだす、世にも不思議なマリオネット型ロボットが登場。UNITED ARROWS green label relaxing期間限定イベント「Marionettebot 恋するマリオネット」」、2012年11月1日
- Alvaro Cassinelli, Jussi Angesleva, Yoshihiro Watanabe, Gonzalo Frasca, Masatoshi Ishikawa「Skin games」、『ITS '12: Proceedings of the 2012 ACM international conference on Interactive tabletops and surface』、2012

年11月、pp. 323-326
- 「START NEWS & OBSESSIONS THE MAKER MOVEMENT」、『WIRED』vol. 6、2012年、pp. 16-17
- 真鍋大度「アーティスト・クリエイターが彩る色彩の世界」、『TOYO INK』、2012年11月26日、ウェブサイト
- Ai Nakajima Sadam Fujioka, Takeshi Usami, Kiyoshi Tomimatsu「NEW CREATIVE POTENTIAL IN THE ANIMATION FIELD BY APPLYING UGC CULTUREA case study of the user generated animation」、『conferência internacional em Ilustração e Animação』、2012年12月、pp. 37-50
- Hiroshi Utsunomiya「Interview 真鍋大度｜メディアアーティスト」、『PAPER SKY』、ニーハイメディア・ジャパン、2012年12月21日、ウェブサイト

2013
- 「MOBILITY AND ART REVIEW – Particles」、『Transfers 2013 No. 1』、2013年
- 「理大ひと」、『東京理科大学報』第189号、2013年
- 「インタラクションを超えて Beyond Interaction」、『FITC TOKYO 2013』、2013年1月27日
- 「村松亮太郎×真鍋大度対談 映像をスクリーンから解放したもの」、『CINRA.NET』、2013年1月29日、ウェブサイト
- 「既成を抜けてフィールドを創り出す」、『CGWORLD Entry vol. 3』、2013年1月30日
- 「テクノロジー＋カルチャーネ申ラボ100 Perfume」、『SWITCH』2013年2月号、スイッチ・パブリッシング
- 「Interfacing Forward」、『The LiP』、2013年2月、ウェブサイト
- illion『UBU』MV「MAHOROBA」ABOUT CREATORS、『BARFOUT!』2013年4月号、ブラウンズブックス
- 「「作家性のない者は滅ぶ」トップクリエイター2人が語る広告の未来」、『エンジニアtype』、2013年4月8日、ウェブサイト
- 「新しい仕事と、僕らの未来。」、『BRUTUS』2013年4月15日号、マガジンハウス
- 「クリエイターを訪ねる〜品田英雄が聞く、あの人の昨日・今日・明日〜」、『音事協magazine：社団法人日本音楽事業者協会会報』vol. 18、日本音楽事業者協会、2013年
- 「TALK about HITS」、『オリジナルコンフィデンス』2013年5月6日号、オリコン・エンタテインメント
- TOKYO FM「TOUGH THE MEETING」、『SHOCK THE RADIO powered by G-SHOCK』、2013年5月17日、ラジオ
- 日本テレビ「人体がスクリーンに!? 超ハイテクピカピカ系ライブ続々!」、『ズームイン!!サタデー』、2013年6月29日
- 真鍋大度「common」、『ユリイカ』2013年7月臨時増刊号［総特集 岡村靖幸］、青土社、pp. 127-130
- 「Disney for Gentlemen 男だってディズニー」、『BRUTUS』2013年7月1日号、マガジンハウス
- 「世界に衝撃を与えたPerfumeのカンヌパフォーマンス、その舞台裏に迫る——ライゾマ・真鍋大度氏、石橋素氏に聞いた」、『エンジニアtype』、2013年8月5日、ウェブサイト
- 日本テレビ「フェイスプロジェクションマッピング」、「ズームイン!!サタデー」、2013年9月14日

- 「光のアートにおける「最新」とは？「真鍋大度（ライゾマティクス）」を考える」、『スタジオ・ボイス』特別号「MY NAME IS BEAMS」、INFASウェーブ、2013年

- 「ギズに「Perfume inspired by ライゾマティクス」展のスペシャルコメントを頂いたよ（動画）」、『ギズモード・ジャパン』、2013年9月27日、ウェブサイト

- 「特集：カンヌで何が起こったか？〈座談会：真鍋大度×MIKIKO×TAKCOM「Perfumeライブパフォーマンスの舞台裏」〉」、『コマーシャル・フォト』2013年10月号、玄光社、2013年

- 「Close up」、『Time&Space』2013年10・11月号、KDDI

- ライゾマティクス 真鍋大度氏へのインタヴュー「ライゾマティクス・真鍋大度が語るPerfumeとメディアアートの今。」、『.fatale』、2013年10月8日、ウェブサイト

- 「真鍋大度1/3 Perfumeでメディアアートに革命［INTERVIEW］」、『FASHION HEADLINE』、2013年10月29日、ウェブサイト

- 「真鍋大度2/3 Perfume以前の舞台芸術の経験［INTERVIEW］」、『FASHION HEADLINE』、2013年10月30日、ウェブサイト

- 「真鍋大度3/3 音楽、Perfume、次は金融へ［INTERVIEW］」、『FASHION HEADLINE』、2013年10月31日、ウェブサイト

- 野間恒毅「ライゾマ真鍋大度さんに聞く、ライゾマ展 inspired by Perfumeの舞台裏」、『ギズモード・ジャパン』、2013年11月2日、ウェブサイト

- 毎日放送「コンピューターを使って新たな表現に挑み続ける男の、制作の秘密と頭の中とは？ プログラマー真鍋大度」、「情熱大陸」、2013年11月3日

- 「音と光、映像を駆使したインタラクティブアート アーティスト・真鍋大度氏との対談①」、『週刊ロビ』38号、2013年11月13日

- 渋谷ヒカリエに「形の無い」Xマスツリー、ライゾマティクス監修、『シブヤ経済新聞』、花形商品研究所、2013年11月15日、ウェブサイト

- 東京都・渋谷ヒカリエにライゾマティクス制作の「のぼれる」Xmasツリー登場、『livedoorNEWS』、2013年11月15日、ウェブサイト

- 「SWITCH presents メディアアートとスタートアップ」、『六本木アートカレッジ』、2013年11月24日

- 真鍋大度、細貝淳一「『下町ボブスレー』の舞台裏」、『Qonversations』、2013年12月2日、ウェブサイト

- NHK「Art of Trading Data」、「NHK WORLD NEWSLINE」、2013年12月25日

2014
- 畑麻衣子「アンリアレイジ森永×ライゾマティクス真鍋が語るファッションとテクノロジー［ASVOFF TOKYO］」、『FASHION-HEADLINE』、2014年1月7日、ウェブサイト

- 「アートのお仕事図鑑」、『美術手帖』2014年2月号、美術出版社

- 加藤孝司「あの人の「スタンダード」と「ニュースタンダード」」、『excite ism』、2014年1月14日、ウェブサイト

- 「孫の力 vol. 16、東京五輪を100倍楽しむ方法」、『WANDERLUST』、2014年1月25日

- 上阪徹「Perfumeのメディアアートを創る鬼才・真鍋大度に迫る」、『リクルートTech総研』、リクルートキャリア、2014年1月31日、ウェブサイト

- 「最近やったアートワーク、広告ワーク」、『FITC TOKYO 2014』、2014年2月16日、ウェブサイト

- 宮下哲「［ファッショニスタの逸品］ふだんあまり聞こえない「音」が気になる：真鍋大度さん」、『朝日新聞デジタルマガジン&［and］』、2014年2月20日、ウェブサイト

- 「［INFLUENCER］ファッション界がラブコール！今気になる、二人のアーティストのこと」、『装苑』2014年4月号、文化服装学院出版局

- kentaro inoue「40 真鍋大度（メディアアーティスト）×大野茉莉（サウンドアーティスト）」、『六本木未来会議』、2014年3月19日、ウェブサイト

- 「私の知ってる、勝手なあの人」、『BRUTUS』2014年4月1日号、マガジンハウス

- 「JTQ代表 谷川じゅんじ×RHIZOMATIKS代表 齋藤精一×LEXUS INTERNATIONAL Executive Vice President 福市得雄 Talk Session」開催、『INTERSECT BY LEXUS』、LEXUS TOKYO、2014年5月7日、ウェブサイト

- 「IAMAS移転特集」、『岐阜新聞』、2014年5月22日

- 「1/日本人口、「形」-forme-」、日本文教出版、2014年3月31日

- 真鍋大度「わたしがオススメする人文書3冊」、『文藝』2014年夏号、河出書房新社

- 「［イベント映像演出の世界 vol. 05］屋内テクノ・フェスティバル《electraglide 2013》」、『PRONEWS』、2014年4月16日、ウェブサイト

- NHKラジオ「すっぴん」、2014年4月16日、ラジオ

- 文化放送「スパカン!」、2014年4月18日、ラジオ

- J-WAVE「THE HIDDEN STORY」、STUDIO VIVA、2014年4月25日、ラジオ

- 長瀬光弘「［連載：Tehuのトップクリエイター七番勝負］憧れの真鍋大度氏に聞く！「メディアアーティストって何ですか？」」、『エンジニアtype』、2014年4月30日、ウェブサイト

- 「WE ROBOTS」、『OTDM short movie project』、OTDM、2014年5月1日

- 『TOO MUCH Magazine』issue5、2014年4月

- NHK「まず動け、未来はその先にある プログラマー/アーティスト 真鍋大度」、「プロフェッショナル 仕事の流儀」、2014年5月12日

- 「Transcranial – Collaborative project by Klaus Obermaier, Daito Manabe and Kyle McDonald」、『CREATIVE APPIICATIONS NETWORK』、2014年5月11日、ウェブサイト

- SPACE SHOWER TV「映像作家の世界 真鍋大度ワークス」、スペースシャワーネットワーク、2014年5月29日

- 「テクノライズミー」、『SPUR』6月号、集英社

- 「ぼくの、わたしの、こう育てられた。」、『BRUTUS』2014年6月1日号、マガジンハウス

- 「フットボール・ピープルたちのコミュニケーション術」、『SWITCH』2014年6月号、スイッチ・パブリッシング

- 「Creator's file #001 アイデアの扉」、『Pen』2014年6月号、阪急コミュニケーションズ

- Akiko Saito (text) / Daniel Robson (translation)「「Photo Tour」ODAIBA, TSUKISHIMA: Daito Manabe」、『100 Tokyo』、CINRA、ウェブサイト、2014年6月6日

- 泉彩子「「仕事とは? vol. 123」真鍋大度さん(プログラマー・メディア ア ティスト)の「仕事とは?」」、『就職ジャーナル』、リクルートホールディングス、2014年6月11日、ウェブサイト

- 「El hombre que hacía bailar a los drones」、『El Diario』、eldiario.es、2014年6月14日、ウェブサイト

- 「Collecting Data from One's Own: an interview with Daito Manabe」、『PostDigital Node』、2014年6月19日、ウェブサイト

- SPACE SHOWER TV「千原ジュニアの鼓膜」、スペースシャワーネットワーク、2014年6月26日

- DAITO MANABE「Artichoke 11 (the official magazine of the degree course in Visual Communication at SUPSI)」、『SUPSI』、2014年6月26日

- 「Creators' Bonding, SANKEI Express」、『7/5 フジサンケイビジネスアイ』、7/5 フジサンケイビジネスアイ、2014年6月30日

- 「中島信也×伊藤直樹×朴正義×齋藤精一×猪子寿之がクリエイティブの"教育"を語る座談会」、『To Creator』、イマジカデジタルスケープ、2014年7月1日、ウェブサイト

- 「トップクリエイターインタビュー」、『CREATIVE VILLAGE』、クリーク・アンド・リバー社、2014年7月3日、ウェブサイト

- 「理系の友達」、『UOMO』2014年7月号、集英社

- TOKYO FM「LOVE CONNECTION「スターバックスミュージックバリスタ」」、2014年6月26日・7月3日、ラジオ

- 「ライゾマティクス ディレクター 真鍋大度さん」、creativevillage、2014年7月4日、ウェブサイト

- TOKYO FM「坂本美雨のDear Friends」、Atelier E.A.U、2014年7月15日、ラジオ

- 「あの人に訊いた、夢と理想のサマーバケーション」、『Pen』2014年8月号、阪急コミュニケーションズ

- 「10人+ひとりのスパイク・ジョーンズ論。」、『フィガロジャポン』2014年8月号、阪急コミュニケーションズ

- 「テクノロジー + カルチャー ネ申ラボ ver.2.0」、『SWITCH』2014年8月号、スイッチ・パブリッシング

- J-WAVE「Mercedes me MUSIC FACTORY」、2014年8月16日、ラジオ

- 「学びを活かす仕事」、『マナビゲート2014』、2014年8月23日

- 日本テレビ「ヨコハマ・パラトリエンナーレ2014」、「NEWS ZERO」、2014年8月26日

- 伊藤健吾「真鍋大度氏が中高生向けプログラミング教室を開いたら、技術は「人と人をつなぐ魔法」になった」、『エンジニアtype』、2014年8月27日、ウェブサイト

- 「My Food Bible 100 あなたのフードスタイルを変える100冊」、『SWITCH』2014年9月号、スイッチ・パブリッシング

- Fernanda Quiroz「Lo más esperado en el Cervantino: Rhizomatiks + Elevenplay」、『W RADIO』、2014年9月10日

- 「クリエイターズトーク、KINARI vol. 11」、『Percus.』、2014年9月13日

- 「なぜ音楽は真鍋大度を必要とするのか:Red Bull Music Academyのレクチャーで語られたこと」、『WIRED』、2014年9月15日、ウェブサイト

- 「「齋藤精一さんに会いに行く。」、『差し出しかたの教室／受け入

- れかたの学校」」、弘文堂、2014年9月22日、ウェブサイト

- 日本テレビ「エンタメよ〜いPON!」、『PON!』2014年9月23日

- 「ファッション通信」、『BS-J』、2014年9月27日、

- 「36人のクリエーターに聞く私が影響を受けた本、写真、映画、音楽。」、『装苑』2014年9月号、文化服装学院出版局

- 「100人の欲しいものリスト。」、『BRUTUS』2014年10月1日号、マガジンハウス

- 「コミュニケーションの最前線を行く」、『K-OPT』、エム・シー・アンド・ピー、2014年10月1日

- 高岡謙太郎「インタビュー:真鍋大度「身体に電流が流れるレクチャーイベントとは?」」、『Time Out Tokyo』、コンタクト・イースト、2014年10月10日

- 「ろう者ダンスの新時代 背中から音楽が聞こえる」、『AERA』2014年10月13日号、朝日新聞出版

- 「ENTERTAINMENT NEWS!! ART」、『Hanako』2014年10月23日号、マガジンハウス

- 「みんなの新TOKYO 港区・千代田区・中央区」、『フィガロジャポン』2014年11月号、阪急コミュニケーションズ

- 「あの人に会いたいvol. 35」、『MEN'S NON-NO』2014年11月号、集英社

- 「理大人列伝」、『科学フォーラム』365号、東京理科大学広報課、2014年

- 「情熱接客キャンペーン」、『United Arrows』、ユナイテッドアローズ、2014年11月1日、ウェブサイト

- 「男らしさを考える委員会。」、『BRUTUS』2014年11月1日号、マガジンハウス

- 日本テレビ「SENSORS」、AX-ON、2014年11月3日

- エフエム岐阜「未来授業」、2014年11月8日、ラジオ

- 深沢慶太「革新的表現を生み出す創造への意欲とは」土田耕作と真鍋大度との対談、『Creators' Bonding』、SUNデザイン研究所、2014年11月17日、ウェブサイト

- 「MY STANDARD JOURNEY」、『G-SHOCK BOOK』、BYOB、2014年11月21日

- 「インタラクティヴ・アートからデータ・アートへ」、『目白大学社会学部メディア表現学科 公開講演会』、2014年11月26日

- 「Light Brings Technology to Culture」、『外務省広報誌にぽにか』no. 14、平凡社、pp. 14–17、2014年11月、ウェブサイト

- 「ベッドサイドテーブルブック特集」、『SPUR』2014年12月号、集英社

- 「アノ人の企画書が見たい!トップクリエイターの「勝てる」企画の通し方」、『Web Designing』2014年12月号、マイナビ出版

- Verena Dauerer「Code + culture: new media art from Japan」、『Japan Times Web』、2014年12月6日、ウェブサイト

- 「LECTURE: Daito Manabe」、『SWITCH X RBMA Tokyo 2014 SPECIAL ISSUE』、コンタクト・イースト、2014年12月20日

- 「Provisio コンピテンシーの道程」、『日本アイビーエム』、2014年、pp. 30–32

2015
- 小林正明「"Thirty years of Mac" for the rest of us.」、『Mac Fan』2015年1月号、マイナビ出版

- 佐々木敦規×真鍋大度「進化するライヴの感動体験」、『オリ

ジナルコンフィデンス』2015年1月1日号、オリコン・エンタテインメント

- 小島歌織「REPORTメディアアート・ラボから考える都市文化vol.2「ラボから生まれるアート ライゾマティクス」」、ART AleRT SAPPORO All Rights Reserved、2015年1月30日、ウェブサイト

- 「SNAP, FOREVER コンピューターはファッションフォトグラファーの夢を見るか?」、『GINZA』2015年2月号、マガジンハウス

- yosuke iizuka「Skate Drawing」Rhizomatiks / Presented by 六本木未来会議【前編】、六本木未来会議、2015年2月4日、ウェブサイト

- 「ポストメディウム時代のメディアアート〜アート部門受賞作品発表会 vol.2」(登壇:真鍋大度ほか)、SuperDeluxe、2015年2月6日

- 「アートとプロトタイピング」、『FITC TOKYO 2015』、2015年2月8日

- 「OK GO スペシャル ライブ at YouTube Space Tokyo 2周年記念イベント」、YouTube Channnel、2015年2月10日

- 「書籍『電通デザイントークVol. 2』齋藤精一×中村勇吾×飯田昭雄「つくる機会をつくる」」、『ウェブ電通報』、電通、2015年2月13日、ウェブサイト

- テレビ朝日「最先端エンターテインメントの右腕×プログラマー・真鍋大度」、『夏目と右腕』、2015年2月14日

- 「クリエイターが撮った#MyMomentAtOkura」、『Numero TOKYO』2015年3月号、扶桑社

- 「Watch a Modern Dance Battle Between Drones and a Human」、『the creators project』、2015年3月1日、ウェブサイト

- yosuke iizuka「Skate Drawing」Rhizomatiks / Presented by 六本木未来会議【後編】、六本木未来会議、2015年3月4日、ウェブサイト

- 盛山諒「ヤバいから見てっ! ライゾマティクス真鍋大度の動画と作品(本人による解説つき):SENSORS IGNITION 2015」、『週刊アスキー』、2015年3月6日、ウェブサイト

- 「AMIT2015シンポジウム デザイン・ザ・フューチャー」、『アートフェア東京2015』、2015年3月21日

- Sami Emory「The Future Is Here, And It's a Japanese Pop Concert」、『the creators project』、2015年3月23日、ウェブサイト

- 「クリエイターのヒミツ基地。」、『東京ウォーカー』2015年3月号、KADOKAWA

- 「教育とテクノロジーの"最前線" 若者たちが見つめたEdu×Tech Fes 2015」、『Web Designing』2015年4月号、マイナビ出版

- 「トッププログラマーが語る人工知能:真鍋大度&山本一成」、Apple Store銀座店、2015年4月2日、ウェブサイト

- 「自由な発想で、無機質なデータに新しい価値を与える——メディアアーティスト 真鍋大度さんインタビュー」、『mugendai』、2015年4月9日、ウェブサイト

- 「僕らを走らせるひと」、『走るひと』2015年4月号、1milegroup

- 「クリエイターのヒミツ基地。」、『東京ウォーカー』2015年4月号、KADOKAWA

- J-WAVE「Appleに選ばれたクリエイター真鍋大度 テクノロジーと音楽の未来を語る」、「SAPPORO BEER OTOAJITO」、

2015年4月25日、ラジオ

- 日本テレビ「「世界的テクノロジスト真鍋大度」×「演出振付家MIKIKO」番組、初対談!」、「SENSORS」、2015年4月26日

- 「あの私的でエモーショナルな体験にあった背景」、『GQ JAPAN』、コンデナスト・ジャパン、2015年5月12日、ウェブサイト

- 大崎龍史「チームラボとRhizomatiksの違い:メディアアートは、人と都市の関係をどうハックするか?【後編】」、『GUERILLA LOCAL』、2015年5月12日、ウェブサイト

- 「クリエイション大国へようこそ!」、『Numero TOKYO』2015年5月号、扶桑社

- 「Daito Manabe」、『RTVE.es』、2015年6月

- 「話題のクリエイターが選ぶ、カッコいいミュージックビデオ」、『フィガロジャポン』2015年7月号、CCCメディアハウス

- 齋藤あきこ「[アートプロジェクト]ライゾマティクス・齋藤精一」、『JDN』、2015年7月6日、ウェブサイト

- 真鍋大度×石橋素×石橋治子×関口真一郎「Experience Driven Showcase #11 安川電機100周年式典を、ライゾマティクスが演出!」、『電通報』、2015年7月7日、ウェブサイト

- 「ライゾマティクス 齋藤精一のクリエイティブ考「アーティストにKPIを求めるなんてバカげてる」」、『キャリアハック』、2015年7月21日、ウェブサイト

- 「Interviews - Daito Manabe」、『NEURAL』Issue50 Winter 2015、2015年8月

- 「現場主義で最先端の表現を極めたい R&Dの強化から始まった一気通貫のモノづくり」、『WORKSIGHT』、コクヨ、2015年8月3日、ウェブサイト

- 星暁雄「鮮烈な演出を支えるのは、枯れた技術と入念なテスト ライゾマティクス リサーチのプログラマーに聞く」、『CodeZine』、2015年8月5日、ウェブサイト

- 星暁雄「本番で絶対に失敗しないメンタリティをつけるには? ライゾマティクス リサーチの若手プログラマーに聞く」、『CodeZine』、2015年8月7日、ウェブサイト

- 塩谷舞「否定も、悲観も、熱弁もしない。日本メディアアートシーンを牽引する、真鍋大度とは?」、『partner』、2015年8月15日、ウェブサイト

- 「[ドローン女が行く!vol. 01]ドローン×ヒューマンインタラクション。ライゾマティクスが語るドローンの未来」、『drone.jp』、2015年8月27日、ウェブサイト

- 「[特別インタビュー]メディアアーティスト真鍋大度が初めて語るハッカソン、人工知能、DJで変貌する音楽の未来とは?」、『All Digital Music』、2015年8月27日、ウェブサイト

- 大陸新秩序「[CEDEC 2015]インタラクティブアートがエンターテイメントの世界に進出。2日めの基調講演「Data Art and Entertainment」をレポート」、『4gamer.net』、2015年8月27日、ウェブサイト

- 秋山健一「[CEDEC 2015]データのビジュアル化に秘められた可能性とは? 第一人者・真鍋大度氏による基調講演「Data Art and Entertainment」リポート」、『ファミ通.com』、2015年8月28日、ウェブサイト

- 「真鍋大度とKEIZOmachine!がLiveの活用法を伝授! Ableton User Meeting Tokyoアニバーサリー・イベントレポー

● 「ト」、『soundrope』、2015年8月30日、ウェブサイト

● 「Timeline of Technology & Performing Arts」、『SWITCH』2015年9月号、スイッチ・パブリッシング

● 「Drones on the Dance Floor」、『GOOD』ISSUE 34、2015年9月8日、ウェブサイト

● 「ライゾマティクス真鍋大度&石橋素が語る「僕たちがドローンを使いはじめた理由」」、『クーリエ・ジャポン』、2015年9月24日、ウェブサイト

● 真鍋大度「メディアアートで世界を面白がる 21世紀をつくるニッポン人名鑑」、『AERA』、朝日新聞出版、2015年9月28日

● 「プログラマー 真鍋大度's playlist」、『Hi-Res Playlist×EYESCREAM』、2015年10月1日、ウェブサイト

● 「[特別対談記事]エンジニアが導く新たな表現の世界 橋本善久(リブゼント・イノベーションズ)×真鍋大度(ライゾマティクス)」、『CGWORLD Entry』vol.13、ボーンデジタル、2015年、pp. 6–9

● 「わたしたちの原点 最先端技術をプログラミングで可視化 数学と音楽との融合が新たなアートを生み出す」、『大学の力[週刊朝日進学MOOK]』、朝日新聞出版、2015年、p. 76

● Takatoshi Takebe「[SPECIAL REVIEW]今、最も体感すべきテクノロジーと音楽の祭典「POST」とは何だったのか? 10時間に及ぶトークセッションを中心にLIVERARYが全力レポ。」、『LIVERARY』、2015年10月11日、ウェブサイト

● 「Blackmagic Design製品事例:ライゾマティクスリサーチが手がけた「NEXT WORLD LIVE」の場合」、『PRONEWS』、プロニュース、2015年10月13日、ウェブサイト

● LUMINE「21世紀をつくるニッポン人名鑑」、『朝日新聞』、2015年10月22日

● 「集団創作 アートに新風 個性持ち寄り作品に献身」、『日本経済新聞』、2015年10月24日

● 高橋範光『道具としてのビッグデータ──最適解を導き、成果につなげる8つのルール』、日本実業出版社、2015年

● 「[PEOPLE]future fusion サカナクション山口一郎が挑むMusic×Technology×Fashionの未来」、『Numéro Tokyo』2015年11月号、扶桑社、pp. 188–191

● 「NF_Interview 01 真鍋大度」、『SWITCH』2015年11月号、スイッチ・パブリッシング、pp. 47

● 「特集:音楽×アートの現在」、『ぴあ MUSIC COMPLEX』vol.2、ぴあ、2015年

● 真鍋大度「萬斎さんのこと」、『狂言ござる乃座52ndパンフレット』、2015年11月4日

● 遊佐怜子「橋本善久×真鍋大度 特別対談「必要なのはアーティストだけじゃない!」エンジニアが導く 新たな表現の世界」、『CGWORLD.jp』、2015年11月4日、ウェブサイト

● 松本雅延「ライゾマティクス真鍋大度が語る「テクノロジーと表現の融合」−1/2[INTERVIEW]」、『FASHION HEADLINE』、2015年11月5日、ウェブサイト

● 松本雅延「ライゾマティクス真鍋大度が語る「アップルウォッチの創造性」−2/2[INTERVIEW]」、『FASHION HEADLINE』、2015年11月5日、ウェブサイト

● 「進路にまつわるアンケート」、『This! 001』、小学館、2015年

● J-WAVE『ALL AREA PASS』、2015年11月21日、ラジオ

● 日本テレビ「SENSORS SALON第8回 人工知能の現在と未来」、『SENSORS SALON』、2015年11月27日

● 日本テレビ「[5日間連続公開]クリエイター、僧侶、研究者が語る「人工知能の現在と未来」」、『SENSORS』、2015年11月27日、ウェブサイト

● 日本テレビ「ライゾマ真鍋大度らが語る、ゴッホやピカソを凌駕する人工知能×アート論」、『SENSORS』、2015年11月29日、ウェブサイト

● 「音楽ライブ、クールに演出 映像や光、踊りとシンクロ 先鋭技術融合し脚光」、『日本経済新聞』、2015年11月30日

● 日本テレビ「「人工知能は悟れるのか?」光明寺松本僧侶×東大松尾豊 研究者対談」、『SENSORS』、2015年11月30日、ウェブサイト

● oricon ME『コンフィデンス』、2015年12月1日

● 日本テレビ「「あなたは人工知能と恋愛できますか?」アーティスト市原えつこが創造する未来の恋愛」、『SENSORS』、2015年12月1日、ウェブサイト

● 日本テレビ「「アニメ大国・日本は人工知能競争で勝てる」東大松尾豊の提言」、『SENSORS』、2015年12月2日、ウェブサイト

● 「八重洲口グランルーフでインスタレーション デッキの風を光と音に変換」、『日本経済新聞』、花形商品研究所、2015年12月2日、ウェブサイト

● 日本テレビ「修行するAI、人工知能近未来予測」、『SENSORS』、2015年12月3日、ウェブサイト

● 「ジャイアントステップ」、『Quick Japan』vo. 123、太田出版、2015年

● 真鍋大度「あの人が選ぶ今年の3枚 2015年ベストディスクレビュー特集」、『ARBAN』、2015年12月22日、ウェブサイト

2016

● 「クリエイターを育てるクリエイターたち」、『Numero TOKYO』2016年1・2月号、扶桑社、p. 114

● NHK Eテレ「日本賞50周年記念番組:U18 ぼくらの未来」、2016年1月3日

● 「「風の印象感じて欲しい」。風を可視化、新感覚のプロジェクトに迫る」、『サイエンスニュース』、カンゼン、2016年1月5日、ウェブサイト

● 真鍋大度「COVER STORY」、『コンフィデンス』、2016年1月11日

● 「僕らを走らせる31名の音楽」、『走るひと3』、1milegroup、2016年

● 「アクサのテレマティクス保険、担当者「楽しく、お得に、安全を届ける」」、『レスポンス』、イード、2016年1月21日、ウェブサイト

● 真鍋大度「第2特集:音楽×映像の関係」、『ぴあ MUSIC COMPLEX』vol. 3、ぴあ、2016年

● 「ソーシャリー・エンゲージド・アート」と、三者三様の活動のあり方−Relight Session vol. 2 レポート[1/3]、『Relight Project』、特定非営利活動法人インビジブル、2016年1月28日、ウェブサイト

● 真鍋大度「岡村靖幸さんニューアルバムに対するコメント」、『TV Bros.』2016年1月30日号、東京ニュース通信社

● 真鍋大度「テクノロジー、アート、エンターテインメントを融合し 誰も見たことがない映像と音で新境地を切り拓く」、『金沢工業大

学卒業生／OB会報誌 Back Up』、2016年

- 真鍋大度「光と私」、『CK VIEWS』vol. 15、カラーキネティクス・ジャパン、2016年
- 真鍋大度「MUSIC VIDEO 音楽を魅せるクリエイターたち—テクノロジーで魅せる 真鍋大度」、『装苑』、2016年2月号、文化出版局
- Lance Ulanoff「Watch this magician effortlessly control 24 drones, indoors」、『Mashable』、2016年2月11日、ウェブサイト
- J-WAVE「KIRIN ICHIBAN SHIBORI ONE AND ONLY」、2016年2月16日、ラジオ
- NHK「プログラミング〜真鍋大度〜」、「NHK Eテレ 課外授業 ようこそ先輩〜センセイの頭の中〜」、2016年2月19日
- 「奇跡的にできた絶妙なバランスで成り立つ 唯一無二のクリエイティブ集団「Rhizomatiks」」、『CREATORS STATION』、フェローズ、2016年2月24日、ウェブサイト
- 真鍋大度「［連載・ヒットするデザイン］世界中が熱狂！進化を続けるPerfumeライブ演出の秘密」、『PRESIDENT』、2016年2月29日
- 真鍋大度、ハイロック「デジタル新世紀へ突入！フューチャリスティックな便利生活」、『フィガロジャポン』2016年3月号、阪急コミュニケーションズ
- Yu Murooka「Interview with Daito Manabe」、『THE FASHION POST』、2016年3月3日、ウェブサイト
- 「東京の24時間を旅する本〜TOKYO 24HOURS JOURNEY〜」、『TOKYO DAY OUT』、2016年3月3日
- 「第3部 ゲームのみらい—メディアアーティスト対談：落合陽一×真鍋大度」、『ゲームってなんでおもしろい?』、2016年3月9日
- 「コムアイのフリー対談連載「さぐりさぐり」vol. 31」、『Nylon』、カエルム、2016年3月10日、ウェブサイト
- 谷川じゅんじ（JTQ）×齋藤精一（Rhizomatiks）「MEDIA AMBITION TOKYO」対談インタビュー、『NEOL』、STOP、2016年3月11日、ウェブサイト
- 杉本昭彦、中村勇介「Key Person AIによりクラフトマンシップは価値を失う 人に求められるのは文脈作り」、『日経Big Data』、2016年3月16日
- 木村浩康「プログラマーと実現するデータドリブンなデザインプロセス」、『ブレーン』2016年4月号、宣伝会議、ウェブサイト
- 「真鍋大度（メディアアーティスト）」、川村元気『理系に学ぶ。』、ダイヤモンド社、2016年
- 真鍋大度「MOVIES FOR LIFE／映画が教えてくれること。」、『& Premium』2016年4月号、マガジンハウス
- 「COMMUNITY」、『WWD.JAPAN』、2016年4月1日、ウェブサイト
- Charlotte Sarrola「#24 Tokyo Daito MANABE」、『i Heart』、2016年4月5日
- 日本テレビ「SHOWBIZ BRAVO」、『ZIP!!』、2016年4月8日
- 「ライゾマティクスリサーチ・真鍋大度のルーツを探る—NYで音楽に打ち込んだ大学時代」、『SENSORS』、2016年4月8日、ウェブサイト
- 「5 MINUTES WITH: DAITO MANABE+NOSAJ THING」、『RED BULL STUDIOS TOKYO』、2016年4月15日、ウェブサイト

- 「Así crea sus obras Daito Manabe, el artista digital más importante de nuestro tiempo」、『El PAIS』、2016年4月17日、ウェブサイト
- 「都会にできた巨大な工房は人々をどう変える? TechShop Japan有坂庄一×ライゾマティクス齋藤精一」、『HIP』、森ビル、2016年4月18日、ウェブサイト
- BSフジ「人 Gens」、『ESPRIT JAPAN』、2016年4月25日
- SPACE SHOWER TV「サカナクションのNFパンチ」、スペースシャワーネットワーク、2016年4月29日
- 「Perfumeというカルチャー」、『装苑』2016年5月号、文化出版局
- 「テクノロジーを使って誰も見たことのない表現を探る テクニカルディレクター石橋素」、『cakes』、2016年5月19日、ウェブサイト
- 「［ドローン・マジック］ライゾマティクス・石橋素氏インタビュー」、『ROBOTEER』、ROBOTEER、2016年5月26日、ウェブサイト
- 「プロジェクションマッピングだけじゃない! 新しいことをする会社、ライゾマティクス齋藤精一さん。」、『TOKYO ONGOING』、TOKYO FM、2016年6月4日、ウェブサイト
- 齋藤あきこ「パリ日本文化会館発 真鍋大度、石橋素への質問」、『をちこちMagazine』、2016年6月30日、ウェブサイト
- 「世界的クリエイター・真鍋大度は "どこでも眠れるたくましさ" を持つ」、『フミナーズ』、2016年7月11日、ウェブサイト
- 日本テレビ「真鍋大度×アルスエレクトロニカ演出監督対談「メディアアートが社会に与えるインパクト」」、『SENSORS』、2016年7月16日
- 日本テレビ「『ポケモンGO』で盛り上がる位置情報ゲームの魅力を探る 真鍋大度×Ingress川島優志」、『SENSORS』、2016年7月21日
- 真鍋大度「Levi's特集企画」、『PRODISM』、2016年7月21日、ウェブサイト
- 中脇雅裕「音楽クリエイターのためのイメージ・トレーニング!」ゲスト：真鍋大度 時代を切り開くメディア・アーティストの脳内」、『サウンド&レコーディングマガジン』、2016年7月25日
- 篠田哲生「グランドセイコー 伝統とテクノロジー、その見事な融合。」、『Pen Online』、2016年8月5日、ウェブサイト
- Miho Iizuka「「DAOKO meets 真鍋大度」デジタル育ちとアナログ育ちが捉えるテクノロジーの過去・現在・未来」、『DiFa』、2016年8月5日、ウェブサイト
- 齋藤精一×豊田啓介×西牟田悠「可変する建築」（後編）、『AdverTimes』、宣伝会議、2016年8月6日、ウェブサイト
- ARINA TSUKADA「テクノロジーがコンテンツだった時代は終わった：真鍋大度」、『WIRED』、2016年8月19日、ウェブサイト
- テレビ朝日「ELEVENPLAY × Rhizomatiks Research "24 drones"」、『ミュージックステーション』、2016年8月26日
- 「100人の、マイ・スタンダードTシャツ」、『MEN'S NON-NO』2016年9月号、集英社
- J-WAVE「ACOUSTIC COUNTY」、2016年9月5日、ラジオ
- NHK Eテレ「U18 ぼくらの未来」、2016年10月17日
- 「今、アナログが新しい! レコードとカセット」、『UOMO』2016年10月号、集英社
- 「男の利き手／vol. 100 真鍋大度」、『Numero TOKYO』2016

年10月号、扶桑社

● 本木雅弘、真鍋大度『本木雅弘×真鍋大度 仕事の極意』、KADOKAWA、2016年

● 「日本の美しい写真が話題に「PHOTO METI PROJECT」が目指す、ストックフォトサービスのその先とは」、『AdGang』、PR TIMES、2016年11月11日、ウェブサイト

● AKIKO SAITO「Rhizomatiks Research Chronicle 真鍋大度＋ライゾマティクスリサーチ AR/VR集成 2012-2016 ─ Perfumeからリオ五輪2016閉会式まで」、『WIRED』、2016年11月16日、ウェブサイト

● 真鍋大度「［クリエーターインタビュー］進化するテクノロジーで世の中をおもしろく」、『広告朝日』、2016年11月18日、ウェブサイト

● 黒田隆憲「後藤英が真鍋大度に訊く、五輪閉会式の裏とメディアアートの未来」、『CINRA.NET』、2016年11月28日、ウェブサイト

● 「ろう者の世界からどう音楽を表現する? 南村千里×ライゾマの挑戦」、『CINRA.NET』、2016年12月6日、ウェブサイト

● 日本テレビ「ズムサタいち押し!「リオ五輪 名場面TOP10＆是非とも知って頂きたいあれこれ」、「ズームイン!!サタデー」、2016年12月10日

● 真鍋大度「ルフと私」、『トーマス・ルフ展』、2016年12月10日、ウェブサイト

● 『ENSEMBLE』、TABLE ENSEMBLE、2016年12月20日

● 川上康介「メディアアーティスト・真鍋大度 稀有な才能を支える右腕」、『GOETHE』、2016年12月24日、ウェブサイト

● 「真鍋大度 リオ五輪で確信した「日本型ライブ」の真の強み」、『NewsPicks』、2016年12月30日、ウェブサイト

2017
● 「［特集 ライゾマティクス］Rhizomatiks 世界に誇る"フルスタック"集団 ライゾマティクスのすべて」、『美術手帖』2017年1月号、美術出版社

● J-WAVE『J-WAVE NEW YEAR SPECIAL EYES FOR THE FUTURE』、2017年1月2日、ラジオ

● 「常に時代の最前線に立つ クリエイター 真鍋大度さん」、マイナビバイト、2017年1月4日、ウェブサイト

● 「TOKYO 24H Interview 5 #worktime、WWD JAPAN (Tiffany East West Collection)」、2017年1月6日、ウェブサイト

● 「PAMTASM CONCEPTUAL BOOK (P.A.M.FACETASM)」、2017年1月7日、ウェブサイト

● 「佐藤オオキ(nendo)のひらめきのスイッチ」、『Casa BRUTUS』、マガジンハウス、pp. 128-129

● 「DJの経験からリオ五輪閉会式の映像演出まで。また、真鍋大度が捉える「東京」とは」、『HIGHFLYERS』、2017年1月12日、ウェブサイト

● 新國翔大「ライゾマティクス 真鍋大度の軌跡 サラリーマン時代を経て、無名の青年が世界を魅了するまで。」、『キャリアハック』、エン・ジャパン、2017年1月16日、ウェブサイト

● 横石崇編「File 1 テクノロジーで身体表現は変化する:真鍋大度」、『これからの僕らの働き方──次世代のスタンダードを創る10人に聞く』、早川書房、2017年

● 「2. 一流企業を1年で退職しフリーターを経験後、IAMASでテ

クノロジーを使った表現方法を習得。それまでを支えた精神とは」、『HIGHFLYERS』、2017年1月26日、ウェブサイト

● NHK WORLD「J-Music Creators 真鍋大度」、『J-MELO』、2017年1月30日

● 「ファッション・グル4人が指南──東京を"体験"するデザイン名所14選」、『GQ JAPAN』2017年2月号、コンデナスト・ジャパン

● 「［カバーインタビュー］真鍋大度＋石橋素」、『AXIS』vol.185、2017年2月号、AXIS

● FaltyDL『Heaven is for Quitters』Release Tour、『SWITCH』2017年2月号、スイッチ・パブリッシング、pp. 126

● 「［interview］真鍋大度 人に求められるのは文脈作り」、日経トップリーダー、日経ビッグデータ編『AIが同僚──あなたはたのしく一緒に働けるか』日経BP、2017年

● 青山鼓「［EVENT REPORT］Tiffany & Co. × Forbes JAPAN スペシャルトークショー」、『Forbes JAPAN』、2017年3月号、リンクタイズ、pp. 110-111

● 「第2特集「音楽とアートの関係」:真鍋大度、石橋素(Rhizomatiks Research)、MIKIKO (ELEVENPLAY)鼎談」、『ぴあMUSIC COMPLEX』vol. 8、ぴあ、2017年、pp. 90-97

● テクノロジーを駆使して新たな表現を生み出すRhizomatiks Researchのエンジニアチームが明かす舞台裏、『fabcross』、メイテックフィルダーズ、2017年2月3日、ウェブサイト

● 「「アディダス バイ カラー」最新作をスニーカー賢者が評価 ステージや映像でも引き立ちそうなカラーリングと素材:真鍋大度 ライゾマティクスリサーチ ディレクター」、『WWD JAPAN』、2017年2月9日

● 「3. Perfumeとの仕事が大きな転機に。U2やマッシヴ・アタックが世界を驚かせたメディアアートから5年間の葛藤と打開策とは」、『HIGHFLYERS』、2017年2月9日、ウェブサイト

● 毎日新聞社広告局「クリエーターの目」、『SPACE』、2017年2月16日

● 「"最先端"の病を脱し、エレガントな組み合わせを見出す。光と動きの「ポエティクス／ストラクチャー」真鍋大度(ライゾマティクスリサーチ)×ユッシ・アンジェスレヴァ(ART+COM)」、Bound Bow、2017年2月17日、ウェブサイト

● 「制約の中で表現獲得」、『愛媛新聞』、2017年2月18日

● 「4. 人生を変えたライゾマ創設メンバーとの出逢い。テクノロジーと表現をさらに最大化させた、MIKIKOやその他の仲間の重要性とは」、『HIGHFLYERS』、2017年2月26日、ウェブサイト

● 「真鍋大度・LOCUS」、『SWITCH』2017年3月号、スイッチ・パブリッシング

● フジテレビ「バディーズ〜私と大切な仲間たち〜真鍋大度、齋藤精一」、2017年3月9日

● 「2016 毎日デザイン賞」、『毎日新聞』、2017年3月10日

● 「ライゾマティクス代表取締役社長 齋藤精一さん」、『CREATIVE PLATFORM OITA』、特定非営利活動法人BEPPU PROJECT、2017年3月16日、ウェブサイト

● NHK BSプレミアム「未来へ伝統×最先端が挑む日本最古の舞〜狂言師・野村萬斎×メディアアーティスト・真鍋大度の挑戦〜」、2017年3月31日

● 「新しい音楽の聴き方 "サンプリングミュージック"」、『GINZA』

2017年4月号、マガジンハウス

● 「真鍋大度・LOCUS」、『SWITCH』2017年4月号、スイッチ・パブリッシング

● 「特集「はじまりの音楽」」、『BRUTUS』2017年4月15日号、マガジンハウス、pp. 24–25

● 「TOKYO MUSIC ODYSSEY 2017」、SPACE SHOWER、2017年4月

● 「the Digital Innovator_コンテキストに価値があるモノだけが生き残る」、『corporate mag』、2017年4月

● ラジオ日本「真夜中のハーリー＆レイス」、2017年4月2日、ラジオ

● テレビ朝日「関ジャム完全燃SHOW」、2017年4月2日

● 宋文「Sónar Hong Kong 2017―與視覺藝術家Daito Manabe訪談」、『HYPEBEAST』、2017年4月3日、ウェブサイト

● 「MIKIKO・真鍋大度が語る「国境を超えるクリエイティブの秘訣」」、『SENSORS』、2017年4月4日、ウェブサイト

● 片山正通「片山正通教授の「未来」の「仕事」のつくり方(CASA BOOKS instigator 3)」、マガジンハウス、2017年

● 島貫泰介「「オリンピアード文化通信 第5回」時代に逆らい、未来を考える。ライゾマティクス真鍋大度の流儀」、『ネットTAM』、2017年4月10日、ウェブサイト

● 「AI DJ or Vinyl DJ テクノロジーが導くDJの新たな境地」、『Intel IQ』、2017年4月10日、ウェブサイト

● 「水道橋にアートを、新ギャラリー「アーモ」でライゾマ×イレブンプレイが新作を世界初演」、『Fashionsnap.com』、2017年4月10日、ウェブサイト

● 「「EOS M6×6senses：写真×メディアアート」表現の未来を拓く真鍋大度が、写真に見る可能性とは？」、『Pen Online』、2017年4月20日、ウェブサイト

● Tatsuya Noda「東京ドームシティの新名所AaMoで真鍋大度とMIKIKOが新作ダンスインスタレーション発表」、『FASHION HEADLINE』、2017年4月24日、ウェブサイト

● 「[ひと]真鍋大度さん 2016毎日デザイン賞を受賞」、『毎日新聞』、2017年4月26日朝刊

● 「圧倒！ライゾマ×ELEVENPLAYの新作、そして未来へ…！」、『Numero TOKYO』、2017年4月26日、ウェブサイト

● 「La instal·lació interactiva i sense límits de Daito Manabe que arribarà al Sónar」、ara.cat、2017年4月27日、ウェブサイト

● 「[フロントランナー]五輪閉会式からPerfume舞台まで 真鍋大度さん」、『朝日新聞デジタルbe on Saturday』、2017年4月28日、ウェブサイト

● 「[フロントランナー]ライゾマティクスリサーチ主宰・真鍋大度さん 生の表現を技術で新次元へ」、『朝日新聞』、2017年4月29日朝刊、ウェブサイト

● J-WAVE「CHINTAI TOKYO DISTRICT 秋元梢があなたとシェアするREAL TOKYO LIFE」、2017年4月30日、ラジオ

● 「ユース・ファッションのいま/世界を席巻するスケーターファッション」、『GQ JAPAN』2017年5月号、コンデナスト・ジャパン

● 「真鍋大度・LOCUS」、『SWITCH』2017年5月号、スイッチ・パブリッシング

● 「街に意思をもたせる：ライゾマティクス 齋藤精一氏の「CityOS」構想とAIの関係性とは」、『THINK Business』、IBM、2017年5月12日、ウェブサイト

● 首都大学東京インダストリアルアート学域「技術の面白さ、その先に行くにはコンセプトが必要です」、『AXIS Web magazine』、2017年5月16日、ウェブサイト

● 「Perfumeライブ、リオ閉会式FHOのARシステムを開発した男。Rhizomatiks Research花井裕也が生み出す映像世界」、『パーソルテクノロジースタッフ』、パーソルテクノロジースタッフ、2017年5月18日、ウェブサイト

● 野田達哉「東京ドームシティの新名所AaMoで真鍋大度とMIKIKOが新作ダンスインスタレーション発表」、『FASHION HEADLINE』、2017年5月24日、ウェブサイト

● 「「デジタルは深く人を支える」齋藤精一が語る仕事(1-4)」、『朝日新聞ひろば』、朝日新聞社、2017年5月29日、ウェブサイト

● 「真鍋大度 ライゾマティクスリサー×きゅんくん ロボティクスファッションクリエイター：デジタルの世界に、男女は存在するのか？」、『フィガロジャポン』2017年6月号、阪急コミュニケーションズ

● 「6人のサムライのお仕事道「型と基礎」」、『GINZA』2017年6月号、マガジンハウス、pp. 162–167

● 「真鍋大度・LOCUS」、『SWITCH』2017年6月号、スイッチ・パブリッシング

● 岡村靖幸、真鍋大度「あの娘と、遅刻と、勉強と」、『TV Bros.』2017年6月3日号、東京ニュース通信社、p. 28

● 「[pioneer Interview]芸術×娯楽×社会実験 求め続ける新しい表現」、『NIKKEI The Style（日本経済新聞）』、2017年6月4日朝刊日曜版

● 「ライゾマ・齋藤精一氏が考える、未来の都市の姿「もっと個性を活かし、東京全体をデザインすべき」」、『ORICON NEWS』、オリコン、2017年6月11日、ウェブサイト

● Barcelona「Sónar presenta "Phosphere", un espectáculo inmersivo del artista Daito Manabe」、EFE、2017年6月14日、ウェブサイト

● 「Descalzos por el atómico mundo de Daito Manabe y otros espacios inmersivos del Sónar+D」、eldiario.es、2017年6月14日、ウェブサイト

● 「El Sónar presenta "Phosphere", un espectáculo inmersivo del artista Daito Manabe」、ecoDiario.es、2017年6月14日、ウェブサイト

● 「Un Sónar sin límites」、EL Periódico、2017年6月15日、ウェブサイト

● 「The Magic of Light a the Sónar Festival with Brian Eno and Daito Manabe」、Arshake、2017年6月15日、ウェブサイト

● 「ARRANCA LA PRIMERA JORNADA DEL SÓNAR 2017」、NON STOP PEOPLE、2017年6月15日、ウェブサイト

● 「Rhizomatiks10～実空間の表現に革命を起こしたRhizomatiksの10年間、そしてこれから～」、『にぎわい空間研究所』、2017年6月16日、ウェブサイト

● 「Karma Peiró「Sónar +D: la creativitat tecnològica que no et pots perdre」」、Naciodigital、2017年6月16日、ウェブサイト

● TOKYO FM「高須光聖×ライゾマ代表齋藤精一 渋谷大開発を空想する」、「空想ラジオ」、2017年6月18日、ラジオ

- Bruno Garca「ESPECIAL Crónica: Sónar+D 2017」、『clubbingspain.com』、2017年6月19日、ウェブサイト

- Anna Savina「Daito Manabe on choreographing equations and making use of deep brain data」、『Freunde von Freunden』、2017年6月22日、ウェブサイト

- 「International Arts-Science Residency at Jodrell Bank」、Jodrell Bank Discovery Centre、2017年6月23日、ウェブサイト

- Mireia Pascual「Sónar+D 2017 - Speculative features」、『METALmagazine』、2017年6月26日、ウェブサイト

- 「Siete mai stati al Sónar Barcellona」、『youMark!』、2017年6月28日、ウェブサイト

- 「L'espectacle «Phosphere» de Daito Manabe dona el tret de sortida al Sónar」、『Naciodigital』、2017年6月28日、ウェブサイト

- 齋藤あきこ「ホームページ番外地 第0回」インタラクションデザイナーはどこを見る：木村浩康」、『JDN』、2017年6月29日、ウェブサイト

- 「真鍋大度・LOCUS」、『SWITCH』2017年7月号、スイッチ・パブリッシング

- 萩原雄太「真鍋大度はなぜ大舞台に強い？「紅白」やリオ閉幕式の成功に迫る」、『CINRA.NET』、2017年7月4日、ウェブサイト

- NHK BSプレミアム「未来へ　伝統×最先端が挑む日本最古の舞 ～狂言師・野村萬斎×真鍋大度の挑戦～」、2017年7月6日

- 「World Premiere // COSMOS 2017 // international art-science residency」、『SHIFT』、2017年7月7日、ウェブサイト

- ARINA TSUKADA「真鍋大度、evalaによる最高のイマーシヴ・エクスペリエンス：バルセロナ「Sónar+D」現地レポート」、『WIRED』、2017年7月9日、ウェブサイト

- 「Daito Manabe, and the COSMOS Project, 2017」、『MICHAEL9MURRAY』、2017年7月10日、ウェブサイト

- 岡村靖幸、真鍋大度「あの娘と、遅刻と、勉強と」、『TV Bros』、2017年7月15日号、東京ニュース通信社、p. 28

- 『POPEYE特別編集 本と映画のはなし』、マガジンハウス、2017年

- DJ Pangburn「These Ghostly Dancers Are the Closest We've Come to 'Star Wars' Holograms」、『VICE MAGAZINE』、2017年7月24日

- 「「コムアイの脳ミソの中がまとまらなくて。」ゲスト 真鍋大度」、『POPEYE』2017年8月号、マガジンハウス

- 「真鍋大度・LOCUS」、『SWITCH』2017年8月号、スイッチ・パブリッシング

- 「ライゾマ齋藤社長が池田純に語った、"スポーツとテクノロジー"融合の未来。」、『Number Web』、文藝春秋、2017年8月8日、ウェブサイト

- 「大好きカルチャー最前線！」、『anan』2017年8月9日号、pp. 38–39

- 「スポーツは、もっとやれる」齋藤精一（ライゾマティクス）、『VICTORY』、VICTORY、2017年8月11日、ウェブサイト

- 杉原環樹「真鍋大度と阿部一直が語る、ダン・フレイヴィンから連なる「メディア・アートへの系譜」」、『美術手帖』、美術出版社、2017年8月25日、ウェブサイト

- 「テクノロジー賢者に学ぶ原理と潮流 2 メディアアートの旗手 齋藤精一」、『週刊東洋経済プラス』、東洋経済新報社、2017年8月26日、ウェブサイト

- 「エゴを出せ—「優等生」の日本人にライゾマティクスが伝えたいこと」、『"未来を変える"プロジェクト』、パーソルキャリア、2017年8月28日、ウェブサイト

- 「真鍋大度・LOCUS」、『SWITCH』2017年9月号、スイッチ・パブリッシング

- 「[#Illustrator30_30 #Ai30th 記念連載]vol. 25 デザイナー 木村浩康さん」、『Adobe Blog』、アドビ システムズ、2017年9月7日、ウェブサイト

- SATORU KANAI「ライゾマティクスリサーチが「機械とテックによる表現」に託すもの：CeBIT 2017バックステージレポート #3」、『WIRED』、2017年9月18日、ウェブサイト

- 大高志帆「渋谷から「ファッション×テクノロジー」でムーブメントを起こす」、『NewsPicks』、2017年9月28日、ウェブサイト

- 「真鍋大度・LOCUS」、『SWITCH』2017年10月号、スイッチ・パブリッシング

- 福光恵「見るより着て感じる障害者の世界 横浜でパラトリエンナーレ開催」、『AERA』、2017年10月9日、ウェブサイト

- 真鍋大度、石橋素「Things on Stage——パフォーマンス作品における開発と実践」、『デジタルプラクティス』vol. 8 no. 4 (Oct. 2017)、情報処理学会、2017年

- 「Rhizomatiks Research 真鍋大度氏、石橋素氏インタビュー パフォーマンス作品における技術と演出、その先に」、『情報処理学会』、2017年10月15日、ウェブサイト

- 「Blackmagic Design製品事例：ライゾマティクスリサーチによるダンスインスタレーション『phosphere』の場合」、『PRONEWS』、プロニュース、2017年10月20日、ウェブサイト

- 「BMD製品導入事例：ライゾマティクスリサーチ、ダンスインスタレーション『phosphere』にURSA Mini 4KおよびUltraStudi 4Kを使用」、『eizine』、アールテクニカ、2017年10月20日、ウェブサイト

- 「真鍋大度 × Nosaj Thing「Live at Sónar Hong Kong 2017」ドキュメンタリー映像」、『lute』、2017年10月24日、ウェブサイト

- Zoe Mutter「Behind the scenes video: Bluedot's intergalactic masterpiece of projection」、『AV magazine』、2017年10月31日、ウェブサイト

- 「真鍋大度・LOCUS」、『SWITCH』2017年11月号、スイッチ・パブリッシング

- 「その男、グランドセイコー「新たな価値を創造するイノベーターたち」」、『日本経済新聞』、2017年11月2日

- JUN ISHIDA「未来を切り拓く男たち The Innovative Spirits」、『T JAPAN: The New York Times Style Magazine』、2017年11月8日、ウェブマガジン

- 「渋谷を3Dデータ化したら、街の価値がもっと見えてくると思う。」、『KEYPERSON』、渋谷文化プロジェクト、2017年11月14日、ウェブサイト

- 大高志帆「人工的に「流れ星」を作り出す。夢を形にするふたり」、『NewsPicks』、2017年11月17日、ウェブサイト

- 「業界の壁を飛び越え、新しい世界を切り開く。ライゾマティク

ス齋藤精一が語る「Data + Technology + Creative + Art + City」」、『AREA JAPAN』、オートデスク、2017年11月20日、ウェブサイト

- 4 Parede「ANDROIDES DANÇAM COM SAPATILHAS ELÉTRICAS?」、『Quarta Parede』、2017年11月21日、ウェブサイト
- 「真鍋大度・LOCUS」、『SWITCH』2017年12月号、スイッチ・パブリッシング
- 「ライゾマティクスリサーチ《phosphere》の世界的称賛の理由。音楽とアートの実験場Sónarレポート(後編)」、『boundbaw』、2017年12月7日、ウェブサイト
- 深沢慶太「岐阜県のIAMAS—日本の未来を担う"人づくり"の最前線」、『AXIS Magazine』、2017年12月28日
- 「連載「アーキテクチュアル・シンキング」パースやプレゼンの表現など、建築のプロセスはどれもアートだ」、『NIKKEI DESIGN』、2017年12月28日、pp. 6–7

2018
- テレビ朝日『別冊アサ(秘)ジャーナル』、2018年1月28日
- NHK WORLD「Direct Talk "A Technological Wizard Shaping Art Daito Manabe"」、2018年1月29日
- Alisa Yamasaki「Big in Japan: The Illustrator 30 (Part Four) — Hiroyasu Kimura」、『Adobe Create Magazine』、2018年1月31日、ウェブサイト
- 「[Good Tools For Me vol. 66]愛用のイヤフォンを教えてください」、『Casa BRUTUS』2018年2月号、マガジンハウス、pp. 190–191
- 「真鍋大度が関わり続ける、最前線の音楽の現場」、『KODE』、2018年2月5日、ウェブサイト
- 齋藤あきこ「真鍋大度のDJプレイの裏側」、『KODE』、2018年2月6日、ウェブサイト
- 齋藤あきこ「真鍋大度が語る「ベストアクト」」、『KODE』、2018年2月7日、ウェブサイト
- 齋藤あきこ「真鍋大度が語るメディアアートフェス「アルス」の魅力」、『KODE』、2018年2月8日、ウェブサイト
- 山田智子「IAMAS OB/OG interview 005」、『IAMAS web』、2018年2月12日、ウェブサイト
- J-WAVE「特別番組 J-WAVE HOLIDAY SPECIAL KAMARQ presents EXPAND YOUR WORLD」、2018年2月15日、ラジオ
- 「ドルチェ&ガッバーナのショーでドローン飛行を成功させたライゾマティクスに一問一答」、『WWD』、2018年2月27日、ウェブサイト
- 秦野邦彦「[クリエイター連載]真鍋大度「Perfume×TECHNOLOGY」presents Reframe」、『TVガイドperson』vol. 67、東京ニュース通信社、2018年、pp. 86–89
- 深沢慶太「真鍋大度:テクノロジー×アートの遙かなる行方」、『nippon.com』、2018年3月15日、ウェブサイト
- NHK Eテレ「にっぽんの芸能」、野村萬斎×真鍋大度「三番叟 FORM II」、2018年3月16日
- Kunihiro Miki「[対談:AKIKO KIYAMA×真鍋大度 和楽器を再構築し、狂言を再解釈する」、『TimeOut TOKYO』、2018年3月19日、ウェブサイト
- 「都市のこれからを考える—R不動産 林氏、ライゾマティクス 齋藤氏、WIRED 若林氏」、『LivingTech』、LivingTech運営事務局、2018年3月26日、ウェブサイト
- 「[特集ART COLLECTIVE]企業と協働する集団の戦略とは? Rhizomatiks/チームラボ/WOW/THE EUGENE Studio」、『美術手帖』2018年4月号、美術出版社
- 「ライゾマティクスリサーチ 真鍋大度×ファッションを学ぶ20代」、『装苑』2018年4・5月合併号、文化出版局
- ライゾマティクスリサーチ「広告をアップデートするテクノロジー ゴールはできるかできないかの境界線上に置く」、『ブレーン』2018年4月号、宣伝会議、pp. 32–35
- 「「デジタル×建築」新次元テクノロジーアートの担い手と劇的融合」、『日経アーキテクチュア』2018年4月26日号、日経BP、p. 60
- Vivian Yeung「Digital artist Daito Manabe is turning music videos into sensory experiences」、『Crack magazine』、2018年4月27日、ウェブサイト
- NHK BS プレミアム「内村五輪宣言!Perfume×Technology presents Reframe」、2018年4月29日
- Elena Giulia Rossi「Interview I Daito Manabe」、『Arshake』、2018年5月4日、ウェブサイト
- "CREATIVE ACTION"、『TEDxShibuya』、2018年5月17日、ウェブサイト
- 「ライゾマティクスの"原寸日本建築"を体験する!「建築の日本展:その遺伝子のもたらすもの」」、『HILLS LIFE DAILY』、森ビル、2018年6月6日、ウェブサイト
- 「文化庁 メディア芸術祭メモランダム vol. 1」、『ソトコト』2018年7月号、木楽舎、p. 115
- NATSUMI MATSUZAKA「掘って掘って積んで積んで:ライゾマティクスの最新のドローン、AR、etc…を支える「リサーチ」と「作業」」、『WIRED』、2018年7月3日、ウェブサイト
- Jin Sugiyama「Rhizomatiks Research真鍋大度がDJ少年だった過去から〈フジロック出演〉までを語る#fujirock」、『富士電子瓦版』、2018年7月6日、ウェブサイト
- NHK BS プレミアム「Perfume×Technology presents Reframe」、2018年7月7日
- 「ライゾマティクス齋藤精一氏「建築のプロセスはどれもアートだ」」、『日経クロストレンド』、日経BP、2018年7月10日、ウェブサイト
- 真鍋大度「あの人が選ぶ"2018上半期"ベストディスク」、『ARBAN』、2018年7月13日、ウェブサイト
- 羽村玄「連載:外から見える土木・第42回」、『土木学会誌』、2018年7月15日、社団法人土木学会、pp. 54–55
- 「「ホームページ番外地 第3回」木村靖裕(homunculus Inc.)」、『JDN』、2018年7月17日、ウェブサイト
- Giulia Trincardi「Daito Manabe ci ha spiegato l'importanza di empatizzare con la tecnologia」、『Motherboard Italia』、Vice、2018年7月19日、ウェブサイト
- 詹士賢_羽瀬靖青Hase Yasuo「科技藝術的極致!是誰打造如夢似幻的「東京八分鐘」?日本科技藝術團隊真鍋大度&石橋素&編舞家MIKIKO專訪」、『MOT TIMES－明日誌』、2018年7月19日、ウェブサイト
- 「納期はたったの1週間!Rhizomatiks Researchの迅速な開発を支えるデジタルツール」、『fabcross powered by MEITEC』、

2018年7月20日

- Victoria Gill「Lovell lights: turning a telescope into an art installation」、BBC、2018年7月21日、ウェブサイト
- Keiko Kusano「アップル〈WWDC〉に潜入、真鍋大度が見た未来とは?」、『CasaBRUTUS』、マガジンハウス、2018年7月27日、ウェブサイト
- Yasuo Matsunaka「Rhizomatiks Researchがオリジナルのデバイスで開く新たな地平」、『The Conversation』、2018年7月30日、ウェブサイト
- 「無人機、全息投影、AR與舞蹈 看Rhizomatiks 真鍋大度、石橋素與 Mikiko如何完美融合科技與藝術」、『Cool3c』、2018年8月3日、ウェブサイト
- JOJO「[演唱會煉成術]歡迎來到未來世界!Perfume幕後推手 MIKIKO、真鍋大度、石橋素專訪」、『kkbox』、2018年8月4日、ウェブサイト
- 「「エステー鹿毛執行役 100番勝負 第5回」鹿毛康司 vs 真鍋大度 音楽で身につけた一流の仕事術(前編・後編)」、『日経xTREND』、2018年8月10日、ウェブサイト
- Federico Fianchini「ZEBRA CROSSING. Intervista esclusiva a DAITO MANABE」、『Sentieri Selvaggi』、2018年8月12日
- 「L'ingegnere che fa danzare i droni」、『la Lettura』、2018年8月19日
- 「[オフィス訪問レポ vol.16]まるで秘密基地、謎だらけの「ライゾマティクス」に潜入」、『Fashionsnap.com』、2018年8月23日、ウェブサイト
- 「子どものパソコン活用への期待[PR]パソコンは本当にやりたいことを加速させるツール」、『日経xTREND』、2018年8月24日、ウェブサイト
- 「カルチャーの最先端はどう生まれる? あの熱狂のつくり手・7人」、『anan』2018年9月12日号、マガジンハウス、pp. 55–56
- 「ART + TECHNOLOGY Series - Episode 15"Is Drone art a phase?"」、『Bloomberg』、2018年9月11日、ウェブサイト
- J-WAVE「特別番組 J-WAVE HOLIDAY SPECIAL KAMARQ presents EXPAND YOUR WORLD」、2018年9月17日、ラジオ
- 「クールジャパン最前線 キラキラ 光の芸術」、『読売KoDoMo新聞』、読売新聞、2018年9月27日、ウェブサイト
- 「ライゾマ齋藤精一が訴える「東京にはボブ・マーリーが必要だ」」、『CINRA.NET』、2018年10月5日、ウェブサイト
- 「2020を機に、東京はどう変わるのか? ライゾマティクス齋藤精一が見据える「東京の街づくり」」、『Yahoo! JAPANニュース』、2018年10月5日、ウェブサイト
- 「[ライブレポート]プラネタリウムでライゾマ・真鍋大度の音楽とテクノロジーの足跡を辿るトークショー」、『iFLYER』、2018年10月9日、ウェブサイト
- 「万年筆だけじゃない モンブランの新たな魅力に迫る」、『WWD JAPAN』、2018年10月12日、ウェブサイト
- 「心を開放する旅、本、音楽。」、『BRUTUS』2018年10月15日号、マガジンハウス
- 「[interview 2]真鍋大度(ライゾマティクスリサーチ)社会実験からメディアイベントへ──テクノロジーとアートの最前線を駆け抜ける」、『RedBull』、2018年10月16日、ウェブサイト
- Pablo Maille「discrete figures La chorégraphie augmentée à l'intelligence artificielle」、『Usbek & Rica』、2018年10月18日、ウェブサイト
- 庄野祐輔「[Event Report]A CONVERSATION WITH DAITO MANABE──真鍋大度と音楽。DJとしての活動、パフォーマンス演出から、楽器制作までその軌跡を語る」、『UNCANNY』、2018年10月22日、ウェブサイト
- 「真鍋大度さん(RhizomatiksResearch代表)インタビュー」、『Eastern Sound Factory』、2018年10月24日、ウェブサイト
- 「[CAST People #8]渋谷と365日インスタレーションする人──一過性ではない、その場所に根付く作品で人と空間をつなぐ」、『SHIBUYA CAST.』、2018年11月13日、ウェブサイト
- 「コンピューターの手癖をなくしてグラフィックに定着させるには」、『advanced』、2018年12月6日、ウェブサイト
- 川又英紀「[記者の眼]ライゾマを追った2018年、ダンス公演でAIの可能性と限界を見た」、『日経xTECH』、2018年12月19日、ウェブサイト
- 「異分野とつなげ文化を生む余白つくる、ライゾマティクス・齋藤精一氏」、『日経xTECH』、2018年12月19日、ウェブサイト
- 鹿児島MBCラジオ「People's」、2018年12月22日、ラジオ
- 真鍋大度「あの人が選ぶ"2018下半期"ベストディスク」、『ARBAN』、2018年12月24日、ウェブサイト
- 「その人のアイデアや技術や発想、つくるものなどをもって、これからの東京をおもしろくしてくれる!と期待している方をおひとり挙げてください」、『HILLS LIFE』94号、2018年12月29日
- 「[2018年ベストバイ]ライゾマティクス真鍋大度が今年買って良かったモノ」、『Fashionsnap.com』、2018年12月30日、ウェブサイト

2019
- 川又英紀「docomo×Perfumeの5Gライブに潜入、その瞬間を共有した」、『日経xTECH』、2019年2月1日、ウェブサイト
- 「真鍋大度氏、音声だけで展開するサスペンス『THE GUILTY／ギルティ』は「音響彫刻のような映画」」、『映画.com』、2019年2月2日、ウェブサイト
- 「真鍋大度が惚れ込んだ"耳で観る音響彫刻映画"とは? 映画『THE GUILTY／ギルティ』先行上映トークイベント」、『NB Press Online YouTube』、2019年2月4日、ウェブサイト
- H.USAMI「真鍋大度が惚れ込んだ"耳で観る音響彫刻映画"とは?映画『THE GUILTY／ギルティ』先行上映トークイベント」、『NB Press Online』、2019年2月5日、ウェブサイト
- 「真鍋大度、エブリオブギガス feat. mcアスナロら出演。写真×音楽の実験的イベント「NIGHT DEVELOPING#4」開催」、『LIVERARY』、2019年2月5日、ウェブサイト
- 川又英紀「Perfumeファン1万2000人のスマホ、Wi-Fi同時接続できたか?」、『日経xTECH』、2019年2月8日、ウェブサイト
- 原田優輝「「ギリギリ」の境界線上で生まれる表現とは?『未来の学校祭』をきっかけに見つめ直す、未来のアート、文化、社会のあり方」、『JDN』、2019年2月21日、ウェブサイト
- 「渋谷キャストにて、齋藤精一氏、豊田啓介氏らと『クリエイティブ思考で未来の都市を考える(仮)』公開企画会議を開催!」、『ニ

コニコニュース』、2019年3月14日、ウェブサイト

● Sam Byford「Behind the scenes with Perfume, Japan's most futuristic pop group」、『The Verge』、2019年3月29日、ウェブサイト

●「真鍋大度：身体と、実験と、一回性と」、岡村靖幸『あの娘と、遅刻と、勉強と（Bros.books）』、徳間書店、2019年、pp. 146-163

●「DAITO MANABE RHIZOMATIKS」、『+81 Magazine』、河出書房新社、2019年、pp. 115-125

● 坂本泉「［第6回ライブ・エンターテイメントEXPO］初日に開講されたセミナーをダイジェスト 〜ソニーミュージック水野氏／ぴあ村上氏／亀田氏＆いしわたり氏／ライゾマ真鍋氏〜」、『Musicman』、2019年5月13日、ウェブサイト

●「青柳菜摘、真鍋大度、三上晴子ら出展 ICC「オープン・スペース 2019」展」、『CINRA.NET』、2019年5月18日、ウェブサイト

● 猪口貴裕「「コンボが決まる気持ちよさは、音楽的な感じがするんです」真鍋大度氏が語るストリートファイターの魅力」、『e-sports press』、2019年5月22日、ウェブサイト

● 服部桂『VR原論──人とテクノロジーの新しいリアル』、翔泳社、2019年、pp. 351-352

●「「SXSW」で日本人が世界から突きつけられた課題とは？『ジャパン・プレゼンスを考える』レポート」、『FINDERS』、シー・エヌ・エス・メディア、2019年6月6日、ウェブサイト

● SHUNTA ISHIGAMI「「最適化」と「完璧」の先にテクノロジーの未来はある：「人とテクノロジーの関係」MATトークレポート」、『WIRED』、2019年6月7日、ウェブサイト

● 近藤雄生「アートとテクノロジーの融合によって、未来の世界が見えてくる」、『テレスコープマガジン』、ナノテクミュージアム、2019年6月28日、ウェブサイト

●「ライゾマの真鍋大度が選曲＆ナビゲートする新番組スタート」、『radiko news』、2019年7月5日、ラジオ

●「《やりたいこと》は拡張し続ける──真鍋大度の好奇心と情熱。「A CONVERSATION WITH DAITO MANABE」レポート」、『Red Bull』、2019年7月5日、ウェブサイト

●「真鍋大度／Daito Manabe – artist programmer」、『J weekly』、2019年7月6日、ウェブサイト

●「夢を叶えるために…ライゾマ・齋藤精一が学生に語る［KYOCERA TECHNOLOGY COLLEGE］」、『d menu ニュース』、NTTドコモ、2019年7月26日、ウェブサイト

●「真鍋大度の履歴書：前人未到の場所こそ、リスクが少ない」、『ぼくらの履歴書』、エン転職、2019年7月30日、ウェブサイト

●「想像力を刺激する展望施設「SHIBUYA SKY」にかける想い 新屋潤×ライゾマティクス プロジェクトディレクター 有國恵介」、『CITY UP!』、JR東日本生活サービス事業PR事務局、2019年8月31日、ウェブサイト

● HTB北海道テレビ「世界的アーティストの真鍋大度氏が札幌でトークイベント」、『HTBニュース』、2019年9月1日

● 真鍋大度＋坂本洋一＋石井達哉「「オープン・スペース 2019 別の見方で」出品作家インタヴュー」、『チャンネルICC』、2019年9月11日、ウェブサイト

● テレビ朝日「真鍋大度 アーティスト」、『白の美術館』、2019年9月18日

●「大丸心斎橋店、86年ぶりに建て替えた本館がついに開業。旧本館から復元した内外装を見てみた」、『トラベルWatch』、インプレス、2019年9月20日、ウェブサイト

●「sight update session エンジニアへのラブコール：ライブパフォーマンス×テクノロジー」、『sight』、2019年10月11日、ウェブサイト

● 川又英紀「位置情報を数センチ単位で計測、ライゾマが描く未来都市の姿を追う」、『日経xTECH』、10月16日、ウェブサイト

●「ライゾマティクス・真鍋大度が語る、"チームにアイデアを共有する方法"とは」、『dメニューニュース』『gooニュース』、2019年10月21日、ウェブサイト

● Akihiro Aoyama「真鍋大度が語る、音楽がもたらす創造の世界」、『Always Listening』、オーディオテクニカ、2019年10月25日、ウェブサイト

● 川又英紀「センチ誤差の位置情報で動く台車、増上寺のイベントでライゾマが初投入した自動走行ロボの実力」、『日経xTECH』、2019年11月22日、ウェブサイト

●「ピアノ、ゲーム、スケボー、DJ──全てがアーティスト・真鍋大度の原点になっている」、『sight』、2019年11月26日、ウェブサイト

● CROSS FM「ライゾマティクスリサーチの真鍋大度が語る、暮らしのデザインと仕事術」、『#casa』、2019年12月2日、ラジオ

●「株式会社ライゾマティクス創業──デジタル技術と表現の渦の中でもがいた真鍋大度の13年」、『sight』、2019年12月4日、ウェブサイト

●「真鍋大度（ライゾマティクス）が選ぶ2019年ベストアルバム」、『ARBAN』、2019年12月6日、ウェブサイト

●「ライゾマがメディアアートで目指すもの 最新技術に温もりを添えて」、『CINRA.NET』、2019年12月13日、ウェブサイト

●「［2019年ベストバイ］ライゾマティクス真鍋大度が今年買って良かったモノ」、『Fashionsnap.com』、2019年12月19日、ウェブサイト

●「誰も使っていないけど、これ絶対面白い──テクノロジーを作品に先取りする真鍋大度の未来創造論」、『sight』、2019年12月23日、ウェブサイト

●「真鍋大度 アートと先端技術の融合で「少し先」の未来を見せる」、『NewsPicks』、2019年12月29日、ウェブサイト

●「「デザインミュージアムをつくろう！キックオフ公開会議」議事録②横山いくこ×林保太×田根剛×齋藤精一」、『DesignDESIGN MUSEUM』、2019年12月29日、ウェブサイト

2020
●「AXIS Design Round-table「グッドデザインて何だ？」齋藤精一・山田遊・広野萌・佐々木智也」、『AXIS web magazine』、AXIS、2020年1月7日、ウェブサイト

● 鳥居裕介「最先端のアートは音楽とともに生まれる コンセプター坂井直樹さん×アーティスト真鍋大度さん」、『わたしのオト』、J-CASTニュース、2020年1月22日、ウェブサイト

● ライゾマティクス＋Perfumeの現在形。「Rhizomatiks inspired by Perfume 2020」をレポート、TOKYO ART BEAT、2020年1月25日、ウェブサイト

●「Rhizomatiks真鍋大度×MIKIKOによる「ライブパフォーマンス×テクノロジー」はいかに生まれたのか［前編］」、『sight』、

2020月1月29日、ウェブサイト

- 「スクエアプッシャー、真鍋大度が手がけたMVで「超近未来の東京」を描く」、『Rolling Stone』、2020年1月30日、ウェブサイト

- 「Rhizomatiks真鍋大度×MIKIKOによる「ライブパフォーマンス×テクノロジー」はいかに生まれたのか［後編］」、『sight』、2020年2月6日、ウェブサイト

- Maho Ise「不安や恐れではない。近未来への期待。」、『ソトコト』2020年2月号、sotokoto online

- 「「連載：自分の仕事をつくる」器用貧乏な自分にしかできない仕事がある：有國恵介」、『Business Network Lab』、Sansan、2020年2月28日、ウェブサイト

- 照沼健太「「街をハックする」真鍋大度が、スクエアプッシャーのMVを監督した理由と、その技術」、『ギズモード・ジャパン』、2020年3月3日、ウェブサイト

- J-WAVE「#1真鍋大度が解き明かす「テレコミュニケーションとテレプレゼンスアート」坂本龍一×真鍋大度が語る、音楽とアートの「役割」」、「TOPPAN INNOVATION WORLD ERA」、2020年4月5日、ラジオ

- 「齋藤精一が語るテック屋の危機感「技術の時代こそ哲学を」」、『CINRA.NET』、2020年4月23日、ウェブサイト

- J-WAVE「世界の紛争解決に最新テクノロジー/AIを活用！ライゾマティクス・真鍋×国連政策官・高橋尚子が対談」、「TOPPAN INNOVATION WORLD ERA」、2020年5月1日、ラジオ

- J-WAVE「サカナクション・山口一郎×真鍋大度 コロナ禍の今だからこそ届けられるエンタメとは？」、「TOPPAN INNOVATION WORLD ERA」、2020年5月3日、ラジオ

- 照沼健太「ライゾマティクス真鍋大度とMUTEK竹川潤一が見せる、"アグレッシブなSTAY HOME"」、『ギズモード・ジャパン』、2020年5月23日、ウェブサイト

- Sayuri Kobayash、「昔から変わらない広尾の、地元に愛される憩いの場：アーティスト・真鍋大度さんの超私的スポット」、『GINZA』2020年6月号、マガジンハウス

- 真鍋大度・花井裕也「AR/VR技術によるライブ映像演出」、『電子情報通信学会誌』vol. 103 no. 6、2020年6月、pp. 564–570

- 「Communicators - with Innovative mind」、理想科学工業広報誌『理想の詩』2020年夏号、pp. 2–8

- 「東京の大改造ビジョンをどう描くか、大手デベロッパー4社とクリエーターが議論」、『日経xTECH ACTIVE』、2020年6月2日、ウェブサイト

- J-WAVE「真鍋大度、ムロツヨシ＆上田誠と組んだ「非同期テック部」の活動を語る」、「TOPPAN INNOVATION WORLD ERA」、2020年6月7日、ラジオ

- 「アートから制度づくりまで、インスタレーションに挑み続ける。ライゾマティクス・アーキテクチャー齋藤精一×馬場正尊」、『REWORK』、オープン・エー、2020年6月9日、ウェブサイト

- J-WAVE「［サカナクション Part1］シンガーソングライター長谷川白紙さん対談」、「MITSUBISHI JISHO MARUNOUCHI MUSICOLOGY」、2020年6月13日、ラジオ

- J-WAVE「［サカナクション Part2］シンガーソングライター長谷川白紙さん対談」、「MITSUBISHI JISHO MARUNOUCHI MUSICOLOGY」、2020年6月20日、ラジオ

- NHK-FM「「かけるインタビュー」コーナーにアーティスト・プログラマ・DJの真鍋大度が登場！知られざるクラシック愛を語る」、「×（かける）クラシック」、2020年6月21日、ラジオ

- 照沼健太「真鍋大度らが手がけた"2020年の分岐点"を描いたミュージックビデオが、栄誉賞を受賞」、『ギズモード・ジャパン』、2020年6月24日、ウェブサイト

- J-WAVE「Perfume×真鍋大度が考える、ライブ・エンターテインメントの未来」、「TOPPAN INNOVATION WORLD ERA」、2020年7月5日、ラジオ

- J-WAVE「［#5真鍋大度×Niantic川島優志］ARを通した、新しい価値体験 マスクをつけたまま楽しむ！新しいエンターテインメントの形」、「TOPPAN INNOVATION WORLD ERA」、2020年8月2日、ラジオ

- 高岡謙太郎「絶景の山頂でライブ、湖の真ん中でDJ、ウイルス防止スーツ……飛沫感染を防ぐために世界各地で行われていることRhizomatiks真鍋大度、huezとしくにに聞いた演出側からの意見も」、『音楽ナタリー』、2020年8月7日、ウェブサイト

- 「［対談］デジタルショーの作り方：ホワイトマウンテニアリング相澤陽介＆ライゾマティクス真鍋大度」、『fashionsnap.com』、2020年8月7日、ウェブサイト

- 「今見つめ直す、「私にとってのラグジュアリーvol. 8」」、『VOGUE JAPAN』、コンデナスト・ジャパン、2020年8月15日、ウェブサイト

- 「J-WAVE TOKYO +ONGAKU」、『メトロミニッツ』、2020年8月20日、スターツ出版

- 「未来とファッション vol.1 デジタル"ファッションとは、自分の境界線を外に出すもの"」、『星の商人No. 2』、伊藤忠商事、2020年8月24日

- 「阿部亮平研究室#2」、『SODA』2020年9月号、ぴあ、pp. 52–55

- 「世界で一番新しいステージパフォーマンスを目撃してほしい」ライゾマティクス真鍋大度によるPerfumeコンセプトライブ"Reframe"の見どころ」、『映画.com』、2020年9月3日、ウェブサイト

- 真鍋大度「INTERVIEW 02 DAITO MANABE Rhizomatiks」、『Reframe THEATER EXPERIENCE with you』、2020年、pp. 12–17

- J-WAVE「「非同期テック部」真鍋大度×上田誠が語る、演劇とテクノロジーの未来」、「TOPPAN INNOVATION WORLD ERA」、2020年9月6日、ラジオ

- 尾田和実「ライゾマティクス真鍋大度は、Perfumeの映画作品で何をリフレームしたか？」、『ギズモード・ジャパン』、2020年9月9日、ウェブサイト

- xuxu、刘向林「新媒体艺术家真锅大度：我要创造实体作品，而不只是提出问题」、『藝術商業』、2020年9月14日、ウェブサイト

- 「阿部亮平研究室#3」、『SODA』2020年11月号、ぴあ、pp. 52–55

- 「THURE Magazine vol.1 作り手としてどれだけ人の心に残るものを作るか」、『THULE』、2020年9月25日、ウェブサイト

- BSテレビ東京「S/S MEN'S ONLINE Part. 2」、「ファッション通信」、2020年9月26日
- 木村浩康(Rhizomatiks Design)「第一線で活躍するクリエイターが語る書体選びのノウハウ My MORISAWA PASSPORT わたしの"推し"フォント」、『＋DESIGNING』vol. 50、マイナビ出版、2020年
- J-WAVE「Perfume「"P. O. P" Festival」を真鍋大度が振り返る」、「TOPPAN INNOVATION WORLD ERA」、2020年10月2日、ラジオ
- J-WAVE「ライゾマ・真鍋大度×White Mountaineering・相澤陽介が考える、これからの表現の可能性」、「TOPPAN INNOVATION WORLD ERA」、2020年10月4日、ラジオ
- 安達友絵「「DVD棚、見せてください。第30回」技術と共に歩んできた映画の歴史から、"前例のない表現"に挑む勇気をもらう」、『PINTSCOPE』、2020年10月8日、ウェブサイト
- Lia Coleman, Eugene Lee「Flesh & Machine、Neocha Magazine」、2020年10月12日、ウェブサイト
- 「Daito Manabe: "Sónar is the most important festival in my career"」、『Alterna2』、2020年10月14日、ウェブサイト
- 「Daito Manabe and Motoi Ishibashi Making Particles Dance」、Pen Magazine(FR)、2020年11月2日、ウェブサイト
- 「あなたにとって"信用"できるモノ・コト #6 Rhizomatiks／真鍋大度」、『EQUALAND』、2020年11月5日、ウェブサイト
- 「真鍋大度、ライゾマティクスが示す唯一無二のクリエイティブとは」、『B』、SONY、2020年11月13日、ウェブサイト
- 照沼健太「12Kカメラで、コロナ禍の制約へ挑戦。真鍋大度が語る「テクノロジーへの信頼」と「自由」」、『ギズモード・ジャパン』、2020年12月20日、ウェブサイト
- 長谷川祐子「長谷川祐子の『ハイパーサブジェクトアートレポート』」、『ONBEAT』13号、2020年12月25日

2021
- J-WAVE「ライゾマ・真鍋大度が訊く、データ活用の最前線」、「TOPPAN INNOVATION WORLD ERA」、2021年1月3日、ラジオ
- J-WAVE「演出振付家・MIKIKO×ライゾマ・真鍋大度が考える、エンタテインメントの未来」、「TOPPAN INNOVATION WORLD ERA」、2021年1月3日、ラジオ
- TBS「Version Up!〜我が家の暮らし〜」、2021年1月10日
- TBS「Version Up!〜我が家の暮らし〜」、2021年1月17日
- 「《泛.南.島》一生牛流轉 Circle of Life Ebook」、『Pan Zine』、2021年1月4日
- J-WAVE「J-WAVE SONAR MUSIC」、2021年1月21日、ラジオ
- 『Beshknow』、2021年1月22日
- 「第一線のクリエイターの就活」、『クリ活2 クリエイターの就活本：デジタルクリエイティブ編』、宣伝会議、2021年
- J-WAVE「ライゾマ・真鍋大度が訊く、Cryptartの最前線」、「TOPPAN INNOVATION WORLD ERA」、2021年2月7日、ラジオ
- 「「人間邂逅782」仲暁子×真鍋大度 一点突破の創造力」、『PRESIDENT』2021年2月12日号、プレジデント社、2021年2月12日

- 「音楽と酒。酒と音楽を語るリスニングバーへ。」、『BRUTUS』2021年2月15日号、マガジンハウス
- 「[COVERCHORD CULTURE]クリエイターにきく、愛してやまない漫画。Japan's best MANGA selected by leading creatives」、『COVERCHORD』、2021年2月20日
- 大杉真心「「フミエタナカ」がMIKIKO＆ライゾマティクスと協業」、『WWD JAPAN』、2021年2月23日、ウェブサイト
- 「[特集：なにしろラジオ好きなもので。3]あしたのラジオ② J-WAVE「4人のクリエイター、4つのあした。」のん／後藤正文／真鍋大度／小橋賢児」、『BRUTUS』2021年3月15日号、マガジンハウス
- 「Rhizomatiks, Augmented Choreography With his collective, Daito Manabe manipulates light and transposes the contours of dancers into data to explore their movements.」、『Pen Online(FR)』、2021年3月1日
- J-WAVE「真鍋大度×小橋賢児、イノベーションをテーマに対談」、「TOPPAN INNOVATION WORLD ERA」、2021年3月7日、ラジオ
- 「[対談]コロナ時代の音楽の実学：村井純、真鍋大度」、『KEIO SFC JOURNAL』第20巻第2号、2021年
- RIE NOGUCHI「自然と向き合う「葉山」での時間と道具論：齋藤精一、シチズンPROMASTERを身につける」、『WIRED』、2021年3月31日、ウェブサイト
- 「岡村靖幸×真鍋大度。旧知の二人が語る、アートとエンタメとテクノロジーと。」、『Casa BRUTUS』2021年4月号、マガジンハウス
- 中島良平「話題沸騰の展覧会「ライゾマティクス_マルティプレックス」で、リサーチと開発、アートとエンタテインメントの横断を体感する」、『Pen Online』、2021年4月2日、ウェブサイト
- 「アーティスト 真鍋大度の時間時答」、『SEIKO 140周年特設記念サイト 時間時答』、2021年4月3日、ウェブサイト
- NHK Eテレ「ライゾマティクス まだ見ぬ世界へ」、「日曜美術館」、2021年4月4日
- 橋爪勇介「真鍋大度が語るクリプトアートの問題点と可能性。「CryptoArt Experiment」が目指すものとは?」、『美術手帖』、2021年4月17日、ウェブサイト
- 「マシーンドラム×真鍋大度×Rhizomatiks、現実と仮想の世界を行き来する革新的AVライブを4月24日ストリーミング配信」、『BARKS』、2021年4月19日、ウェブサイト
- TOKYO FM「坂本龍一、Perfume…さまざまなコラボで話題のRhizomatiks・真鍋大度が語る15年の歩み」、『DIGITAL VORN Future Pix』、2021年4月17日、ラジオ
- TOKYO FM「Rhizomatiks・真鍋大度「脳に電極を埋め込むことで…」"貪欲なクリエイティブ精神"に脱帽」、『DIGITAL VORN Future Pix』、2021年4月24日、ラジオ
- 「Perfume映像だけじゃない!「ライゾマ」の全貌に迫る展覧会」、産経新聞、2021年4月20日、ウェブサイト
- Ittousai、「ライゾマティクス真鍋大度インタビュー コロナ禍とテクノロジー、「ARメガネ」で変わる社会」、『engadget日本版』、2021年4月28日、ウェブサイト
- 吉村栄一「[教授動静〈番外編〉第1回]真鍋大度、坂本龍一

を語る」、『GQ JAPAN web』、2015年4月30日、ウェブサイト

● 秋元雄史「なぜ「デジタルアート」は日本人が世界をリードしているのか?」、『幻冬舎GOLD ONLNE』、2021年5月2日、ウェブサイト

ライゾマティクス｜プロジェクトリスト

編｜ライゾマティクス／森山朋絵

Rhizomatiks
List of projects

ed. Rhizomatiks / Tomoe Moriyama

凡例　各作品について、下記の項目・記載順で作成、概ね年代順に掲載した。

タイトル
発表年
アーティスト名義（自社〈社名／チーム名／個人名〉または自社を含む連名）
発表形式（インスタレーション／ウェブサイト等）
会場（ウェブサイトは「online」、video他は「−」と表記）
イベント名称（ない場合は「−」または記載なし）
クライアント名称（ない場合は「−」または記載なし）

Note　For each work, the following items are listed in chronological order.

Title
Date
Artist's name (a company name, a team name, a personal name or a collaborative joint name)
Presentation format (installation, website, etc.)
Venue ("online" for website, " – " for video, etc.)
Name of the event (" – " or blank for none)
Name of the client (" – " or blank for none)

1
G-Display
– 1999
– Motoi Ishibashi + Motoki Kouketsu
– installation
– NTTインターコミュニケーション・センター［ICC］、東京
– NTTインターコミュニケーション・センター［ICC］

2
2003 rhizomatiks
– 2003
– Rhizomatiks
– installation
– ダートマス大学、ハノーバー、アメリカ

3
ルイ・ヴィトン神戸店
オープニングパーティー
インスタレーション
– 2004
– Motoi Ishibashi + Motoki Kouketsu
– installation
– 神戸市美術館、兵庫
– –
– ルイ・ヴィトン

4
カルティエ タンク "Advance the hands on the clock"
– 2005
– Daito Manabe + Motoi Ishibashi
– Interactive video
– カルティエ銀座、東京／
カルティエ心斎橋、大阪
– カルティエ

5
リステア神戸 "Touch a Glove"
– 2005
– RESTIR × DGN
– Interactive video
– 北野クラブ ソラ、兵庫
– リステア神戸店
オープン記念パーティー
– リステア神戸

6
Tripon
– 2006
– Vokoi + Daito Manabe + Satoshi Horii
– VJ
– Metamorphose

7
wiimote DJ
– 2006
– Daito Manabe
– DJ
– 渋谷Phase、東京

8
I'mPULSE 2006 in Beijing
– 2006
– Daito Manabe
– workshop
– ベルリン、ドイツ

9
RFID VJ
– 2006
– Daito Manabe + Motoi Ishibashi + Seiichi Saito
– installation / VJ
– 川口 SKIPシティ、埼玉

10
RFID Light Sequencer
– 2006
– Daito Manabe + Motoi Ishibashi
– installation
– NTTインターコミュニケーション・センター［ICC］、東京
– ICC キッズ・プログラム
– NTTインターコミュニケーション・センター［ICC］

11
マツダ CX7 Show room
インスタレーション
– 2006
– Motoki Kouketsu + Motoi Ishibashi
– installation
– 銀座、東京
– マツダ

12
d-labo -Atlas-
– 2007
– Lee Myeong Hee(matt) + DGN
– installation
– スルガ銀行ミッドタウン支店横
コミュニケーションスペース
「d-labo」、東京
– スルガ銀行

13
d-labo -Hyper Library-
– 2007
– DGN + rhiozomatks
– installation
– スルガ銀行ミッドタウン支店横
コミュニケーションスペース
「d-labo」、東京
– スルガ銀行

14
d-labo -Time-
– 2007
– Lee Myeong Hee(matt) + DGN
– installation
– スルガ銀行ミッドタウン支店、
東京
– スルガ銀行

15
Sonic Floor
- 2007
- Daito Manabe + Motoi Ishibashi
- installation
- 北九州イノベーションギャラリー
  （産業技術継承センター）、福岡

16
検索ワークショップ "PodPod"
- 2007
- Daito Manabe + Motoi Ishibashi
  + Satoshi Horii
- workshop
- 川口市立映像・情報メディアセンター
  メディアセブン、埼玉

17
I'mPULSE 2007 in Goteborg
- 2007
- Daito Manabe
- workshop
- イェーテボリ、スウェーデン

18
Okosanu
- 2007
- Milosh + Zenial + Daito Manabe
- performance
- Le Cube、パリ、フランス

19
Proce55ing Life
- 2007
- Daito Manabe + Motoi Ishibashi
- installation
- NTTインターコミュニケーション・
  センター[ICC]、東京
- ICC キッズ・プログラム 2007
  「サウンド×イメージ — 音を見て，
  映像を聞こう」展

20
true／本当のこと
- 2007
- Takayuki Fujimoto, Tsuyoshi Shirai,
  Takao Kawaguchi, Takuya Minami,
  Daito Manabe, Satoshi Horii,
  Seiichi Saito, Motoi Ishibashi,
  Masaki Teruoka, Noriko Kitamura
- performance
- 山口情報芸術センター[YCAM]、山口
- 公益財団法人山口市文化振興財団

21
Le Placard
- 2007
- Daito Manabe
- event
- ライゾマティクス、白金、東京
- Le Placard

22
Interactive Lighting System for
a Poledance
- 2007
- Daito Manabe + Motoi Ishibashi
- performance
- 青海南ふ頭公園 駐車場、東京

23
劇場版どうぶつの森 わくわくヴィレッジ
インスタレーション（フィッシング）
- 2007
- Rhizomatiks
- installation
- ひらかたパーク、大阪
- DAC

24
劇場版どうぶつの森 わくわくヴィレッジ
インスタレーション（花火）
- 2007
- Rhizomatiks
- installation
- ひらかたパーク、大阪
- DAC

25
デジタルアートフェスティバル2007
アドトラック
- 2007
- Motoi Ishibashi
- installation
- トーキョーワンダーサイト 渋谷
- デジタルアートフェスティバル2007
- デジタルアートフェスティバル東京
  2007実行委員会
  （NHK、株式会社NHKエンタープライズ）

26
Command line wave
- 2008
- Daito Manabe + Motoi Ishibashi
- installation

27
Face visualizer, instrument, and
copy
- 2008
- Daito Manabe
- experiment
- –

28
ライゾマスクリーンセーバー（2008 ver.）
- 2008
- Rhizomatiks
- application
- –
- –

29
NIKE6.0 RAMP GIG'08
- 2008
- Rhizomatiks
- installation
- 幕張メッセ、千葉

Nike Japan

30
smiles less noise
- 2008
- TRIPON (vokoi, Daito Manabe,
  Satoshi Horii)
- video
- 渋谷スクランブル交差点 Sib.TV、
  東京
- TAICOCLUB Art Project

31
Clandestino Festival 2008
- 2008
- Daito Manabe + Motoi Ishibashi
- performance
- イェーテボリ、スウェーデン
- Clandestino Festival 2008

32
ISS Audio Visual System
- 2008
- DGN
- Interactive video
- 日本科学未来館5階常設展示
  『こちら、宇宙ステーション/ISS』、東京

33
true in Singapore
- 2008
- Takayuki Fujimoto, Tsuyoshi
  Shirai, Takao Kawaguchi, Takuya
  Minami, Daito Manabe, Satoshi
  Horii, Seiichi Saito, Motoi
  Ishibachi, Masaki Teruoka,
  Noriko Kitamura
- sound
- エスプラネード・シアター、シンガポール

34
チェンマイ大学ワークショップ
- 2008
- Daito Manabe
- workshop
- タイ チェンマイ大学

35
タイ孤児院ワークショップ
- 2008
- Daito Manabe
- workshop
- School for life, Chiang Mai

36
electric stimulus to face
- 2008
- Daito Manabe
- experiment
- –

37
scoreLight
- 2009
- Alvaro CASSINELLI / MANABE

Daito / KURIBARA Yusaku /
Alexis ZERROUG
- installation
- 第13回文化庁メディア芸術祭受賞
  作品展
- 国立新美術館、東京

38
Party in the mouth
- 2009
- Daito Manabe + Motoi Ishibashi
  + Tomoaki Yanagisawa
- event

39
PlayStation Playface – Web site
- 2009
- Rhizomatiks
- web
- online
- ソニー株式会社

40
lights on!
- 2009
- YesYesNo with Joel Gethin
  Lewis, Damian Stewart and
  Daito Manabe
- sound
- アルスエレクトロニカセンター、リンツ、
  オーストリア
- Ars Electronica Center

41
Ars Electronica Center Open
Days
- 2009
- Daito Manabe
- DJ and performance
- アルスエレクトロニカセンター、リンツ、
  オーストリア
- Ars Electronica Center

42
LED in my mouth
- 2009
- Daito Manabe
- experiment
- –

43
モノクロームサーカス Cage
- 2009
- Rhizomatiks
- Performance
- アトリエ劇研、京都

44
NIKEiD.STUDIO Fukuoka
- 2009
- Rhizomatiks
- Interactive video
- Nike Fukuoka、福岡
- Nike Japan

45
Scratchワークショップ
- 2009
- Motoi Ishibashi + Tomoaki Yanagisawa
- workshop
- 川口市立映像・情報メディアセンター メディアセブン、埼玉

———————

46
Session with I Am Robot And Proud
- 2009
- Rhizomatiks
- performance
- ベルサール六本木、東京

———————

47
BAR TALK Nº1
- 2009
- Daito Manabe
- talk
- マドリード、スペイン
- Barfutura

———————

48
Medialab-Prado
- 2009
- Daito Manabe
- talk
- Medialab-Prado Madrid、マドリード、スペイン

———————

49
Clandestino Festival 2009
- 2009
- Daito Manabe
- performance
- Röda Sten、イェーテボリ、スウェーデン
- Clandestino Festival 2009

———————

50
Flying Tokyo#2
- 2009
- Rhizomatiks
- event
- 5TANDA SONIC、東京
- Flying Tokyo#2

———————

51
Pa++ern
- 2009
- Daito Manabe + Motoi Ishibashi
- installation
- B GALLERY、東京

———————

52
The Way Sensing Go
- 2009
- Daito Manabe + Motoi Ishibashi + Kanta Horio + Tomoaki Yanagisawa
- installation

———————

NTTインターコミュニケーション・センター[ICC]、東京
- NTTインターコミュニケーション・センター[ICC]

———————

53
デジタル×カラダ de ワークショップ
- 2009
- Daito Manabe + Motoi Ishibashi
- workshop
- 世田谷文化生活情報センター ワークショップルームA、東京
- デジタル×カラダ de ワークショップ

———————

54
freeze!—2009 International MedTech Art Show
- 2009
- Daito Manabe
- installation
- 国立台湾美術館、台湾
- freeze!—2009 International MedTech Art Show

———————

55
Flying Tokyo#3
- 2009
- Rhizomatiks
- event
- 5TANDA SONIC、東京
- Flying Tokyo#3

———————

56
BODY HACK electric stimulus to/from body
- 2009
- Daito Manabe
- Workshop
- リクルート MTLカフェ スペース、東京

———————

57
Geminoid in Ars Electronica Festival 2009 サウンドデザイン
- 2009
- Daito Manabe
- installation
- アルスエレクトロニカセンター、リンツ、オーストリア
- Ars Electronica Festival 2009

———————

58
Night Lights
- 2009
- YesYesNo with Daito Manabe
- installation
- Ferry Terminal Building、オークランド、ニュージーランド

———————

59
Pa++ern sounds for embroidery
- 2009
- Daito Manabe + Motoi Ishibashi
- live
- 九州大学、福岡

———————

60
Time Lapse Plant
- 2009
- Takayuki Fujimoto + Daito Manabe + Motoi Ishibashi
- installation
- BankART Studio NYK、神奈川

———————

61
ソニー make.believe
- 2010
- Rhizomatiks
- web / installation
- online
- ソニー株式会社

———————

62
BodyHackワークショップ、パフォーマンス(香港)
- 2010
- Daito Manabe
- performance / workshop
- 香港

———————

63
BodyHackワークショップ(TEI'10)
- 2010
- Daito Manabe, Motoi Ishibashi, Masaki Teruoka and Seiichi Saito
- workshop
- MITメディアラボ、ボストン、アメリカ
- TEI'10: 4th International Conference on Tangible, Embedded and Embodied Interaction

———————

64
やくしまるえつこ と d.v.d "ファイナルダーリン" ミュージックビデオ
- 2010
- Daito Manabe
- video
- –

———————

65
electric stimulus to face
- 2010
- Daito Manabe
- installation
- サイバーアーツジャパン— アルスエレクトロニカの30年
- 東京都現代美術館、東京
- 公益財団法人東京都歴史文化財団 東京都現代美術館

———————

66
Search'n Search
- 2010
- Motoi Ishibashi + Daito Mababe + YCAM staff
- workshop
- 山口情報芸術センター[YCAM]、山口／ NTTインターコミュニケーション・センター[ICC]、東京
- 公益財団法人山口市文化振興財団 (YCAM実施分)

———————

67
NIKE MUSIC SHOE
- 2010
- Rhizomatiks
- product / video
- –
- Nike Japan

———————

68
Nike Tulio Twitter Statue
- 2010
- Rhizomatiks
- CF
- –
- Nike Japan

———————

69
やくしまるえつこ "ヴィーナスとジーザス" ミュージックビデオ
- 2010
- Daito Manabe
- Music video

———————

70
やくしまるえつこ YAKUSHIMARU 3D SCAN | TIME-OF-FLIGHT CAMERA
- 2010
- Daito Manabe and Satoshi Horii
- web
- online

———————

71
スポンテニア "Jam" ミュージックビデオ
- 2010
- Daito Manabe
- video
- –

———————

72
BodyHack Workshop #4
- 2010
- Daito Manabe
- workshop
- 東京造形大学、東京

———————

73
evala live visuals for Evala at UNIT
- 2010
- Rhizomatiks
- VJ
- UNIT
- UNIT 6th Anniversary Premier Showcase feat. Cluster

———————

74
fade out

- 2010
- Daito Manabe + Motoi Ishibashi
- installation
- 大分市美術館、大分
- 大分市美術館

75
KeizoMach!ne live visuals for
KeizoMach!ne at Womb
- 2010
- Rhizomatiks
- VJ
- WOMB、東京

76
DELL ALIENWARE
"DEKOTORA × LED × PC"
- 2010
- Rhizomatiks
- video
- –
- DELL

77
Pa++ern at Japan Media Art
Festival in Istanbul
- 2010
- Daito Manabe + Motoi Ishibashi
- installation
- ペラ美術館、イスタンブール、トルコ

78
points
- 2010
- Daito Manabe + Motoi Ishibashi
- installation
- せんだいメディアテーク、宮城

79
pa++ern at おおがきビエンナーレ
2010
- 2010
- Daito Manabe + Motoi Ishibashi
- installation
- 大垣、岐阜

80
The Way Sensing Go 2010
- 2010
- 4nchor5 La6
- installation
- クンストパラスト美術館、
  デュッセルドルフ、ドイツ

81
LED Balloon Test
- 2010
- Rhizomatiks
- experiment-

82
BodyHackワークショップ
（マンチェスター）
- 2010
- Daito Manabe

workshop
- マンチェスター、イギリス
- MadLab

83
BodyHackワークショップ（ルガーノ）
- 2010
- Daito Manabe
- workshop
- ルガーノ、スイス
- Aula di formazione continua

84
BodyHackワークショップ
（21_21 DESIGN SIGHT）
- 2010
- Daito Manabe
- workshop
- 21_21 DESIGN SIGHT、東京

85
結成10周年、メジャーデビュー5周年
記念! Perfume LIVE @東京ドーム
「1 2 3 4 5 6 7 8 9 10 11」
Lighting Balloon System
2010
- Rhizomatiks
- live
- 東京ドーム、東京
- 結成10周年、メジャーデビュー5周年
  記念! Perfume LIVE @東京ドーム
  「1 2 3 4 5 6 7 8 9 10 11」
- 株式会社アミューズ

86
結成10周年、メジャーデビュー5周年
記念! Perfume LIVE @東京ドーム
「1 2 3 4 5 6 7 8 9 10 11」
Balloon Explosion System
- 2010
- Rhizomatiks
- live
- 東京ドーム、東京
- 結成10周年、メジャーデビュー5周年
  記念! Perfume LIVE @東京ドーム
  「1 2 3 4 5 6 7 8 9 10 11」
- 株式会社アミューズ

87
結成10周年、メジャーデビュー5周年
記念! Perfume LIVE @東京ドーム
「1 2 3 4 5 6 7 8 9 10 11」3D Scan
Visuals
- 2010
- Rhizomatiks
- live
- 東京ドーム、東京
- 結成10周年、メジャーデビュー5周年
  記念! Perfume LIVE @東京ドーム
  「1 2 3 4 5 6 7 8 9 10 11」
- 株式会社アミューズ

88
結成10周年、メジャーデビュー5周年
記念! Perfume LIVE @東京ドーム

「1 2 3 4 5 6 7 8 9 10 11」
Interactive Visuals
- 2010
- Rhizomatiks
- live
- 東京ドーム、東京
- 結成10周年、メジャーデビュー5周年
  記念! Perfume LIVE @東京ドーム
  「1 2 3 4 5 6 7 8 9 10 11」
- 株式会社アミューズ

89
BodyHackワークショップ（パリ）
- 2010
- Rhizomatiks
- workshop
- パリ、フランス

90
Sony VAIO｜VAIO ASSIST
TORCH PROJECT
- 2010
- Rhizomatiks
- web / installation / event
- 高円寺「なみのゆ」、東京
- ソニー株式会社

91
electric stimulus to body +
myoelectric sensor test
- 2010
- Daito Manabe
- experiment
- –

92
Google で、もっと。
Google トップページに新年の抱負
- 2010
- Rhizomatiks
- CF video
- –
- グーグル

93
uv laser to face failed
- 2011
- Daito Manabe
- Experiment
- –

94
ラフォーレ原宿
ラフォーレグランバザール "Geee"
CM
- 2011
- Rhizomatiks
- CF
- –
- ラフォーレ原宿

95
faceprojection failed
- 2011
- Daito Manabe

- experiment
- –

96
Sound Clouds
- 2011
- Tangible Interaction +
  Rhizomatiks
- installation
- イエールタウンパーク、バンクーバー、
  カナダ

97
川口隆夫 "テーブルマインド"
- 2011
- Rhizomatiks
- performance
- 川崎市アートセンター
  アルテリオ小劇場、神奈川

98
particles
- 2011
- Daito Manabe + Motoi Ishibashi
- installation
- 山口情報芸術センター[YCAM]、山口

99
TOFFIE POP CULTURE
FESTIVAL 2011
- 講師
- 2011
- Daito Manabe
- レクチャー
- ケープタウン市庁舎、ケープタウン、
  南アフリカ
- TOFFIE POP CULTURE
  FESTIVAL 2011

100
kinect × laser for Sonar Sound
Tokyo
- 2011
- Motoi Ishibashi
- installation
- 新木場STUDIO COAST /
  ageHa、東京
- Sonar Sound Tokyo

101
salyu × salyu "muse'ic
visualiser"
- 2011
- Shingo Ohno a.k.a. Merce
  Death, Genki Ito, Nao Tokui,
  Seiichi Saito, Hidenori Chiba,
  Shizuo Takahashi
- application
- –

102
Love donation at SonarSound
Tokyo
- 2011
- rhizomatiks + 4nchor5 Lab

- 渋谷CLUB QUATTR、東京
- もしもしクアトロ

134

FAマガジン Face projection for
FA Magazine
- 2012
- Daito Manabe
- graphic
- –
- FAマガジン

135

Perfume global site project #001
- 2012
- Rhizomatiks
- web
- online
- 株式会社アミューズ

136

ロッテ ZEUS「SNOW STORM」
- 2012
- Rhizomatiks
- CF
- –
- ロッテ

137

東急電鉄 アーバンコアサイネージ
「Inforium」
- 2012
- Rhizomatiks
- signage
- 渋谷ヒカリエ、東京
- 東急電鉄

138

Perfume "Spring of Life"
ミュージックビデオ
- 2012
- Rhizomatiks
- music video
- –
- 株式会社アミューズ

139

NIKE BUILDING TWIST
- 2012
- Rhizomatiks
- installation
- 横浜 赤レンガ倉庫、神奈川
- Nike Japan

140

pulse
- 2012
- Daito Manabe + Motoi Ishibashi
- installation
- 東京

141

サントリー GATORADE RUN
「FUN RACE MACHINE」
- 2012

- Rhizomatiks
- installation
- 二子玉川ライズ、東京
- ゲータレード ランPresents 二子玉川
  FUN RACE
- サントリー

142

Perfume 3rd Tour「JPN」
"Spring of Life"
- 2012
- Rhizomatiks
- live
- 日本武道館、東京
- Perfume 3rd Tour「JPN」
- 株式会社アミューズ

143

ラフォーレ原宿 2012夏 GB
「find you」
- 2012
- Rhizomatiks
- video
- –
- ラフォーレ原宿

144

NIKE MUSIC SHOE in Italy
- 2012
- Rhizomatiks
- installation
- NIKE Stadium、ミラノ、イタリア
- Nike

145

Perfume "Spring of Life" at
MTV VMAJ 2012
- 2012
- Rhizomatiks
- live
- 幕張メッセイベントホール、千葉
- MTV VMAJ 2012 (MTV VIDEO
  MUSIC AWARDS JAPAN 2012)
- 株式会社アミューズ

146

NIKE FuelBand "FuelFest"
- 2012
- Rhizomatiks
- event
- バターシー発電所、ロンドン、イギリス
- Nike

147

Perfume global site project #002
- 2012
- Rhizomatiks
- web
- online
- 株式会社アミューズ

148

Perfume 氷結 SUMMER NIGHT
- 2012
- Rhizomatiks

- live
- 渋谷ヒカリエ、東京
- 氷結 SUMMER NIGHT
- 株式会社アミューズ

149

Intel Ultrabook
"In! ハイパーねぶた"
- 2012
- Rhizomatiks
- video / installation / web
- 青森
- 青森ねぶた祭り
- インテル

150

やくしまるえつこ
"ロンリープラネット(Post)"
ミュージックビデオ
- 2012
- Daito Manabe + Rhizomatiks
- music video
- –

151

Perfume Global Compilation
"LOVE THE WORLD"
- 2012
- Rhizomatiks
- graphic
- –
- 株式会社アミューズ

152

Perfume "FAKE IT"
ミュージックビデオ
- 2012
- Rhizomatiks
- music video
- –
- 株式会社アミューズ

153

CREATE THE FUTURE
PROJECT 3rd ACTION
- 2012
- Rhizomatiks
- workshop
- キャンピカ明野、山梨

154

TOTO × toto "Super Great
Toilet Keeper"
- 2012
- Rhizomatiks
- video / installation
- –
- TOTO × toto

155

human laser projector
- 2012
- Rhizomatiks
- experiment

---

live
- 渋谷ヒカリエ、東京

156

Physicalizing Data by
Rhizomatiks Inspired by
Perfume
- 2012
- Rhizomatiks
- インスタレーション
- 明治神宮外苑絵画館前(中央会場)、
  東京
- TOKYO DESIGNERS WEEK
  2012「コンテナ展」
- 株式会社アミューズ

157

Tokyo Designers Week
"富士通デザインコンテナ"
- 2012
- Rhizomatiks
- installation
- 明治神宮外苑、東京
- Tokyo Designers Week
- 富士通デザイン株式会社

158

Tokyo Designers Week
"scoreLight"
- 2012
- Alvaro Cassinelli + Daito
  Manabe + Alexis Zerroug
- installation
- 明治神宮外苑、東京

159

Nosaj Thing "Eclipse Blue"
ミュージックビデオ
- 2012
- Daito Manabe + Rhizomatiks +
  Takcom
- music video
- –

160

FaltyDL "Straight & Arrow"
ミュージックビデオ
- 2012
- Daito Manabe
- music video / web
- –

161

slitscan sculpture
- 2012
- Daito Manabe + Motoi Ishibashi
  + MIKIKO
- experiment
- –

162

やくしまるえつこ dimtakt
- 2012
- Rhizomatiks
- live
- 象の鼻パーク、神奈川

163
UNITED ARROWS green label relaxing "Marionettebot 恋するマリオネット"
- 2012
- Rhizomatiks
- installation
- UNITED ARROWS green label relaxing
- 渋谷マークシティ店1階 店頭ショーウィンドー、東京
- ユナイテッドアローズ

164
electraglide2012
- 2012
- Rhizomatiks
- event
- 幕張メッセ ホール9-11、千葉
- electraglide
- 2012
- BEATINK

165
2012 NHK TROPHY / ARIGATO SKATING
- 2012
- Rhizomatiks
- performance
- セキスイハイムスーパーアリーナ、宮城
- 日本スケート連盟

166
キラキラウィンターファーム
- 2012
- Rhizomatiks
- installation
- マザー牧場、群馬
- マザー牧場イルミネーション
- 2012-2013
- 日本電波塔株式会社

167
KDDI au「驚きを、常識に。」 〜FULL CONTROL YOUR CITY〜
- 2012
- Rhizomatiks
- CF / application / web / event
- –
- KDDI

168
NIKE AIR FORCE ONE ART INSTALLATION
- 2012
- Rhizomatiks
- installation
- 渋谷 PIVOT POINT 2F、東京
- AIR FORCE ONE ART INSTALLATION
- Nike Japan

169
第63回NHK紅白歌合戦 Perfume "Spring of Life"
- 2012
- Rhizomatiks
- TV番組
- NHKホール、東京
- 第63回NHK紅白歌合戦
- 株式会社アミューズ

170
LOVE+1+1
- 2013
- Yakushimaru Etsuko + Daito Manabe + Motoi Ishibashi + Kaoru Sugano
- installation
- 森美術館、東京
- LOVE展：アートにみる愛のかたち— シャガールから草間彌生、初音ミクまで

171
森永製菓 ハイチュウ "ハミガキコントローラー"
- 2013
- Rhizomatiks
- application
- –
- 森永製菓

172
pulse 3.0
- 2013
- Rhizomatiks
- performance
- 山口情報芸術センター［YCAM］、山口
- 公益財団法人山口市文化振興財団

173
illion "MAHOROBA" ミュージックビデオ
- 2013
- Daito Manabe
- music video
- –

174
Perfume "未来のミュージアム" ミュージックビデオ
- 2013
- Rhizomatiks
- music video /web
- –
- 株式会社アミューズ

175
motor music test
- 2013
- Daito Manabe + Motoi Ishibashi
- experiment
- –

176
shape

- 2013
- ELEVENPLAY × Rhizomatiks
- performance
- 山口情報芸術センター［YCAM］、山口
- sound tectonics #13 「pulse live version」
- 公益財団法人山口市文化振興財団

177
illion MAHOROBA @O2 Shepherd's Bush Empire, London, UK
- 2013
- Rhizomatiks
- live
- O2 Shepherd's Bush Empire、 ロンドン、イギリス

178
ray
- 2013
- ELEVENPLAY × Rhizomatiks
- performance
- 山口情報芸術センター［YCAM］、山口
- sound tectonics #13 「pulse live version」
- 公益財団法人山口市文化振興財団

179
following
- 2013
- ELEVENPLAY × Rhizomatiks
- performance
- 山口情報芸術センター［YCAM］、山口
- sound tectonics #13 「pulse live version」
- 公益財団法人山口市文化振興財団

180
illion γ @O2 Shepherd's Bush Empire, London, UK
- 2013
- Rhizomatiks
- Live
- O2 Shepherd's Bush Empire、 ロンドン、イギリス

181
KDDI au "Perfect Sync."
- 2013
- Rhizomatiks Architecture
- CF / web / application
- –
- KDDI

182
cube
- 2013
- ELEVENPLAY × Rhizomatiks
- performance
- 新木場STUDIO COAST / ageHa、東京
- Sonar Tokyo Festival 2013

183
symmetry
- 2013
- ELEVENPLAY × Rhizomatiks
- performance
- 山口情報芸術センター［YCAM］、山口

184
NIKE GUNYARI BATTLE
- 2013
- Rhizomatiks
- performance / installation / product / event / video / live
- 六本木ヒルズアリーナ、東京
- Nike Japan

185
Visualization of Perfume's history
- 2013
- Rhizomatiks
- installation
- online
- 株式会社アミューズ

186
KDDI au "Perfect Sync. LIVE"
- 2013
- Rhizomatiks Architecture
- CF / web / application / event
- 両国国技館、東京
- KDDI

187
Perfume global site project #003
- 2013
- Rhizomatiks
- web
- online
- 株式会社アミューズ

188
Perfume Cannes Lions International Festival of Creativity
- 2013
- Rhizomatiks
- live
- Palais des Festivals et des Congrès、カンヌ、フランス
- カンヌライオンズ 国際クリエイティビティ・フェスティバル
- 株式会社アミューズ / ユニバーサルミュージック合同会社

189
Perfume WORLD TOUR 2nd "Spending All My Time" Dynamic projection system
- 2013
- Rhizomatiks
- live
- O2 Shepherd's Bush Empire、 ロンドン、イギリス

- Perfume WORLD TOUR 2nd
- 株式会社アミューズ
——————

190
Perfume WORLD TOUR 2nd
Logo Design
- 2013
- Rhizomatiks
- graphic
- –
- 株式会社アミューズ
——————

191
Rhizomatiks Circle
- 2013
- Rhizomatiks
- video
- –
——————

192
AMAZING DOME powered by
LEXUS New IS "ドライヴィングVJ"
- 2013
- Rhizomatiks
- installation / VJ / exhibition /
  product / film / showcase /
  event / live
- 幕張メッセ、千葉
- FREEDOMMUNE 0 〈ZERO〉
  ONE THOUSAND 2013
- トヨタ
——————

193
太田雄貴 Fencing Visualized
- 2013
- Rhizomatiks
- video
- –
——————

194
Rhizomatiks inspired by
Perfume
- 2013
- Rhizomatiks
- installation
- NTTインターコミュニケーション・
  センター[ICC]、東京
- 「Rhizomatiks inspired by
  Perfume」展
——————

195
「建築家にならなかった建築家たち」
展
- 2013
- Rhizomatiks
- installation / 企画監修
- EYE OF GYRE / GYRE 3F、東京
- 「建築家にならなかった建築家たち」
  展
- GYRE
——————

196
traders
- 2013
- Rhizomatiks

installation
- 東京都現代美術館、東京
- 東京アートミーティング（第4回）
  「うさぎスマッシュ展
  世界に触れる方法（デザイン）」
- 公益財団法人東京都歴史文化財団
  東京都現代美術館
——————

197
Perfume "1mm" ミュージックビデオ
- 2013
- Rhizomatiks
- music video
- –
- 株式会社アミューズ
——————

198
Timo Maas "Tantra"
ミュージックビデオ
- 2013
- Rhizomatiks
- music video
- –
——————

199
Hikarie WONDER TREE
- 2013
- Rhizomatiks
- installation
- 渋谷ヒカリエ、東京
- 東急電鉄
——————

200
Nosaj Thing Nosaj Thing AR Live
2013
- 2013
- Rhizomatiks
- DJ / VJ
- 幕張メッセ、千葉
- electraglide 2013
——————

201
Perfume 4th Tour in DOME
「LEVEL3」 "Sleeping Beauty"
- 2013
- Rhizomatiks
- live
- 東京ドーム、東京 他
- Perfume 4th Tour in DOME
  「LEVEL3」
- 株式会社アミューズ
——————

202
Perfume 4th Tour in DOME
「LEVEL3」 "Spending all my
time"
- 2013
- Rhizomatiks
- live
- 東京ドーム、東京 他
- Perfume 4th Tour in DOME
  「LEVEL3」
- 株式会社アミューズ

——————

203
Perfume Music Player
- 2013
- Rhizomatiks
- application
- –
- 株式会社アミューズ
——————

204
Perfume Music Player Web
- 2013
- Rhizomatiks
- web
- online
- 株式会社アミューズ
——————

205
第64回NHK紅白歌合戦
Perfume "Magic of Love"
- 2013
- Rhizomatiks
- TV番組
- NHKホール、東京
- 第64回NHK紅白歌合戦
- 株式会社アミューズ
——————

206
RADWIMPS GRAND PRIX 2014
実況生中継 "トレモロ"
- 2014
- Rhizomatiks
- live
- Zepp Tokyo、東京 他
- RADWIMPS GRAND PRIX 2014
  実況生中継
——————

207
right brain
- 2014
- ELEVENPLAY
- video
- –
——————

208
GM CORPORATION /
ELECTRON
- 2014
- Rhizomatiks
- branding / web / event / film
- –
- GM CORPORATION
——————

209
golf by seven dreamers
- 2014
- Rhizomatiks
- branding / exhibition / web /
  film
- –
- seven dreamers
——————

210
247
- nastent by seven dreamers

- 2014
- Rhizomatiks
- branding / web / CF / film /
  video
- –
- seven dreamers
——————

211
/ laundroid by seven dreamers
- 2014
- Rhizomatiks
- branding / exhibition / web /
  product / CF / film / event /
  video / lighting
- –
- seven dreamers
——————

212
LEXUS AMAZING VISION
- 2014
- Rhizomatiks
- web / branding / UIdesign
-
- Lexus international
——————

213
ARASHI LIVE TOUR 2014 THE
DIGITALIAN "Hope in the
darkness" 筋電位演出
- 2014
- Rhizomatiks
- live
- 東京ドーム、東京 他
- ARASHI LIVE TOUR 2014 THE
  DIGITALIAN
- ヤングコミュニケーション
——————

214
(centiscript)
- 2014
- Rhizomatiks
- application
- –
——————

215
NUNO
- 2014
- Rhizomatiks
- web / film
- –
- NUNO
——————

216
D&AD 2014 D&AD Annual
book | Page Design
- 2014
- Rhizomatiks
- graphic
- –
- D&AD
——————

217
Ravijour "TRUE LOVE
TESTER"
- 2014

- Rhizomatiks
- product / application / film-
- Verygry Co.,Ltd.

218
やくしまるえつこ "X次元へようこそ"
ミュージックビデオ
- 2014
- Rhizomatiks
- music video
- –
- みらいレコーズ

219
Solaris Protocol
- 2014
- Rhizomatiks
- installation
- NTTインターコミュニケーション・センター[ICC]、東京
- NTTインターコミュニケーション・センター[ICC]

220
TOYOTA LEXUS "physical presence"
- 2014
- Rhizomatiks
- installation
- 六本木ヒルズ 森タワー52階 東京シティビュー、東京
- Media Ambition Tokyo 2014
- TOYOTA

221
fly
- 2014
- ELEVENPLAY × Rhizomatiks Research
- performance
- スパイラルホール、東京
- ELEVENPLAY Dance Installation【モザイク】

222
Squarepusher × Z-MACHINES
- 2014
- Rhizomatiks
- music video
- –

223
鴨川シーワールド "Coral Message"
- 2014
- Rhizomatiks
- installation
- 鴨川シーワールド トロピカルアイランド内、千葉
- ソニーPCL株式会社

224
Perfume Dome Tour Emulator
- 2014
- Rhizomatiks
- web

- online
- 株式会社アミューズ

225
CCJC POWERADE "POWER AWARD"
- 2014
- Rhizomatiks
- installation / product / showcase / event / film
- アクアシティお台場3F アクアアリーナ／渋谷マークシティ1F マークイベントスクエア、東京
- CCJC

226
NHK「プロフェッショナル仕事の流儀 真鍋大度」
- 2014
- Daito Manabe
- TV番組
- NHK(日本放送協会)

227
Perfume SAYONARA 国立競技場 FINAL WEEK「JAPAN NIGHT」
- 2014
- Rhizomatiks
- live
- 国立競技場、東京
- 株式会社アミューズ

228
Intel Technology Night in Akiba 2013
- 3Dプロジェクションマッピング
- 2014
- Rhizomatiks
- installation
- ベルサール秋葉原、東京
- Intel Technology Night in Akiba 2013
- インテル株式会社

229
Sonar Music Festival2014 ELEVENPLAY show
- 2014
- Daito Manabe + MIKIKO + ELEVENPLAY
- performance
- バルセロナ、スペイン
- Sonar Music Festival 2014

230
Perfume "Cling Cling" World
- 2014
- Rhizomatiks
- live
- 原宿アストロホール、東京
- Perfume "Cling Cling" World
- 株式会社アミューズ

231
センシング・ストリームズ—不可視、

不可聴
- 2014
- Ryuichi Sakamoto + Daito Manabe
- installation
- モエレ沼公園ガラスのピラミッド「HIDAMARI」、北海道
- 札幌国際芸術祭(SIAF2014)特別展示「センシング・ストリームズ」展

232
Nike RISE 'House of Mamba' LED court
- 2014
- Rhizomatiks
- installation
- 上海、中華人民共和国
- Nike

233
Perfume 5th Tour 2014 「ぐるんぐるん」"intro"
- 2014
- Rhizomatiks
- live / video
- 国立代々木第一体育館、東京 他
- Perfume 5th Tour 2014 「ぐるんぐるん」
- 株式会社アミューズ

234
Perfume 5th Tour 2014 「ぐるんぐるん」"エレクトロ・ワールド"
- 2014
- Rhizomatiks
- live / video
- 国立代々木第一体育館、東京 他
- Perfume 5th Tour 2014 「ぐるんぐるん」
- 株式会社アミューズ

235
Perfume WORLD
- 2014
- Rhizomatiks
- web
- online
- 株式会社アミューズ

236
Perfume 5th Tour 2014 「ぐるんぐるん」Logo Design
- 2014
- Rhizomatiks
- graphic
- –
- 株式会社アミューズ

237
hanacam test / Seamless Mixed Reality Experiment
- 2014
- Rhizomatiks Research
- experiment
- –

238
MUTEK MEXICO 2014 "Pulse"
- 2014
- Rhizomatiks × ELEVENPLAY
- performance
- メキシコシティ、メキシコ
- MUTEK MEXICO 2014

239
Perfume Font
- 2014
- Rhizomatiks
- web
- online
- 株式会社アミューズ

240
Perfume WORLD TOUR 3rd "GAME"
- 2014
- Rhizomatiks
- live
- HAMMERSTEIN BALLROOM、ニューヨーク、アメリカ 他
- Perfume WORLD TOUR 3rd
- 株式会社アミューズ

241
Perfume WORLD TOUR 3rd "Hold Your Hand"
- 2014
- Rhizomatiks
- live
- HAMMERSTEIN BALLROOM、ニューヨーク、アメリカ 他
- Perfume WORLD TOUR 3rd
- 株式会社アミューズ

242
Perfume WORLD TOUR 3rd "INTRO"
- 2014
- Rhizomatiks
- live
- HAMMERSTEIN BALLROOM、ニューヨーク、アメリカ 他
- Perfume WORLD TOUR 3rd
- 株式会社アミューズ

243
Perfume WORLD TOUR 3rd Logo Design
- 2014
- Rhizomatiks
- graphic
- –
- 株式会社アミューズ

244
The Human Sized Synthesizer
- 2014
- Red Bull Music Academy × Rhizomatiks
- installation / exhibition /

product / event / live
- 渋谷パルコ、東京
- RED BULL MUSIC ACADEMY
  TOKYO 2014
- Red Bull Music Academy

245
岡村靖幸 "彼氏になって優しくなって
(YouTube Version)" ミュージックビデオ
- 2014
- Rhizomatiks
- music video
- –

246
shadow
- 2014
- ELEVENPLAY × Rhizomatiks
  Research
- performance
- 幕張メッセ イベントホール、千葉
  [InterBEE2014]
  第50回開催記念イベント
  INTER BEE EXPERIENCE

247
Tokyo Colors. 2014
- 2014
- Rhizomatiks
- installation
- 東京駅八重洲口 グランルーフ、東京
- 東京駅開業100周年記念イベント
  Tokyo Colors.
- 株式会社鉄道会館

248
RADWIMPS GRAND PRIX 2014
実況生中継 "パーフェクトベイビー"
- 2014
- Rhizomatiks
- live
- Zepp Tokyo、東京 他
- RADWIMPS GRAND PRIX 2014
  実況生中継
- 2014/12/03

249
第65回NHK紅白歌合戦
Perfume "Cling Cling"
- 2014
- Rhizomatiks
- TV番組
- NHKホール、東京
- 第65回NHK紅白歌合戦
- 株式会社アミューズ

250
Nosaj Thing "Cold Stares ft.
Chance The Rapper + The O'My's"
ミュージックビデオ
- 2015
- Rhizomatiks
- music video
- –

251
Your Cosmos
- 2015
- Rhizomatiks
- performance
- Your Cosmos performance Ars
  Electronica、リンツ、オーストリア
  Ars Electronica Festival 2015

252
Björk "Mouth Mantra"
ミュージックビデオ
- 2015
- Rhizomatiks
- music video
- –

253
Cinema Analysis using IBM
Watson™ Visual Recognition
service
- 2015
- Rhizomatiks Research
- graphic
- –

254
trace
- 2015
- ELEVENPLAY × Rhizomatiks
  Research
- performance
- 渋谷某所、東京

255
Honda DCT (Dual Clutch
Transmission) branding
promotion
- 2015
- Rhizomatiks
- branding / web / film / video
- –
- Honda

256
ライゾマスクリーンセーバー (2015 ver.)
- 2015
- Rhizomatiks
- application
- –
- Rhizomatiks

257
NHKスペシャル NEXT WORLD
私たちの未来 – 特設Webサイト
SYMPHONY
- 2015
- Rhizomatiks
- web
- online
- NHK

258
CAPSULE "Another World"
ミュージックビデオ
- 2015
- Rhizomatiks
- music video
- –

259
WEARABLE INFOBAR
PATTERN GENERATOR by
ANREALAGE × Rhizomatiks
- 2015
- ANREALAGE × Rhizomatiks
- web / product / application /
  graphic / event
- –
- KDDI、ISETAN

260
TOYOTA LEXUS「1,220」
- 2015
- Rhizomatiks
- installation
- INTERSECT BY LEXUS –
  TOKYO 青山、東京
- MEDIA AMBITION TOKYO
  2015
- トヨタ

261
Nike Zoom City Arena
- 2015
- Rhizomatiks
- event
- NYC Tribeca、ニューヨーク、アメリカ
- Nike

262
Perfume Translyrics Project
- 2015
- Rhizomatiks
- web
- online
- 株式会社アミューズ

263
ボッテガ・ヴェネタ
"EMOTION OF SOUND"
- 2015
- Rhizomatiks
- promotion video
- –
- ボッテガ・ヴェネタ

264
Perfume live "SXSW 2015"
- 2015
- Perfume / MIKIKO / NAKATA
  Yasutaka / MANABE Daito
  / HANAI Yuya / ISHIBASHI
  Motoi / HORII Satoshi /
  SUGANO Kaoru
- live
- オースティン、テキサス、アメリカ
- SXSW 2015

265
fly - (2015 version)
- 2015
- ELEVENPLAY × Rhizomatiks
  Research
- performance
- スパイラルホール、東京
- MOSAIC Ver.1.5

266
六本木アートナイト2015
- 2015
- Rhizomatiks
- installation
- 六本木周辺、東京
- 六本木アートナイト

267
Perfume×ISETAN "Pick me up"
Logo Design
- 2015
- Rhizomatiks
- graphic
- –
- 株式会社アミューズ

268
Perfume LSG T-shirts 2015
- 2015
- Rhizomatiks
- graphic
- –
- 株式会社アミューズ

269
ミラノ国際博覧会 日本館
「FUTURE RESTAURANT」
- 2015
- Rhizomatiks
- showcase / event
- ミラノ、イタリア
- ミラノ国際博覧会
- JETRO

270
グラフィックデザインの死角
- 2015
- Rhizomatiks
- exhibition
- ギンザ・グラフィック・ギャラリー、東京
- 大日本印刷株式会社

271
motion
- 2015
- YASKAWA × Rhizomatiks ×
  ELEVENPLAY
- performance
- 安川電機本社、福岡
- 安川電機100周年式典
- 安川電機

272
TOON WORKSHOP 'THP-01'

TEASER PV
- 2015
- Rhizomatiks
- film /video
- –
- 株式会社グッドスマイルカンパニー

―――――

273
サカナクション NF
- 2015
- Rhizomatiks
- VJ
- –

―――――

274
segments
- 2015
- Rhizomatiks Research + MIKIKO
- performance
- セキスイスタジアム、北海道
- 真駒内花火大会

―――――

275
24 drones
- 2015
- ELEVENPLAY × Rhizomatiks Research
- performance

―――――

276
Summer Workshop 2015
- 2015
- Rhizomatiks Research + MIKIKO
- workshop
- ライゾマティクス

―――――

277
Perfume Anniversary 10days 2015 PPPPPPPPPP LIVE 3:5:6:9 "STORY"
- 2015
- Rhizomatiks
- live
- 日本武道館、東京 他
- Perfume Anniversary 10days 2015 PPPPPPPPPP LIVE 3:5:6:9
- 株式会社アミューズ

―――――

278
Perfume Anniversary 10days PPPPPPPPPP Logo Design
- 2015
- Rhizomatiks
- graphic
- –
- 株式会社アミューズ

―――――

279
東京理科大学 "理科大サイエンス道場"
- 2015
- Rhizomatiks
- signage / film / video

- 東京理科大学 葛飾キャンパス、東京
- 東京理科大学

―――――

280
ELECTRIC LIGHT SYMPHONY 2015
- 2015
- Orchestra Ensemble Kanazawa × Rhizomatiks
- performance / film / graphic / event / video / live / lighting
- 金沢駅 もてなしドーム、石川
- ELECTRIC LIGHT SYMPHONY 2015
- 石川県庁

―――――

281
WE ARE Perfume -WORLD TOUR 3rd DOCUMENT
- 2015
- Rhizomatiks
- graphic
- –
- 株式会社アミューズ

―――――

282
JINS MEME
- 2015
- Rhizomatiks
- application / web / video / event
- –
- JINS

―――――

283
MAQuillAGE "LADY RED GARDEN"
- 2015
- Rhizomatiks
- installation / event
- Zero Base 表参道、東京
- LADY RED GARDEN
- 資生堂

―――――

284
Synesthesia Suit
- 2015–2017
- Enhance Games + Rhizomatiks + Keio Media Design
- performance / installation / exhibition / product
- Moscone Center サンフランシスコ / 六本木ヒルズ 森タワー52階 東京シティビュー、東京 他
- PlayStation Experience 2015、Media Ambition Tokyo 2016、Sundance Film Festival 2017、SXSW 2017 他
- –

―――――

285
Tokyo Colors. 2015
- 2015
- Rhizomatiks
- installation
- 東京駅八重洲口グランルーフ・八重洲口駅前広場、東京
- Tokyo Colors. 2015
- 株式会社鉄道会館

―――――

286
Dimensions
- 2015
- Yoichi Sakamoto
- installation
- スパイラル エントランス、東京

―――――

287
border
- 2015
- ELEVENPLAY × Rhizomatiks Research
- performance
- スパイラルホール、東京

―――――

288
第66回NHK紅白歌合戦 Perfume "Pick Me Up"
- 2015
- Rhizomatiks
- TV番組
- NHKホール、東京
- 第66回NHK紅白歌合戦
- 株式会社アミューズ

―――――

289
スーパーレジン工業 カンパニーフィルム
- 2016
- Rhizomatiks
- film / video
- –
- スーパーレジン工業

―――――

290
Bound Baw (バウンド・バウ)
- 2016
- Rhizomatiks
- web / online
- 大阪芸術大学

―――――

291
Hermès The Nature of Men
2016
- Rhizomatiks
- event
- 都内、東京
- The Nature of Men
- Hermès

―――――

292
Hermès The Nature of Men
- 2016
- Rhizomatiks
- branding / event
- 都内、東京
- The Nature of Men
- Hermès

―――――

293
Deleted Reality
- 2016

- Daito Manabe + Motoi Ishibashi
- installation
- パリ日本文化会館、パリ、フランス
- 「トランスフィア(超域)」#1 真鍋大度 + 石橋素 創意のランドスケープ

―――――

294
アクサ損害保険株式会社 "MIRAI DRIVE PROJECT"
- 2016
- Rhizomatiks
- web / film / video
- –
- アクサ損害保険株式会社

―――――

295
ON-MYAKU 2016 —see/do/be tone—
- 2016
- Tsuyoshi Shirai × Kenichi Nakagawa × Satoshi Horii
- performance
- 東京文化会館、東京
- ON-MYAKU 2016

―――――

296
Media Ambition Tokyo 2016 SPACE EXPERIMENT
- 2016
- Rhizomatiks Architecture
- installation
- 六本木ヒルズ 森タワー52階 東京シティビュー、東京
- Media Ambition Tokyo 2016

―――――

297
Marco Tempest "24 Drone Flight"
- 2016
- Rhizomatiks
- performance
- –

―――――

298
Everything as it is
- 2016
- Douglas Diaz + Rhizomatiks Architecture
- performance
- 六本木ヒルズ ウェストウォーク2F 仮囲い、東京
- MEDIA AMBITION TOKYO

―――――

299
北加賀屋アパートメント リノベーション計画
- 2016
- Rhizomatiks Architecture
- installation
- 北加賀屋、大阪
- リノベーションプロジェクト 「APartMENT」

―――――

300
横浜DeNAベイスターズ 開幕戦

- 2016
- Rhizomatiks Architecture
- Creative Direction
- event
- 横浜スタジアム、神奈川
- 横浜DeNAベイスターズ

301
chains
- 2016
- Daito Manabe + Yusuke Tomoto + 2 bit Ishii
- installation
- ZKM（カールスルーエ・アート・アンド・メディアセンター）、ドイツ
- GLOBALE: New Sensorium
- バーデン゠ヴュルテンベルク州、カールスルーエ市

302
border installation ver.
- 2016
- Rhizomatiks
- installation
- 山口情報芸術センター[YCAM]、山口
- 公益財団法人山口市文化振興財団

303
Perfume "FLASH"
ミュージックビデオ
- 2016
- Rhizomatiks
- music video
- –
- 株式会社アミューズ

304
Geo-Prism（日本科学未来館 常設展示）
- 2016
- Rhizomatiks
- installation
- 日本科学未来館、東京
- 日本科学未来館

305
Perfume "COSMIC EXPLORER" ウェブサイト
- 2016
- Rhizomatiks
- web
- online
- 株式会社アミューズ

306
Nosaj Thing NO REALITY TOUR 2016
- 2016
- Nosaj Thing x DAITO MANABE
- live
- ロサンゼルス、サンフランシスコ、アメリカ 他
- NO REALITY TOUR 2016
- Coachella Festival 他

307
SOUND & CITY
- 2016
- Rhizomatiks
- event
- 六本木アークヒルズ、東京
- wired magazine 日本語版

308
Perfume 6th Tour 2016
「COSMIC EXPLORER」
"Cosmic Explorer" Wearable System and Interaction design
- 2016
- Rhizomatiks
- live
- 幕張メッセ国際展示場、千葉 他
- Perfume 6th Tour 2016
「COSMIC EXPLORER」
- 株式会社アミューズ

309
Perfume 6th Tour 2016
「COSMIC EXPLORER」
Logo Design
- 2016
- Rhizomatiks
- graphic
- –
- 株式会社アミューズ

310
Enhance branding
- 2016
- Rhizomatiks
- branding / web / logo / namecard
- –
- Enhance

311
America's Got Talent
- 2016
- ELEVENPLAY × Rhizomatiks
- performance
- TV番組
- America's Got Talent (AGT) season11
- NBC

312
東京都－パリ市文化交流事業イブニングイベント
「LOUIS VUITTON: DANCE WITH Machine Visuals」
- 2016
- Rhizomatiks
- VOLEZ, VOGUEZ, VOYAGEZ – LOUIS VUITTON
「空へ、海へ、彼方へ──旅するルイ・ヴィトン」展
- event
- LOUIS VUITTON

313
Perfume 6th Tour 2016
「COSMIC EXPLORER」
幕張メッセ 国際展示場
"Cosmic Explorer"
- 2016
- Rhizomatiks
- live
- 幕張メッセ 国際展示場、千葉
- Perfume 6th Tour 2016
「COSMIC EXPLORER」
- 株式会社アミューズ

314
Björk Making of Björk Digital -livestreaming-
- 2016
- Rhizomatiks
- live
- 日本科学未来館、東京

315
Björk Quicksand
- 2016
- Rhizomatiks
- live
- 日本科学未来館、東京
- BjörkDigital ─ 音楽のVR・18日間の実験

316
Resonair branding
- 2016
- Rhizomatiks
- branding / web / logo / namecard
- –
- Enhance

317
FUTURE FACTORY "ROBOT MANAGER in LUCKY FACTORY"
- 2016
- Rhizomatiks
- web / film / video
- –
- 株式会社グッドスマイルカンパニー

318
WE ARE Perfume -WORLD TOUR 3rd DOCUMENT Blu-ray, DVD Package Design
- 2016
- Rhizomatiks
- graphic
- –
- 株式会社アミューズ

319
Rio 2016 Flag Handover Ceremony to Tokyo 2020
- 2016
- Rhizomatiks
- performance
- エスタジオ・ド・マラカナン、リオデジャネイロ、ブラジル
- Rio 2016 Flag Handover Ceremony to Tokyo 2020

320
Perfume: A Gallery Experience Supported by Rhizomatiks
技術開発、映像制作
- 2016
- Rhizomatiks
- exhibition
- Old Truman Brewery Shop 7、ロンドン、イギリス
- Perfume: A Gallery Experience Supported by Rhizomatiks
- 株式会社アミューズ

321
Perfume: A Gallery Experience Supported by Rhizomatiks
LOGO Design
- 2016
- Rhizomatiks
- graphic
- Old Truman Brewery Shop 7、ロンドン、イギリス
- Perfume: A Gallery Experience Supported by Rhizomatiks
- 株式会社アミューズ

322
Perfume 6th Tour 2016
「COSMIC EXPLORER」
北米ツアー "COSMIC EXPLORER" Costume
- 2016
- Rhizomatiks
- live
- HAMMERSTEIN BALLROOM、ニューヨーク、アメリカ 他
- Perfume 6th Tour 2016
「COSMIC EXPLORER」
北米ツアー
- 株式会社アミューズ

323
Perfume 6th Tour 2016
「COSMIC EXPLORER」
北米ツアー "STORY"
- 2016
- Rhizomatiks
- live
- HAMMERSTEIN BALLROOM、ニューヨーク、アメリカ 他
- Perfume 6th Tour 2016
「COSMIC EXPLORER」
北米ツアー
- 株式会社アミューズ

324
Perfume 6th Tour 2016
「COSMIC EXPLORER」
北米ツアー "COSMIC

EXPLORER" Drone
- 2016
- Rhizomatiks
- live
- HAMMERSTEIN BALLROOM、ニューヨーク、アメリカ 他
- Perfume 6th Tour 2016「COSMIC EXPLORER」北米ツアー
- 株式会社アミューズ

———————

325
Rez Infinite: Area X Reveal Trailer
- 2016
- Rhizomatiks
- branding / film
- –
- Enhance

326
Magic Flying Lantern
- 2016
- MagicLab + Rhizomatiks Research
- performance
- モントリオール、カナダ
- ACI-NA/World 2016

327
ライブハウス「WWW」新店舗「WWW X」ライティング、ファサードデザイン
- 2016
- Rhizomatiks Architecture
- architecture
- RISE Bldg、東京
- –
- SPACE SHOWER NETWORKS inc.

———————

328
30周年記念特別番組 MUSIC STATION ウルトラFES 2016 Perfume "Spending all my time" Dynamic VR Display
- 2016
- Rhizomatiks Research
- TV番組
- –
- 株式会社アミューズ

329
FaltyDL "Shock Therapy" ミュージックビデオ
- 2016
- Rhizomatiks Research
- music video / event
- –
-

330
日建設計総合研究所 10周年記念展示「passion for sustainable cities」映像コンテンツ
- 2016

———————

Rhizomatiks Design
- installation
- 日建設計東京ビル1階ギャラリー、東京
- NSRI 10周年記念展示「passion for sustainable cities」
- 日建設計総合研究所

331
Stripes
- 2016
- Yoichi Sakamoto
- installation
- 神戸国際展示場、兵庫
- バンドーテクノフェア2016
- バンドー化学株式会社

332
CURTAIN WALL THEATRE
- 2016
- Rhizomatiks Architecture
- installation
- 東京ミッドタウン芝生広場、東京
- Tokyo Midtown DESIGN TOUCH 2016

333
城崎文芸館 "Living Literature"
- 2016
- Rhizomatiks
- installation
- 城崎文芸館、兵庫
- –
- 豊岡市

334
Perfume 6th Tour 2016「COSMIC EXPLORER」Dome Edition "COSMIC EXPLORER"
- 2016
- Rhizomatiks Research
- live
- 京セラドーム、大阪 他
- Perfume 6th Tour 2016「COSMIC EXPLORER」Dome Edition
- 株式会社アミューズ

335
Perfume 6th Tour 2016「COSMIC EXPLORER」Dome Edition "Perfumeの掟"
- 2016
- Rhizomatiks Research
- live
- 京セラドーム、大阪 他
- Perfume 6th Tour 2016「COSMIC EXPLORER」Dome Edition
- 株式会社アミューズ

336
2045×LIFE PAINT Supported by VOLVO CAR JAPAN
- 2016

———————

Zachary Liberman + Daito Manabe + Setsuya Kurotaki
- DJ / VJ
- 代官山UNIT、東京
- 2045×LIFE PAINT Supported by VOLVO CAR JAPAN
- ボルボ・カー・ジャパン

337
oscillation
- 2016
- Rhizomatiks Research
- installation
- スパイラルガーデン、東京
- NSK100周年記念展示イベント「SENSE OF MOTION」
- 日本精工株式会社

338
perspective
- 2016
- Zachary Lieberman × ELEVENPLAY × Rhizomatiks Research
- performance
- ACTセンター、光州、韓国
- ACT Festival 2016: Heterotopia—Common spaces unseen
- Asia Culture Center / Korean Ministry of Culture, Sports and Tourism

———————

339
WIRED Audi INNOVATION AWARD 2016
- 2016
- Rhizomatiks
- event / installation / product
- KAIGAN STUDIO、東京
- WIRED Audi INNOVATION AWARD 2016
- Audi Japan KK

———————

340
Perfume A.R.T.S.Y. magazine
- 2016
- Rhizomatiks
- graphic
- –
- 株式会社アミューズ

———————

341
第67回NHK紅白歌合戦 Perfume "FLASH"
- 2016
- Rhizomatiks Research
- TV番組
- NHKホール、東京
- 第67回NHK紅白歌合戦
- 株式会社アミューズ

342
FUSO Tokyo Motor Show Creative Direction

———————

2017
- Rhizomatiks Architecture
- Tokyo Motorshow ブースデザイン / film
- –
- 三菱ふそう

343
吉忠マネキン × Xperia Touch "Touch Show Space"
- 2017
- Rhizomatiks Design
- installation
- –
- 吉忠マネキン株式会社

344
MUSIC STATION ウルトラFES 2017 Perfume "エレクトロ・ワールド"
- 2017
- Rhizomatiks Research
- TV番組
- –
- MUSIC STATION ウルトラFES 2017
- 株式会社アミューズ

345
Audi Tokyo Motor Show 2017 "Formless"
- 2017
- Rhizomatiks Design
- branding / event / installation / film / web
- 東京国際展示場、東京
- Tokyo Motor Show 2017
- Audi Japan KK

346
COSMOS Project – "Celestial Frequencies"
- 2017
- Daito Manabe
- installation
- ジョドレルバンク天文台、マンチェスター、イギリス
- bluedot festival
- Abandon Normal Devices

347
バーチャルアイドル 荷兹 HeZ：男性アイドルオーディション番組「明日之子」
- 2017
- Rhizomatiks Research
- live
- ワジジワ（旧EE-Media）× Rhizomatiks バーチャルアイドルプロジェクト
- ワジジワ（旧EE-Media）

348
Axyz – installation for SHIBUYA CAST.
- 2017

Manabe
- live / web
- Bunkamuraオーチャードホール、東京
- ヴェルディ：オペラ『オテロ』〈演奏会形式〉
- Bunkamura

377
Pokémon GO 相棒ポケモンと記念撮影！
- 2017
- Rhizomatiks Research
- installation
- 東京オペラシティ アートギャラリー 3階、東京
- ナイアンティック、株式会社ポケモン

378
Uncanny valley
- 2017
- Daito Manabe
- experiment
- –

379
ELEVENPLAY × Rhizomatiks Research プロジェクトアーカイブ上映
- 2017
- ELEVENPLAY × Rhizomatiks Research
- screening
- ナヴァラ、スペイン
- "ARTE TECNOLÓGICO – MASTERCLASS DE DAITO MANABE Y MIKIKO"
- Museo Universidad de Navarra

380
真鍋大度 × MIKIKOトーク
- 2017
- Daito Manabe, MIKIKO
- talk
- ナヴァラ、スペイン
- "ARTE TECNOLÓGICO – MASTERCLASS DE DAITO MANABE Y MIKIKO"
- Museo Universidad de Navarra

381
No Reality Live in Shanghai
- 2017
- Nosaj Thing × Daito Manabe
- DJ / VJ
- 上海、中華人民共和国
- Innersect
- 中華人民共和国文化部

382
echo
- 2017
- Rhizomatiks Research、ANREALAGE、ダイアログ・イン・ザ・ダーク
- installation
- 象の鼻テラス屋上、神奈川
- ヨコハマ・パラトリエンナーレ2017
- –

383
Perfume Lighting Project
- 2017
- Rhizomatiks Research
- web
- online
- NHK『内村五輪宣言！〜TOKYO 2020開幕1000日前スペシャル〜』
- 株式会社アミューズ

384
内村五輪宣言！〜TOKYO 2020 開幕 1000日前スペシャル〜 Perfume "TOKYO GIRL"
- 2017
- Rhizomatiks Research
- TV番組
- –
- NHK『内村五輪宣言！〜TOKYO 2020開幕1000日前スペシャル〜』
- 株式会社アミューズ

385
Sony – Neural Network Console
- 2017
- Rhizomatiks Design
- web
- online
- –
- Sony Network Communications Inc.

386
Perfume "Everyday" ミュージックビデオ
- 2017
- Rhizomatiks Research
- music video
- –
- 株式会社アミューズ

387
"No Reality Live"
- 2017
- Nosaj Thing + Daito Manabe
- live
- 日本科学未来館、東京
- MUTEK JP
- 一般社団法人MUTEK Japan

388
全米ツアー「Katy Perry: The Witness Tour」でのPurity Ringのビジュアル演出
- 2017
- Daito Manabe
- live performance
- 全米19箇所、アメリカ
- Katy Perry: The Witness Tour

389
【docomo×Perfume】FUTURE-EXPERIMENT VOL.01 距離をなくせ。
- 2017
- Rhizomatiks Research
- live / web
- 東京／ニューヨーク／ロンドン
- 【docomo×Perfume】FUTURE-EXPERIMENT
- 株式会社NTTドコモ、株式会社電通

390
ANREALAGE展覧会「A LIGHT UN LIGHT」展示制作
- 2017
- Rhizomatiks Research
- installation / exhibition
- パルコミュージアム 池袋パルコ、東京
- ANREALAGE展覧会「A LIGHT UN LIGHT」
- アンリアレイジ、パルコ

391
"No Reality Live"
- 2017
- Nosaj Thing × Daito Manabe
- live
- ベルリン、ドイツ
- Ableton Loop 2017: A Summit for Music Makers

392
FUTURE-EXPERIMENT VOL.02 視点を拡張せよ。
- 2017
- Rhizomatiks Research
- performance
- –
- FUTURE-EXPERIMENT
- 株式会社NTTドコモ、株式会社電通

393
WIRED Audi INNOVATION AWARD 2017
- 2017
- Rhizomatiks Design
- event / installation / product / live
- KAIGAN STUDIO、東京
- WIRED Audi INNOVATION AWARD 2017
- Audi Japan KK

394
OK Go "Obsession" ミュージックビデオ
- 2017
- Rhizomatiks Research
- music video
- –

395
第68回NHK紅白歌合戦 Perfume "TOKYO GIRL"
- 2017
- Rhizomatiks Research
- TV番組
- NHKホール、東京
- 第68回NHK紅白歌合戦
- 株式会社アミューズ

396
SoVeC branding
- 2018
- Rhizomatiks Design
- branding / web / logo / namecard
- –
- SoVeC Corporation
- 2018

397
トヨタ紡織 "VODY"
- 2018
- Rhizomatiks Architecture
- installation
- トヨタ紡織

398
札幌市図書・情報館 "SAPPORO KNOWLEDGE TREE"
- 2018
- Rhizomatiks Design
- signage
- 札幌市図書・情報館、札幌市民交流プラザ、北海道
- 札幌市図書・情報館

399
3D City Experience Lab.「3,393,867,155」
- 2018
- Rhizomatiks
- film
- –
- 経済産業省

400
Powers of Scale
- 2018
- Rhizomatiks Architecture
- exhibition
- 森美術館、東京
- 建築の日本展：その遺伝子のもたらすもの

401
Bloomberg TV ドローン特集
- 2018
- Daito Manabe
- TV番組、online
- –
- Art+Technology series
- Bloomberg TV

427
- Mac—Behind the Mac—Apple
- 2018
- Daito Manabe
- CF
- –
- Apple Inc.

428
- echo ver.02
- 2018
- Rhizomatiks Research、ANREALAGE、ダイアログ・イン・ザ・ダーク
- installation
- 日本科学未来館、東京
- echo｜空間を知覚する服
- –

429
- Hermès「彼女と。」
- 2018
- Rhizomatiks Architecture
- branding / event
- 国立新美術館、東京
- 「彼女と。」
- Hermès

430
- invisible war
- 2018
- Daito Manabe + 2bit
- video installation
- Hôtel Salomon de Rothschild（ロスチャイルド館）、パリ、フランス
- ジャポニスム2018「深みへ—日本の美意識を求めて—」
- 国際交流基金

431
- MEET THE MEDIA GURU EVENT
- 2018
- Daito Manabe
- talk
- ミラノ、イタリア
- Meet the Media Guru
- MEET DIGITAL COMMUNICATION Srl Impresa Sociale

432
- 内村五輪宣言！～TOKYO 2020 開幕2年前スペシャル～！Perfume “無限未来”
- 2018
- Rhizomatiks Research
- TV番組
- –
- 内村五輪宣言！～TOKYO 2020 開幕2年前スペシャル～！
- 株式会社アミューズ

433
- 株式会社スーパーアプリ Prhythm ZERO（プリズムゼロ）
- 2018
- Rhizomatiks Design
- web / UIdesign / graphic
- –
- 株式会社スーパーアプリ

434
- Pokémon Synchronicity
- 2018
- Rhizomatiks
- performance / event / lighting
- みなとみらい内港（日本丸メモリアルパーク芝生エリア付近）、神奈川
- ピカチュウ大量発生チュウ! Science is Amazing!
- 株式会社ポケモン

435
- Perfume 7th Tour 2018「FUTURE POP」
- 2018
- Rhizomatiks Research
- live
- 横浜アリーナ、神奈川 他
- Perfume 7th Tour 2018「FUTURE POP」
- 株式会社アミューズ

436
- phosphere
- 2018
- Rhizomatiks Research × ELEVENPLAY
- performance
- デン・ハーグ、オランダ
- TodaysArt 2018

437
- Emergence of 3D Knit
- 2018
- Rhizomatiks Architecture
- branding / installation
- ジュ・ド・ポーム美術館、パリ、フランス
- The Art and Science of LifeWear: Creating a New Standard in Knitwear
- ファーストリテーリング

438
- Pokémon GO AR庭園
- 2018
- Rhizomatiks Research
- event
- 毛利庭園、東京
- 森ビル株式会社、ナイアンティック

439
- ANREALAGE 15th “A LIGHT UN LIGHT COLLECTION”
- 2018
- Rhizomatiks Research

- showcase / event
- 東京
- Amazon Fashion Week TOKYO 2019 S/S「AT TOKYO」
- ANREALAGE CO., LTD

440
- 日田の山と川と光と音
- 2018
- Rhizomatiks Architecture
- installation
- 大分県大山ダム、大分
- 日田市水害復興芸術文化事業
- NPO法人 BEPPU PROJECT

441
- 真鍋大度 ∽ ライゾマティクスリサーチ
- 2018
- Rhizomatiks Research
- exhibition
- 鹿児島県霧島アートの森 アートホール、鹿児島
- 真鍋大度 ∽ ライゾマティクスリサーチ
- 鹿児島県文化振興財団／南日本新聞社／MBC南日本放送

442
- Light Field Theater “point light” “color light” “point lights” “wireframe””
- 2018
- Daito Manabe + Youichi Sakamoto + Tatsuya Ishii
- installation
- 鹿児島県霧島アートの森 アートホール、鹿児島
- 真鍋大度 ∽ ライゾマティクスリサーチ
- 鹿児島県文化振興財団／MBC南日本放送

443
- phenomena – dome version
- 2018
- Daito Manabe + Satoshi Horii (Rhizomatiks)
- installation
- 鹿児島県霧島アートの森 アートホール、鹿児島
- 真鍋大度 ∽ ライゾマティクスリサーチ
- 鹿児島県文化振興財団／南日本新聞社／MBC南日本放送

444
- discrete figures installation
- 2018
- Rhizomatiks Research + ELEVENPLAY + Kyle McDonald
- performance
- 鹿児島県霧島アートの森 アートホール、鹿児島
- 真鍋大度 ∽ ライゾマティクスリサーチ
- 鹿児島県文化振興財団／南日本新聞社／MBC南日本放送

445
- ARASHI Anniversary Tour 5×20 “Everything” 花道メンバートラッキングシステム
- 2018
- Rhizomatiks
- live
- 東京ドーム、東京 他
- ARASHI Anniversary Tour 5×20
- ヤングコミュニケーション

446
- ARASHI Anniversary Tour 5×20 “Oh Yeah!” “GUTS!” 360 カメラシステム
- 2018 / 2019
- Rhizomatiks
- live
- 東京ドーム、東京 他
- ARASHI Anniversary Tour 5×20
- ヤングコミュニケーション

447
- dissonant imaginary
- 2018
- Daito Manabe + Kamitani Lab
- performance / installation
- 鹿児島県霧島アートの森 アートホール、鹿児島
- 真鍋大度 ∽ ライゾマティクスリサーチ
- 鹿児島県文化振興財団／南日本新聞社／MBC南日本放送

448
- 【docomo×Perfume】FUTURE-EXPERIMENT VOL.04 その瞬間を共有せよ。
- 2018
- Rhizomatiks Research
- live / web
- 横浜アリーナ【docomo×Perfume】FUTURE-EXPERIMENT
- 株式会社NTTドコモ、株式会社電通

449
- 第69回NHK紅白歌合戦 Perfume “Future Pop” “エレクトロ・ワールド”
- 2018
- Rhizomatiks Research
- TV番組
- 横浜アリーナ、神奈川
- 第69回NHK紅白歌合戦
- 株式会社アミューズ

450
- 猿田彦珈琲 “DRIP WORDS −言葉の抽出− ”
- 2019
- Rhizomatiks Design
- installation
- 猿田彦珈琲 誠品生活日本橋店、東京
- –

- 猿田彦珈琲株式会社

451
optical walls
- 2019
- Yoichi Sakamoto
- installation
- milano salone、ミラノ、イタリア
- 三井化学 Material Meets
Creative Team 第7弾
- 三井化学
———

452
LEXUS DESIGN EVENT 2019 |
LEADING WITH LIGHT
- 2019
- Rhizomatiks
- performance / event /
installation
- SUPERSTUDIO PIÙ
- LEXUS DESIGN EVENT 2019
- Lexus international
———

453
LPIXEL / EIRL
- 2019
- Rhizomatiks Design
- branding / web
- –
- LPIXEL 2019
———

454
JPMD Star Wars: MMXX
typography New Year's card
- 2019
- Rhizomatiks Design
- graphic / web
- –
- JPMD
———

455
SHIBUYA SKY（渋谷スカイ）
- 2019
- Rhizomatiks Architecture
- branding / space design /
installation
- 渋谷スカイ、東京
- 渋谷スクランブルスクエア
———

456
大丸 D-WALL
- 2019
- Rhizomatiks Architecture
- installation
- 大丸心斎橋店 本館、大阪
- 大丸
———

457
202X Urban Visionary
- 2019
- Rhizomatiks Architecture
- talk
- co-lab 渋谷キャスト、東京

458
Sónar Barcelona "factors"
- 2019
- Daito Manabe + Satoshi Horii
- installation
- バルセロナ、スペイン
- Sonar360º by MEDIAPRO
- MEDIAPRO
———

459
Sónar Barcelona "dissonant
imaginary Live AV"
- 2019
- Daito Manabe + Kamitani Lab
- live
- バルセロナ、スペイン
- Sónar Festival (Sonar by Day)
- ADVANCED MUSIC, S.L.
———

460
dissonant imaginary
- 2019
- Daito Manabe + Yukiyasu
Kamitani
- talk
- バルセロナ、スペイン
- Sónar Festival (Sonar +D)
- ADVANCED MUSIC, S.L.
———

461
Lecture Demonstration "on
art and tech research and
development"
- 2019
- Daito Manabe
- talk
- リエージュ、ベルギー
- Theatre de Liège
———

462
'discrete figures' Artist Talk:
Daito Manabe, MIKIKO & Kyle
McDonald
- 2019
- Daito Manabe, MIKIKO, Kyle
McDonald
- talk
- サンフランシスコ、アメリカ
- 'discrete figures 2019' Event
Series
- Gray Area Foundation
———

463
THE official web
- 2019
- Rhizomatiks Design
- web
- online
- THE株式会社
———

464
Synesthesia X1-2.44
- 2019
- Synesthesia Lab feat. evala (See

by Your Ears)
- installation / product
- 六本木ヒルズ 森タワー52階
東京シティビュー、東京
- Media Ambition Tokyo 2019
- –
———

465
Perfume WORLD TOUR 4th
「FUTURE POP」
- 2019
- Rhizomatiks Research
- live
- 横浜アリーナ、神奈川 他
- Perfume WORLD TOUR 4th
「FUTURE POP」
- 株式会社アミューズ
———

466
JR東日本 TokyoYardProject
- 2019
- Rhizomatiks Architecture
- branding
- –
- JR東日本
———

467
Perfume Live at Coachella Valley
Music and Arts Festival 2019
- 2019
- Rhizomatiks Research
- live
- カリフォルニア、アメリカ
- Coachella Valley Music and Arts
Festival 2019
- 株式会社アミューズ
———

468
N.E.R.D & Rihanna Sony's 360
Reality Audio at SOMETHING
IN THE WATER "Lemon"
- 2019
- Rhizomatiks
- installation
- ヴァージニア・ビーチ、アメリカ
- Something in the Water
- ソニーホームエンタテインメント＆サウ
ンドプロダクツ株式会社
———

469
読売広告社 HARUMI FLAG
パビリオン
- 2019
- Rhizomatiks Architecture
- installation
- HARUMI FLAG PAVILION、東京
- 読売広告社
———

470
野村萬斎 MANSAI◉解体新書
その参拾 特別版『5W1H』
- 2019
- Rhizomatiks Research
- performance
- 世田谷パブリックシアター、東京

MANSAI◉解体新書 その参拾
特別版
- 文化庁、独立行政法人日本芸術
文化振興会
———

471
Super Flying Tokyo
- 2019
- Rhizomatiks
- event / web
- 日本科学未来館、代官山UNIT、
東京
- Super Flying Tokyo
- 公益財団法人東京都歴史文化財団
アーツカウンシル東京
———

472
KOHH Live at FUJI ROCK
FESTIVAL '19
- 2019
- Rhizomatiks Research
- live
- 新潟県湯沢町苗場スキー場、新潟
- FUJI ROCK FESTIVAL '19
- 日本コロムビア株式会社
———

473
NANA MIZUKI LIVE EXPRESS
2019 "METANOIA"
- 2019
- Rhizomatiks Research
- live
- ZOZOマリンスタジアム、千葉
- NANA MIZUKI LIVE EXPRESS
2019
- ディーエル
———

474
Universe of HEAT TECH
- 2019
- Rhizomatiks Architecture
- event
- Somerset House、ロンドン、イギリス
- The Art and Science of LifeWear:
New Form Follows Function
- ファーストリテーリング
———

475
Arca "Mutant; Faith"
- 2019
- Daito Manabe
- performance
- The Shed New York、アメリカ
- ARCA: MUTANT; FAITH
- The Shed
———

476
Lucid Motion
- 2019
- Daito Manabe × Rhizomatiks
Research
- exhibition
- ARTECHOUSE DC、アメリカ
- Lucid Motion
- ARTECHOUSE

477
discrete figures Special Edition
- 2019
- Rhizomatiks Research × ELEVENPLAY × Kyle McDonald
- performance
- 札幌文化芸術劇場 hitaru、北海道
- discrete figures Special Edition
- 札幌市芸術文化財団 札幌文化芸術劇場 hitaru

478
Perfume "Reframe 2019"
- 2019
- Rhizomatiks Research
- live
- LINE CUBE SHIBUYA(渋谷公会堂)、東京
- Reframe 2019
- 株式会社アミューズ

479
Hermès 夢のかたち
- 2019
- Rhizomatiks Architecture
- branding / event
- 六本木ヒルズノースタワー、東京
- 夢のかたち Hermès Bespoke Objects
- Hermès

480
エイブル Presents 第72回全日本フェンシング選手権大会 Fencing Visualized
- 2019
- Rhizomatiks Research
- interactive video
- LINE CUBE SHIBUYA(渋谷公会堂)、東京
- エイブル Presents 第72回全日本フェンシング選手権大会
- Dentsu Lab Tokyo(共同開発)

481
SENSE ISLAND –感覚の島– 暗闇の美術島
- 2019
- Rhizomatiks Architecture
- branding / event
- 猿島、神奈川
- SENSE ISLAND –感覚の島– 暗闇の美術島
- 横須賀市

482
JIKU #003 AMANOHASHIDATE
- 2019
- Rhizomatiks Architecture
- installation / event
- 成相山 成相寺、京都
- Alternative kyoto もうひとつの京都 太古から未来へと続くみち
- 京都府宮津市

483
Tokyo Tokyo FESTIVAL special 13 Light and Sound Installation "Coded Field"
- 2019
- Rhizomatiks
- event / web
- 浄土宗大本山増上寺、東京
- 港区立芝公園、東京都立芝公園
- Tokyo Tokyo FESTIVAL スペシャル13 Light and Sound Installation "Coded Field"
- 東京都、公益財団法人東京都歴史文化財団 アーツカウンシル東京

484
Sudo Reiko: Making NUNO Textiles
- 2019
- Rhizomatiks Architecture
- installation
- Center for Heritage Arts & Textile、香港
- Sudo Reiko: Making NUNO Textiles
- CHAT

485
高円宮杯 JAL PRESENTS FENCING WORLD CUP 2019 Fencing Visualized
- 2019
- Rhizomatiks
- interactive video
- 幕張メッセ、千葉
- 高円宮杯 JAL PRESENTS FENCING WORLD CUP 2019
- Dentsu Lab Tokyo(共同開発)

486
ポケモンセンターメガトウキョー「Pokémon GO Lab.」店内演出
- 2019
- Rhizomatiks
- installation
- 池袋サンシャインシティ ポケモンセンターメガトウキョー、東京
- –
- 株式会社ポケモン

487
第70回NHK紅白歌合戦 Perfume "FUSION" "ポリリズム"
- 2019
- Rhizomatiks
- TV番組
- NHKホール、東京
- 第70回NHK紅白歌合戦
- 株式会社アミューズ

488
こども本の森 中之島「本のかけら」
- 2020
- Rhizomatiks Design
- installation
- こども本の森 中之島、大阪
- –
- 大阪市

489
高輪ゲートウェイ駅 GATE 01 "FUTURE GATEWAY"
- 2020
- Rhizomatiks Architecture
- installation
- 高輪ゲートウェイ駅、東京
- –
- 東日本旅客鉄道株式会社

490
Staying TOKYO
- 2020
- Rhizomatiks
- event
- online

491
DOUBLE FANTASY ONLINE SHOP SITE
- 2020
- Rhizomatiks Architecture
- web
- online

492
Rhizomatiks inspired by Perfume 2020
- 2020
- Rhizomatiks
- exhibition
- PARCO MUSEUM TOKYO、東京
- Rhizomatiks inspired by Perfume 2020
- PARCO

493
KOHH Live in Concert
- 2020
- Rhizomatiks
- live
- LINE CUBE SHIBUYA(渋谷公会堂)、東京
- KOHH Live in Concert
- 日本コロムビア株式会社

494
Squarepusher "Terminal Slam" ミュージックビデオ
- 2020
- Rhizomatiks
- music video
- –
- WARP RECORDS LIMITED

495
Perfume 8th Tour 2020 "P Cubed" in Dome
- 2020
- Rhizomatiks
- live
- 東京ドーム、東京 他
- Perfume 8th Tour 2020 "P Cubed" in Dome
- 株式会社アミューズ

496
Architecture and Formalization of Digital Models
- 2020
- Daito Manabe
- talk (online)
- ポンピドゥー・センター、IRCAM、パリ、フランス
- Forum Vertigo 2020
- Centre Pompidou、IRCAM

497
dissonant imaginary at Centre Pompidou
- 2020
- Daito Manabe + Kamitani Lab, Kyoto University and ATR
- exhibition
- ポンピドゥー・センター、パリ、フランス
- Exhibition「Neurones: Simulated Intelligences」
- Centre Pompidou

498
GOOD DRIVE
- 2020
- Rhizomatiks Design
- branding / film
- –
- ソニー損害保険株式会社

499
猿田彦珈琲 "NEO TOKONOMA"
- 2020
- Rhizomatiks Design
- installation
- 猿田彦珈琲 The Bridge 原宿駅店、東京
- –
- 猿田彦珈琲株式会社

500
KAZU "Come Behind Me, So Good! (Official video by Daito Manabe + Kenichiro Shimizu)"
- 2020
- Daito Manabe + Kenichiro Shimizu
- music video
- –
- Adult Baby Records

501
Perfume "Challenger" ミュージックビデオ
- 2020

- 2020
- Daito Manabe
- branding / film
- –
- 株式会社ユニクロ、株式会社
  TBWA HAKUHODO

529

SFC 集中講義 データ・ドリブン・アート
- 2020
- Daito Manabe
- workshop
- 慶応義塾大学SFC（湘南藤沢キャンパス）、
  神奈川

530

BLESSING OF THE WIND
- 2020
- Rhizomatiks Design
- installation
- GREEN SPRINGS、東京
- –
- 株式会社立飛ホールディングス

531

ガンダム GLOBAL CHALLENGE
GGCリーダーズ
- 2020
- Rhizomatiks Architecture
- producer
- 横浜、神奈川
- サンライズ

532

Bleague Drills
- 2020
- Rhizomatiks Architecture
- event
- –
- ソニー・ミュージックエンタテインメント

533

CONNECTED WORLD
- 2020
- DJ Krush × Daito Manabe
- DJ / VJ
- online
- Connected World Vol.1
- Es・U・Es Corporation（共同プロデュース）

534

JIKU #009 TANGO_
KOKUBUNJI
- 2020
- Rhizomatiks Architecture
- installation
- 京都府丹後郷土資料館、京都
- Alternative kyoto もうひとつの京都
  現実と空想のはざまで
- 京都府宮津市

535

Online 慶應三田祭「LEMIT」
監修
- 2020
- Daito Manabe
- consulting
- –
- 慶應義塾大学三田祭実行委員会

536

Photon of Wisdom -知恵の光子-
- 2020
- Rhizomatiks Design
- installation
- OCA TOKYO、東京
- –
- 三菱地所株式会社

537

HEERE
- 2020
- Rhizomatiks + Flowplateaux
- web / branding / UIdesign
- online

538

critical line - version 0
- 2020
- Daito Manabe
- installation
- 清春芸術村 光の美術館、山梨
- HOKUTO ART PROGRAM
  edition.0

539

Niantic ARDK demo
- 2020
- Rhizomatiks
- video
- –
- Niantic, Inc.

540

Flying Lotus Presents "The Hit"
- 2020
- Daito Manabe + Rhizomatiks
- VJ
- online
- Flying Lotus Presents The Hit
- Brainfeeder / Timetable

541

坂本龍一 Ryuichi Sakamoto:
Playing the Piano 12122020
- 2020
- Rhizomatiks
- live
- online
- Ryuichi Sakamoto: Playing the
  Piano 12122020
- commmons

542

国土交通省 PLATEAU
- 2020
- Rhizomatiks Architecture
- web
- online
- 国土交通省

543

第71回紅白歌合戦
Perfume "Perfume Medley
2020"
- 2020
- Rhizomatiks
- TV番組
- NHKホール、東京
- 第71回紅白歌合戦
- 株式会社アミューズ

544

ELECTRON EVERYONE デンキ
バリブラシ TVCF
- 2021
- Flowplateaux
- branding / film
- –
- GM CORPORATION

545

2020年ドバイ万博
日本館クリエイティブ・アドバイザー
- 2020
- Seiichi Saito
- consulting
- –
- JETRO

546

border 2021
- 2021
- ELEVENPLAY × Rhizomatiks
- performance
- スパイラルホール、東京
- border 2021
- 文化庁／特定非営利活動法人映像
  産業振興機構（VIPO）

547

Sensing Streams 2021 –
invisible, inaudible
- 2021
- Ryuichi Sakamoto + Daito
  Manabe
- installation
- 木木芸術社区（M WOODS
  HUTONG）、北京、中華人民共和国
- 坂本龙一：观音・听时｜Ryuichi
  Sakamoto: seeing sound, hearing
  time
- M WOODS Art Community

ライゾマティクス_マルティプレックス 出品リスト

凡例　No.、作品名、制作年、技法、協力機関の順に記載、所蔵表記のない作品資料はすべて作家蔵

展示空間の名称については、地下2階展示室入り口より反時計回りに下記のように表記

エントランス(rhizome)、A-1(Rhizomatiks Chronicle)、A-2 (NFTs and CryptoArt-Experiment)、B前室及びB (Rhizomatiks × ELEVENPLAY "multiplex")、C+D(R&D)、F(particles 2021)、G(Epilogue)

作品8(Epilogue)について、既製のソフトウェアは「アプリケーション」、ライゾマティクスで開発・制作したものは「ソフトウェア」と表記

展示室

1
Rhizome
- 2021
- 映像プロジェクション
- 技術協力=パナソニック株式会社

2
Rhizomatiks Chronicle
- 2021
- 映像インスタレーション
- 技術協力=キヤノンマーケティングジャパン株式会社

3
NFTs and CryptoArt-Experiment
- 2021
- 映像メディアインスタレーション
- 技術協力=キヤノンマーケティングジャパン株式会社／株式会社Kyuzan
- Special thanks=KIZUNA / BlockchainPROseed

4
Rhizomatiks × ELEVENPLAY "multiplex"
- 2021
- ARインスタレーション、モバイルロボティクス、ミクストメディア
- 技術協力=パナソニック株式会社

5
R&D(リサーチ&ディベロップメント)
- 2021–
- 記録映像、モバイルロボティクス、サーチライト、コンピュータほか
- 技術協力=株式会社DataSign

5-0　RTK Laser Robotics Experiment／2021
5-1　"Dissonant imaginary" – Daito Manabe + Kamitani Lab, Kyoto University and ATR／2018／5分
5-2　Trojan Horse／2021／44秒／技術協力=株式会社DataSign
5-3　Daito Manabe "morphechore - prototype" (2020)／2020／5分
5-4　Home Sync Light／2020
5-5　Home Sync Light／2020／1分
5-6　Messaging Mask／2020
5-7　Messaging Mask／2020／6分

6
Rhizomatiks Archive & Behind the Scene
- 2006-2021
- 記録映像、ドローンほか実物展示、資料展示

6-1　Points "Air Gun"／2010／Points
6-2　Pスポットライトドローン／2015／ELEVENPLAY × Rhizomatiks Research "shadow"
6-3　ジンバルカメラ／2015／Nosaj Thing – Cold stares ft. Chance The Rapper + The O' My's
6-4　ピラミッドドローン／2014／ELEVENPLAY × Rhizomatiks Research "fly"
6-5　Command line wave／2008
6-6　高速スポットライト／2016／Deleted Reality
6-7　口LED／2009／LED in my mouth
6-8　平面光源ライト／2019／LEXUS DESIGN EVENT 2019／Leading with Light in collaboration with Rhizomatiks
6-9　電気刺激装置／2008／Face visualizer, instrument, and copy
6-10　LEDアーム／2018／Light Field Theater
6-11　小型レーザープロジェクタ／2013／ELEVENPLAY × Rhizomatiks "ray"
6-12　オムニホイール台車／2015／ELEVENPLAY × Rhizomatiks Research "border"
6-13　LED灯具／2010／『結成10周年、メジャーデビュー5周年記念! Perfume LIVE @東京ドーム「1 2 3 4 5 6 7 8 9 10 11」』／Lighting Balloon System
6-14　LED灯具／2014／rate
6-15　Pa++ern T-shirts／2009／Pa++ern
6-16　echo band／2017／echoプロジェクト
6-17　センサー内蔵シューズ／2010／NIKE MUSIC SHOE
6-18　プリント基板・プロトタイプ・治具
6-19　echo ware／2017／echo プロジェクト、所蔵：ANREALAGE
6-20　メッシュフレーム／2018／Rhizomatiks Research × ELEVENPLAY × Kyle McDonald "discrete figures"

rhizomatiks_multiplex:
List of works

Note   The description of the works are given as follows: title, date, medium and collection. Those works for which no source is indicated are courtesy of the artists.

The names of the exhibition spaces are shown below in counterclockwise order from the entrance of the Exhibition Gallery B2F:

Entrance (rhizome), A-1 (Rhizomatiks Chronicle), A-2 (NFTs and CryptoArt-Experiment), B front room and B (Rhizomatiks × ELEVENPLAY "multiplex"), C+D (R&D), F (particles 2021), G (Epilogue)

Ready-made software is written as "applications (not produced by Rhizomatous)" and software developed or produced by Rhizomatous is written to "software".

Exhibition Gallery B2F

1
Rhizome
- 2021
- Projected images, device and other material
- Technical Cooperation by Panasonic Corporation

2
Rhizomatiks Chronicle
- 2021
- Visual image installation
- Technical Cooperation by=Canon Marketing Japan Inc.

3
NFTs and CryptoArt-Experiment
- 2021
- Visual media installation
- Technical Cooperation by=Canon Marketing Japan Inc./ Kyuzan Inc.
- Special thanks=KIZUNA / BlockchainPROseed

4
Rhizomatiks × ELEVENPLAY "multiplex"
- 2021
- AR installation, mobile robotics and mixed media
- Technical Cooperation by=Panasonic Corporation

5
R&D(Research & Development)
- 2021–
- Document video, mobile robotics, search light, computer and more
- Technical Cooperation by=DataSign Inc.

5-0   RTK Laser Robotics Experiment (2021)
5-1   "Dissonant imaginary" – Daito Manabe + Kamitani Lab, Kyoto University and ATR / 2018 / 5 minutes.
5-2   Trojan Horse / 2021 / 44 seconds. / Technical Cooperation by=DataSign Inc.
5-3   Daito Manabe "morphechore - prototype" (2020)/2020 / 5 minutes.
5-4   Home Sync Light / 2020
5-5   Home Sync Light / 2020 / 1 minutes.
5-6   Messaging Mask / 2020
5-7   Messaging Mask / 2020 /

6 minutes.

6
Rhizomatiks Archive & Behind the Scene
2006-2021
- Document video, drones, other actual exhibits and Materials

6-1   Points "Air Gun" / 2010 / Points
6-2   Spotlight Drone / 2015 / ELEVENPLAY × Rhizomatiks Research "shadow"
6-3   Gimbal Camera / 2015 / Nosaj Thing – Cold stares ft. Chance The Rapper + The O' My's
6-4   Pyramid Drone / 2014 / ELEVENPLAY × Rhizomatiks Research "fly"
6-5   command line wave / 2008
6-6   High Frequency Spot Light / 2016 / Deleted Reality
6-7   Mouth LED / 2009 / LED in my mouth
6-8   Planar light source / 2019 / LEXUS DESIGN EVENT 2019 / Leading with Light in collaboration with Rhizomatiks
6-9   Electric Stimulus Device / 2008 / Face visualizer, instrument, and copy
6-10   LED Arm, a robotic arm with small LEDs / 2018 / Light Field Theater
6-11   A small and lightweight laser projector / 2013 / ELEVENPLAY × Rhizomatiks "ray"
6-12   Omni Wheel Track / 2015 / ELEVENPLAY × Rhizomatiks Research "border"
6-13   LED light fixture / 2010 / Lighting Balloon System, 10th Anniversary Since Formation, 5th Major Debut Anniversary! Perfume LIVE @ Tokyo Dome "1 2 3 4 5 6 7 8 9 10 11"
6-14   LED device installed inside the balloon / 2014 / rate
6-15   Pa++ern T-shirts / 2009 / Pa++ern
6-16   echo band / 2017 / echo project
6-17   Sensor Shoes / 2010 / NIKE MUSIC SHOE
6-18   Printed Circuit Board / Prototype / Jigs
6-19   echo ware / 2017 / echo

掲載作品クレジット
Credits of Works

凡例   本リストには、本書の収録作品に関わるクレジットを掲載した。

また、紙面の都合上ここに記載しきれなかった詳細に関しては、下記のウェブサイトに掲載した。(2021年6月)

Notes   This list includes the credits regarding the works included in this catalogue.

In addition, details which could not be included here due to space limitations are available at the following websites.

https://multiplex-catalog.rhizomatiks.com/

Daito Manabe + Motoi Ishibashi《Sonic Floor》
- Concept and Direction: Daito Manabe, Motoi Ishibashi
- Sound, Lighting Programming and Design, Floor Design: Daito Manabe
- Device: Motoi Ishibashi
- Design: Seiichi Saito
- Web Programming: Satoshi Horii, Hidenori Chiba
- On Site Support: Shintaro Wada
- Supported by DGN + Rhizomatiks, Color Kinetics Japan Inc.

Daito Manabe + Motoi Ishibashi《Proce55ing Life》
- Audio, Visual, Network Design and Programming: Daito Manabe
- RFID Device Programming: Motoi Ishibashi (DGN)
- Graphic Design: Seiichi Saito (Rhizomatiks)

Daito Manabe《Face visualizer, instrument, and copy》
- Performance, Direction, Concept, Composition, Sound Design and Programming: Daito Manabe
- Performers: Yasushi Fukuzawa, Rie Yoshioka, Muryo Homma, Yosuke Ushigome
- Hardware Design Support: Masaki Teruoka (VPP, True, Biosignal), Katsuhiko Harada
- Sensor Development: Masaki Teruoka
- Sound Design Support: Taeji Sawai
- Manipulation Support for a Performance: Hiroyuki Hori (Rhizomatiks)
- All Production Support: Rhizomatiks

Daito Manabe《electric stimulus to body + myoelectric sensor test》
- Programming: Daito Manabe
- Engineering: Masaki Teruoka

川口隆夫 "テーブルマインド"
- Choreography, Direction, Performance: Takao Kawaguchi
- Lighting: Takayuki Fujimoto
- Technical Direction, Programming: Daito Manabe + Motoi Ishibashi
- Music: evala (port, ATAK)
- Visual, Programming: Satoshi Horii
- Visual: Seiichi Saito
- Sensor Development: Masaki Teruoka
- Manipulation: Hiroyuki Hori
- Produce: Yasuo Ozawa
- Dramaturge: Tsubasa Wada
- Costume: Noriko Kitamura
- Photographs: Hiroki Taguchi
- Advertisement: Hiroyasu Kimura, Megumi Shima
- Cameraman: Shizuo Takahashi
- Stage Director: Yuji Kobayashi (Off stage)
- Technical Support: Takanori Sudo (ANJI)
- Production: Hiroto Kojima (ANJI), Mami Takahashi (ANJI)

Produced and presented by Kawasaki Art Center

---

illion "MAHOROBA" ミュージックビデオ
- Director: Tetsuya Nagato
- Technical Support: Daito Manabe (Rhizomatiks Research)

FaltyDL "Straight & Arrow" ミュージックビデオ
- Video Commission: Ninja Tune
- Direction: Daito Manabe + Kazuaki Seki
- Produce: Daito Manabe
- Production Company: Rhizomatiks + Triple-O
- Software Development: Daito Manabe
- Device Development: Masaki Teruoka

Daito Manabe + Motoi Ishibashi《Command line wave》
- Concept: Daito Manabe + Motoi Ishibashi
- Sound Programming: Daito Manabe
- Device Programming: Motoi Ishibashi
- Cube Design: Toshiaki Yanagisawa

Alvaro CASSINELLI / MANABE Daito / KURIBARA Yusaku / Alexis ZERROUG《scoreLight》
- Alvaro Cassinelli, Daito Manabe, Yusaku Kuribara and Alexis Zerroug

---

Daito Manabe《LED in my mouth》
- Sound + Light Programming: Daito Manabe
- LED Device Programming: Motoi Ishibashi

Daito Manabe + Motoi Ishibashi + Kanta Horio + Tomoaki Yanagisawa《The Way Sensing Go》
- Concept and Direction: Daito Manabe, Motoi Ishibashi, Kanta Horio, Tomoaki Yanagisawa
- Workshop Participants: KAJII Yuusuke, KIMOTO Keisuke, SANO Masakazu, SUKI Jarashi, TAJIMA Yoshimi, TADA Hitomi, Thomas TELANDRO, TOGA Yuta. HASEGAWA Shouhei, HATANO Yasuhiro, HAYASHI Masahiro, FUJIOKA Sadam, FUJIMOTO Naoaki, Susanna HERTRICH, HORII Satoshi, MATSUMURA Seiichiro, MAMIYA Asami, Moch, YAMAUCHI Hiroshi, YAMAGUCHI Takahiro, Zachary LIEBERMAN
- Special Thanks: Clear Gallery

Daito Manabe + Motoi Ishibashi《Pa++ern》
- Concept: Daito Manabe, Motoi Ishibashi
- Programming: Daito Manabe, Motoi Ishibashi
- Installation Design: Seiichi Saito (Rhizomatiks)
- Web Creative Direction: Daito Manabe, Hidenori Chiba (Rhizomatiks)
- Twitter Server Side Programming: Hiroyuki Hori (Rhizomatiks), Daisuke Nakahama (Rhizomatiks)
- Web Design: Hiroyasu Kimura

(Rhizomatiks)
- Flash Programming: Hidenori Chiba (Rhizomatiks), Keiichi Yoshikawa (BOW), Sumito Kamoi (Rhizomatiks)
- Cooperation: BEAMS Co., Ltd.

———————————

Daito Manabe + Motoi Ishibashi 《fade out》
- Early concepting: Daito Manabe + Rhizomatiks
- Concept: Daito Manabe + Motoi Ishibashi
- Programming: Daito Manabe + Motoi Ishibashi
- Laser Programming: Motoi Ishibashi
- Sound Programming: Daito Manabe
- Thanks to Rhizomatiks, Kanta Horio and Yasushi Fukuzawa

———————————

Daito Manabe + Motoi Ishibashi 《points》
- Concept: Daito Manabe + Motoi Ishibashi
- Software: Daito Manabe
- Hardware: Motoi Ishibashi
- Mechanical: Yukio Akiba
- Video: Muryo Homma
- Support: Tomoaki Yanagisawa

———————————

Daito Manabe + Motoi Ishibashi 《particles》
- Planning, Software Development: Daito Manabe (4nchor5 La6, Rhizomatiks)
- System Design, Hardware Development: Motoi Ishibashi (4nchor5 La6, Rhizomatiks, DGN)
- Rail Structure Design, Production: Seiichi Saito (Rhizomatiks) and Youichi Sakamoto (Rhizomatiks)
- Ball Design and Development: Tomoaki Yanagisawa (4nchor5 La6)
- Lift Structure Design and Production: Yukio Akiba (Gadget)
- Graphic Design: Hiroyasu Kimura (Rhizomatiks) and Megumi Shima (Rhizomatiks)
- Document Video Filming and Editing: Muryo Homma (Rhizomatiks)
- Planning Support: Ichiro Kojima (Rhizomatiks)
- Onsite Support: Kanta Horio (4nchor5 La6)
- Production Support: Kensuke Fujishiro (Rhizomatiks)
- Special Thanks: MIKIKO and poko

———————————

Daito Manabe + Motoi Ishibashi 《16 Forms》
- Direction, 3D Data Editing, Lighting + Sound Design: Daito Manabe
- Robot Arm Programming: Motoi Ishibashi
- Model: MIKIKO

———————————

Daito Manabe + Motoi Ishibashi 《line》
- Software: Daito Manabe
- Robot Arm: Motoi Ishibashi
- Special thanks to Satoru Higa for ofxPCL and kinectUtils

———————————

Your Cosmos 《Your Cosmos》
- Concept, Programming: Daito Manabe (Rhizomatiks)

Music: evala (port, ATAK)
- Visual, Programming: Satoshi Horii (Rhizomatiks)
- Visual, Programming: Satoru Higa (Rhizomatiks)
- Visual, Programmer: Yusuke Tomoto (Rhizomatiks)
- Lyric Generation: Kaoru Sugano (dentsu)
- Lyric Generation: Nao Tokui (Qosmo)
- Lyric Generation: Kouki Yamada

———————————

Rhizomatiks 《traders》
- Concept + Programming: Daito Manabe
- Front Graphic Design + Programming: Satoru Higa
- Floor Graphic Design + Programming: Satoshi Horii
- Network & System Programming: Yusuke Tomoto
- iOS Programming: Nao Tokui
- Sound Design: Taeji Sawai

———————————

Daito Manabe + Yusuke Tomoto + 2 bit Ishii 《chains》
- Daito Manabe, Yusuke Tomoto, 2bit Ishii

———————————

Daito Manabe + Motoi Ishibashi 《Deleted Reality》
- Concept: Daito Manabe, Motoi Ishibashi
- Software: Daito Manabe
- System Design, Hardware Development: Motoi Ishibashi
- Manufacture of Lighting Device: Youichi Sakamoto
- Technical Support: Toshitaka Mochizuki, Hideaki Tai, Momoko Nishimoto

———————————

Rhizomatiks Research 《oscillation》
- Concept, Software Programming: Daito Manabe
- Concept, Hardware Programming: Motoi Ishibashi
- Product Design: Momoko Nishimoto
- Craft: Toshitaka Mochizuki
- Management: Tomoyo Obata

———————————

Daito Manabe + Kamitani Lab 《dissonant imaginary》
- Daito Manabe + Kamitani Lab, Kyoto University and ATR

———————————

Rhizomatiks Research 《Cinema Analysis using IBM Watson™ Visual Recognition service》
- Direction: Daito Manabe
- Programming: Yusuke Tomoto

———————————

Tokyo Tokyo FESTIVAL Special 13
Light and Sound Installation "Coded Field"
- Organizers: Tokyo Metropolitan Government and Arts Council Tokyo (Tokyo Metropolitan Foundation for History and Culture)
- Support: Minato Ward, Tokyo
- Planning and Production: Rhizomatiks

- Production: TOW Co., LTD.
- Technological Support: SPRESENSE™ by Sony Semiconductor Solutions Corporation

———————————

Daito Manabe × Rhizomatiks Research 《Lucid Motion》
- Artistic Direction: Daito Manabe (Rhizomatiks)
- Choreography: MIKIKO (ELEVENPLAY)
- Motion Performer: SARA (ELEVENPLAY) and EMMY (ELEVENPLAY)
- Visuals Programming: Satoshi Horii (Rhizomatiks)
- Visuals Programming: Yuta Asai (Rhizomatiks)
- Visuals Programming: Futa Kera (Rhizomatiks)
- iOS Programming: 2bit
- CG: Shogo Kawata (GORAKU)
- Space Design: Takahito Hosono (Rhizomatiks)
- Music: Hopebox and Daito Manabe (Rhizomatiks)
- Motion Capture: Crescent
- Producer: Takao Inoue (Rhizomatiks)
- Project Management: Naoki Ishizuka, Rina Watanabe, hibiki (Rhizomatiks)

———————————

Daito Manabe & Satoshi Horii 《phenomena – quarantine version》
- Daito Manabe, Satoshi Horii

———————————

Rhizomatiks 《Social Distancing Communication Platform》
- Rhizomatiks

———————————

Rhizomatiks 《Messaging Mask》
- Creative Direction, Technical Direction, Software Engineering: Yuya Hanai
- Technical Direction, Hardware Engineering: Motoi Ishibashi
- Product Design: Toshitaka Mochizuki
- Visual Effect: Futa Kera
- Project Management: Kahori Takemura
- Project Management, Produce: Takao Inoue
- Supervise: Daito Manabe
- (Behind the scene) Video Shooting&Editor: Takashi Ninomiya

———————————

Rhizomatiks 《Home Sync Light》
- Planning, Technical Direction: Motoi Ishibashi
- Lighting Design, Programming: Daito Manabe
- Circuit Design: Hideaki Tai
- Product Design: Tomoaki Yanagisawa, Toshitaka Mochizuki
- Technical Support: Saki Ishikawa, Noriko Ishizuka, Nanami Tanaka
- Co-Development: Rhizomatiks & Evixar Inc.

———————————

Daito Manabe 《morphechore》
- Motion Capture Dancer and Choreographer: Shingo Okamoto

- Supervisor: MIKIKO (ELEVENPLAY)
- Music Co-producer: Hopebox

─────────────

やくしまるえつこメトロオーケストラ "ノルニル"
ミュージックビデオ
- Music: Yakushimaru Etsuko Metro Orchestra "nornir"
- Produce: Yakushimaru Etsuko
- Music and Lyrics: Tica α (a.k.a Yakushimaru Etsuko)
- –
- Cast: Yakushimaru Etsuko
- Direction: Daito Manabe
- Lighting Programming: Daito Manabe
- Visual Programming: Satoru Higa
- Visual Programming (web): Satoshi Horii
- Rail Design: Youichi Sakamoto
- Hardware Programming: Motoi Ishibashi
- Production Support: Muryo Homma

─────────────

やくしまるえつこ "ロンリープラネット（Post）"
ミュージックビデオ
- Music: Yakushimaru Etsuko "Lonely Planet (Post)"
- Produce: Yakushimaru Etsuko
- Music and Lyrics: Tica α (a.k.a Yakushimaru Etsuko)
- –
- Visual Direction: Daito Manabe
- Technical Direction: Motoi Ishibashi
- Video: Muryo Homma

─────────────

Daito Manabe + Motoi Ishibashi
《proportion》
- Music: Yakushimaru Etsuko Metro Orchestra "boys, come back to me"
- Produce: Yakushimaru Etsuko
- Music and Lyrics: Tica α (a.k.a Yakushimaru Etsuko)
- –
- Director, Visual and Lighting Programming: Daito Manabe
- Robot Motion Design and Programming: Motoi Ishibashi
- Set Design and Mechanical Design: Motoi Ishibashi, Youichi Sakamoto
- Device: Motoi Ishibashi
- Video: Muryo Homma
- Special Thanks: Tomoaki Yanagisawa, Toshitaka Mochizuki, Sayaka Iwamoto
- Cooperation: Color Kinetics Japan

─────────────

やくしまるえつこ＋真鍋大度＋石橋素＋菅野薫
《LOVE+1+1》
- Words, Music, Voice, Appearance: Yakushimaru Etsuko
- Concept and programming: Daito Manabe
- Robot arm programming: Motoi Ishibashi
- Data mining: Kaoru Sugano

─────────────

Red Bull Music Academy × Rhizomatiks
《The Human Sized Synthesizer》
- Client: REDBULL
- Creative Direction: Seiichi Saito (Rhizomatiks)

- Technical Direction, Programmer: Daito Manabe (Rhizomatiks)
- Project Management: Ikumi Hirata (Rhizomatiks)
- Project Management: Ayako Watanabe (Rhizomatiks)
- Sound Production: Setsuya Kurotaki (Rhizomatiks)
- Visual Programmer: Satoshi Horii (Rhizomatiks)
- Hardware Production: Tatsuya Motoki (Rhizomatiks)
- Creative Producer, Product Design, Interface Design: Keitaro Shimizu (Rhizomatiks)
- Film: GROUNDRIDDIM
- Live Performance: DJ UPPERCUT (GROUNDRIDDIM), Yoshiteru Himuro, Setsuya Kurotaki (Rhizomatiks)

─────────────

Björk "Mouth Mantra" ミュージックビデオ
- 360 Technical & Visual Development: Rhizomatiks Research
- 360 Technical & Visual Development Director: Daito Manabe
- 360 Technical Development: Yuya Hanai, Muryo Homma
- *Only the credits for Rhizomatiks are listed.

─────────────

Timo Maas "Tantra" ミュージックビデオ
- Creative Director, Software Engineer: Daito Manabe (Rhizomatiks Research)
- Hardware Engineer: Motoi Ishibashi (Rhizomatiks Research)
- Video Director: Muryo Homma (Rhizomatiks Research)
- Installation Designer: Youichi Sakamoto (Rhizomatiks Research)

─────────────

Squarepusher × Z MACHINES
- Movie Director: Daito Manabe (Rhizomatiks Research)

─────────────

Squarepusher "Terminal Slam"
ミュージックビデオ
- Director, Glitch Effects and Interaction Designer: Daito Manabe (Rhizomatiks)
- Film and Editing Director: Kenichiro Shimizu (PELE)
- Machine Learning Engineer: Yuta Asai (Rhizomatiks)
- Video Export Tool Developer: 2bit
- Effects Artist: Aya Takamatsu (Rhizomatiks)
- Ad Graphic Designer: Kaori Fujii (Rhizomatiks)
- CG Director: Junichi Ebe (Freelance)
- Effects Supervisors: Kenta Katsuno (+ Ring), Takeshi Ozaki (+ Ring)
- Effects Artists: Mikita Arai (Freelance), Masaki Takahashi (Freelance)
- Digital Artists: Yuki Hirakawa (+ Ring), Yu Onishi (+ Ring), Kenta Hasegawa (+ Ring), Ayaka Yamaguchi (+ Ring), Takeya Kamimura (+ Ring), Ryuichi Ono (Freelance)
- –

- CG Producer: Toshihiko Sakata (+ Ring)
- VFX Artist: Yoshinobu Okino (Nomad)
- Colorlist: Felipe Szulc (Nomad)
- Cinematographer: Kazuki Takano (TRIVAL)
- Cinematographer, Operator: Takuya Higa (Cyanworksandfilms)
- MIDI Data Designer: Kyoko Koyama
- –
- Cast: SARA (ELEVENPLAY)
- Film Producer: Chikako Nagai (PELE)
- Producer: Takao Inoue (Rhizomatiks)

─────────────

Nosaj Thing "Eclipse Blue" ミュージックビデオ
- Creative Direction, Technical Direction, Programming: Daito Manabe
- Movie Direction: takcom
- Choreography: MIKIKO
- Programming: Satoru Higa (Rhizomatiks)
- Software Manipulation: Motoi Ishibashi (Rhizomatiks)
- Produce: P.I.C.S.
- Support: Rhizomatiks and Creators Project

Flying Lotus Presents "The Hit"
- Music: Nosaj Thing, Daito Manabe
- –
- Visuals: Satoshi Horii
- Visuals: You Tanaka
- Visuals: Yuta Asai
- Depth Recording System: 2bit
- –
- Project Management: Naoki Ishizuka
- *Only the credits for Rhizomatiks are listed.

─────────────

Nosaj Thing "Cold Stares ft. Chance The Rapper + The O'My's" ミュージックビデオ
- Creative Director, Technical Director: Daito Manabe (Rhizomatiks Research)
- Video Director: TAKCOM
- Choreographer: MIKIKO (ELEVENPLAY)
- Cast: Kaori Yasukawa (ELEVENPLAY), Erisa Wakisaka (ELEVENPLAY)
- Technical Director, Hardware Designer, Hardware Engineer: Motoi Ishibashi (Rhizomatiks Research)
- –
- Computer Vision Programmer: Yuya Hanai (Rhizomatiks Research)
- Drone Engineer: Katsuhiko Harada (Rhizomatiks Research), Momoko Nishimoto (Rhizomatiks Research), Youichi Sakamoto (Rhizomatiks Research), Tomoaki Yanagisawa (Rhizomatiks Research)
- Video Producer: Takahiko Kajima (P.I.C.S.)
- Video Production Manager: Syuhei Harada (P.I.C.S.)
- –
- CG Designer: Akira Miwa (McRAY), Kohki Okuyama (McRAY)
- CG Producer: Akira Iio (McRAY)
- 3D Scan and Motion Capture System: Crescent, inc.
- Costume Designer: Yae-pon

─────────────

Ryuichi Sakamoto + Daito Manabe

《センシング・ストリームズ—不可視、不可聴》
- Technical Support
- Sound Programming: Satoshi Hama
- Software Development: Satoru Higa, Yusuke Tomoto
- Hardware Development: Katsuhiko Harada
- Web Site: Hirock Kimura, Keiichiro Watanabe
- English Translation: Neo Sora
- Special Thanks: Motoi Ishibashi, Tomohiro Takahashi, Kyle McDonald, Misaki Horai

————————

Ryuichi Sakamoto: Playing the Piano 12122020
- [Virtual System and Visual Production]
- Director: DAITO MANABE (Rhizomatiks)
- UE4 Engineer: Tatsuya Ishii (Rhizomatiks)
- Realtime Keying System Engineer: Yuya Hanai (Rhizomatiks)
- Visual Programming Engineer: Futa Kera (Rhizomatiks)
- CG Engineer: Aya Takamatsu (Rhizomatiks)
- Video Engineer: Muryo Homma (Rhizomatiks)
- Technical Support: Shintaro Kamijo (Rhizomatiks)
- Camera Assistant: Shizuo Takahashi
- Project Manager: Naoki Ishizuka (Rhizomatiks)
- Producer: Takao Inoue (Rhizomatiks)
- *Only the credits for Rhizomatiks are listed.

————————

OK Go "Obsession" ミュージックビデオ
- Technical Team: Rhizomatiks Research
- Planning, Technical Direction, Software Design, Software Engineering: Daito Manabe
- System Design, Circuit Design, Technical Direction: Motoi Ishibashi
- Software Engineering: Satoshi Horii, Yusuke Tomoto, Shintaro Kamijo, Sadam Fujioka
- Hardware Engineering: Youichi Sakamoto, Toshitaka Mochizuki, Yuta Asai, Saki Ishikawa, Kyohei Mouri
- Simulator Production: Setsuya Kurotaki, Sadakazu Kato
- Producer: Hidenori Chiba
- Assistant Producer: Ichiro Mishima
- *Only the credits for Rhizomatiks are listed.

————————

サカナクション SAKANAQUARIUM 光 ONLINE "ワンダーランド" "ミュージック"
- Visual Effect: Daito Manabe
- Software Engineering: Yuta Asai
- Technical Support: Kyohei Mouri
- Project Management: Naoki Ishizuka
- Produce: Takao Inoue
- *Only the credits for Rhizomatiks are listed.

————————

NHKスペシャル NEXT WORLD
私たちの未来 – 特設Webサイト SYMPHONY
- Art Director, Designer: Hiroyasu Kimura
- *Only the credits for Rhizomatiks Design are listed.

————————

Rio 2016 Flag Handover Ceremony to Tokyo 2020
- Technical Direction and Visual Direction: Daito Manabe
- Technical Direction and LED Props Development: Motoi Ishibashi
- AR System Development: Yuya Hanai
- Field Simulator Development: Yusuke Tomoto
- Visual Programming: Satoshi Horii, You Tanaka
- LED Props Development: Hideaki Tai, Momoko Nishimoto, Tomoaki Yanagisawa, Katsuhiko Harada
- Operation: Shintaro Kamijo
- Technical Support: Muryo Homma, Toshitaka Mochizuki, Saki Ishikawa, Kyohei Mouri, Youichi Sakamoto, Yuta Asai
- *Only the credits for Rhizomatiks are listed.

————————

Mansai Nomura × Daito Manabe《FORM》
- Stage Performance, General Direction: Mansai Nomura
- Stage Performance: Yoshimasa Kanzei (Kanzeiryu Shitehou) and others
- Visual Performance: Daito Manabe (Rhizomatiks Research)
- Sound Performance: evala
- Lighting Performance: Kinsei Fujimoto (Dumb Type/Kinsei R&D)

————————

野村萬斎 MANSAI ◉ 解体新書
その参百 特別版『5W1H』
- Planned by Mansai Nomura
- Visual Design, Technical Direction: Daito Manabe, Motoi Ishibashi, Rhizomatiks Research
- Music: Daito Manabe + Hopebox
- Cast: Mansai Nomura, Yuichi Otsuki, Mansaku no kai
- Venue: Setagaya Public Theatre

————————

Rhizomatiks Research, ANREALAGE, ダイアログ・イン・ザ・ダーク《echo》
- Creative Direction: Daito Manabe (Rhizomatiks Research)
- Technical Direction: Motoi Ishibashi (Rhizomatiks Research)
- Wear Design: Kunihiko Morinaga (ANREALAGE)
- Project Attend: Akira Hiyama (Dialog In The Dark)
- Project Direction: Noriaki Shimura (ANREALAGE)
- echo Device: Hideaki Tai (Rhizomatiks Research)
- Space Design: Tatsuya Motoki (Rhizomatiks Architecture)
- Sound Design: Setsuya Kurotaki (Rhizomatiks Research)
- Product Design: Toshitaka Mochizuki (Rhizomatiks Research), Saki Ishikawa (Rhizomatiks Research)
- Web Design: Hiroyasu Kimura (Rhizomatiks Design), Kaori Fujii (Rhizomatiks Design)

————————

- Web Programming: You Tanaka (Rhizomatiks Research)
- Movie Direction: Tomoyuki Kujirai (juke)
- Project Management: Miyu Hosoi
- Planning: Kenta Suzuki
- Production: Emi Komatsu (ANREALAGE)
- Key Visual: Masaya Muto (NO DESIGN)
- –
- Interpreter: Natsumi Wada
- –
- Support: Xenoma Inc. / Mitsui Chemicals, Inc. / MEIWA GRAVURE CO., LTD / Randez-vous Project Yokohama Committee / SLOW LABEL (Specified Nonprofit Corporation)
- –
- Co-organizer: Miraikan -The National Museum of Emerging Science and Innovation

————————

Dolce&Gabbana Fall Winter 2018/19 Women's Fashion Show ドローン演出
- Technical & Creative Direction: Motoi Ishibashi
- Hardware Engineering: Momoko Nishimoto, Toshitaka Mochizuki, Saki Ishikawa, Muryo Homma, Shintaro Kamijo
- Drone Motion Design: Tatsuya Ishii
- Motion Capture: Yoshitaka Homma (Crescent)

————————

エイブルpresents第73回全日本フェンシング選手権大会 Fencing Visualized Project
- Technical Direction, System Development, Software Engineering: Yuya Hanai
- Planning, Creative Direction: Daito Manabe
- Planning, Technical Direction, Hardware Engineering: Motoi Ishibashi
- Software Engineering: Kyle McDonald (IYOIYO)
- Software Engineering: Kisaku Tanaka (anno lab)
- Visual Programming: Satoshi Horii
- Visual Programming: Futa Kera
- Sound Operation: Shintaro Kamijo
- Videographer: Muryo Homma
- Hardware Engineering&Videographer Support: Toshitaka Mochizuki
- Videographer Support: Shizuo Takahashi
- Hardware Engineering: Kyohei Mouri
- Project Management: Kahori Takemura
- Project Management, Produce: Takao Inoue

————————

White Mountaineering × Rhizomatiks《White Mountaineering | 2021 Spring / Summer Collection Paris Fashion Week©》
- Collection Movie and Music Directed by Daito Manabe (Rhizomatiks)
- Telop Designer: Kaori Fujii (Rhizomatiks)
- Production Manager: Kahori Takemura (Rhizomatiks)
- PR, Administrator: Momoko Aoyagi, Kaori Hashimoto (Rhizomatiks)
- Producer: Takao Inoue (Rhizomatiks)
- *Only the credits for Rhizomatiks are listed.

ThermoArt by DAITO MANABE | UNIQLO HEATTECH JP |
- Technical Direction, System Design, Visual Effect: Daito Manabe (Rhizomatiks)
- System Development, Software Engineering: Yuya Hanai (Rhizomatiks)
- Thermal Camera Calibrationboard Supervise: Motoi Ishibashi (Rhizomatiks)
- Thermal Camera Calibrationboard Engineering: Kyohei Mouri (Rhizomatiks)
- Video Engineering: Muryo Honma (Rhizomatiks)
- Instagram AR Filter Development: Futa Kera (Rhizomatiks)
- Project Management: Kahori Takemura (Rhizomatiks)
- Produce: Takao Inoue (Rhizomatiks)

Arca "Mutant; Faith"
- Guest Artist and Custom Technology Development: Daito Manabe
- *Only the credits for Rhizomatiks are listed.

KAZU "Come Behind Me, So Good! (Official video by Daito Manabe + Kenichiro Shimizu)"
- Director: Daito Manabe (Rhizomatiks)
- Technical Director: Motoi Ishibashi (Rhizomatiks)
- Technical Support: Muryo Homma (Rhizomatiks)
- Production Manager: Kahori Takemura (Rhizomatiks)
- Production Coordinator: Rina Watanabe (Rhizomatiks)
- Producer: Takao Inoue (Rhizomatiks)
- *Only the credits for Rhizomatiks are listed.

YOKO KANNO SEATBELTS「オンライン七夕まつり」"Inner Universe" 映像演出
- Creative & Technical Direction + 3D Scan: Daito Manabe (Rhizomatiks)
- Direction: Tetsuka Niiyama (Freelance)
- CG Design: Shingo Horiuchi (Awaya LLC)
- Technical Support: Muryo Homma (Rhizomatiks)
- Production Management: Kahori Takemura (Rhizomatiks)
- Produce: Takao Inoue (Rhizomatiks)

DJ Krush × Daito Manabe《CONNECTED WORLD》
- [AUDIO VISUAL Special Showcase]
- Visual: Daito Manabe
- [Team Rhizomatiks]
- UE4 Engineering: Tatsuya Ishii
- Realtime Keying System Development: Yuya Hanai
- Visual Programming: Satoshi Horii, Futa Kera
- CG Engineering: Aya Takamatsu
- Video Engineering: Muryo Homma
- Technical Support: Shintaro Kamijo
- Project Management & Translator: Naoki

Ishizuka
- PR: Momoko Aoyagi
Key Visual: Hiroyasu Kimura, Miku Maruno
- Producer: Takao Inoue
- *Only the credits for Rhizomatiks are listed.

Rhizomatiks《Staying TOKYO》
- Rhizomatiks

非同期テック部
- Tsuyoshi Muro, Daito Manabe, Makoto Ueda

ELEVENPLAY《dot.》
- Direction and Choreography by MIKIKO + TOMO
- Software Programing: Daito Manabe, Satoru Higa
- Device Design and Programming: Motoi Ishibashi
- Device Design Support: Tomoaki Yanagisawa And Mocchi
- Lighting Design: Takayuki Fujimoto (dumbtype)
- Music: Ametsub (iPad scene)
- Visual Design: Kazuaki Seki
- Sound Manipulation: KSK
- Video Shooting: Muryo Homma
- Video Projection Support: Aircord
- Led Equipment Support: Color Kinetics Japan

ELEVENPLAY × Rhizomatiks《shape》
- Direction: MIKIKO + Daito Manabe
- Dance: elevenplay
- Choreography and LED Jockey: MIKIKO
- Music: ametsub
- Visual: Daito Manabe
- Computer Vision: Satoru Higa
- LED Support: color kinetics japan
- Supported by Rhizomatiks and YCAM

ELEVENPLAY × Rhizomatiks《cube》
- Direction: MIKIKO + Daito Manabe
- Dance: elevenplay
- Choreography and Led Jockey: MIKIKO
- Music: ametsub
- Visual: takcom
- Computer Vision Programming: Satoru Higa
- Programming: Daito Manabe
- Visual Produced by P.I.C.S.

ELEVENPLAY × Rhizomatiks《ray》
- Direction, Choreography and Led Jockey: MIKIKO (ELEVENPLAY)
- Direction and Programming: Daito Manabe (Rhizomatiks)
- Robot Arm Programming: Motoi Ishibashi (Rhizomatiks)
- Dance: Aya Kohmen (ELEVENPLAY), Erisa Wakisaka (ELEVENPLAY), Kaori Yasukawa (ELEVENPLAY)
- Music: Taeji Sawai

ELEVENPLAY × Rhizomatiks Research《fly》
- Artistic Direction and Choreograph: MIKIKO (elevenplay)
- Music: Ametsub
- Dancer: YUKA NUMATA and ERISA WAKISAKA (elevenplay)
- Artistic Direction and Drone + Light Programming: Daito Manabe (Rhizomatiks)
- Light Drone Design and Development: Motoi Ishibashi, Tomoaki Yanagisawa, Momoko Nishimoto
- Light Drone Development: Tomoaki Yanagisawa, Youichi Sakamoto, Katsuhiko Harada
- Support: Rhizomatiks, elevenplay and P.I.C.S.
- Light Device Development Support: Color kinetics
- Developed for MOSAIC 2015

ELEVENPLAY × Rhizomatiks《right brain》
- Artistic Direction + Choreography: MIKIKO (elevenplay)
- Artistic Direction + Technical Direction: Daito Manabe (Rhizomatiks)
- Computer Vision Programming: Yuya Hanai (Rhizomatiks)
- Visual Programming + Motion Graphic Design: Satoru Higa
- Camera: Muryo Homma (Rhizomatiks)
- Music: Ametsub

ELEVENPLAY × Rhizomatiks Research《shadow》
- Artistic Direction and Choreograph: MIKIKO (elevenplay)
- Music: Ametsub
- Dancer: Kaori Yasukawa (elevenplay)
- Artistic Direction and Drone + Light Programming: Daito Manabe (Rhizomatiks)
- Light Drone Design and Development: Motoi Ishibashi, Tomoaki Yanagisawa
- Light Drone Development: Tomoaki Yanagisawa, Youichi Sakamoto, Katsuhiko Harada, Momoko Nishimoto
- Drone Support: Enroute
- Support: Rhizomatiks, elevenplay and P.I.C.S.
- Light Device Development Support: Color kinetics
- Developed for Showcase at Interbee 2014

ELEVENPLAY × Rhizomatiks Research《24 drones》
- Artistic Direction and Choreograph: MIKIKO (ELEVENPLAY)
- Music: Setsuya Kurotaki (Rhizomatiks Research)
- Dancer: SAYA SHINOHARA (ELEVENPLAY), YUKA NUMATA (ELEVENPLAY), ERISA WAKISAKA (ELEVENPLAY)
- Artistic Direction and Drone + Light Programming: Daito Manabe (Rhizomatiks

Research)
- Drone Design and Development: Motoi Ishibashi (Rhizomatiks Research), Momoko Nishimoto (Rhizomatiks Research), Tomoaki Yanagisawa (Rhizomatiks Research)
- Drone Light Sphere Design: Katsuhiko Harada (Rhizomatiks Research)
- Support: Rhizomatiks and ELEVENPLAY
- Motion Capture System: Crescent, inc.

———————————

ELEVENPLAY × Rhizomatiks Research 《border 2021》
- Organizers: Agency for Cultural Affairs Visual Industry Promotion Organization (VIPO), Rhizomatiks
- Planning and Operation: Visual Industry Promotion Organization (VIPO), Rhizomatiks
- –
- Technical Development, Visual Production: Rhizomatiks
- Creative Direction, Technical Direction, Software Engineering: Daito Manabe (Rhizomatiks)
- Technical Direction, Hardware Engineering: Motoi Ishibashi (Rhizomatiks)
- MR System Engineering: Yuya Hanai (Rhizomatiks)
- Visual Programming: Satoshi Horii (Rhizomatiks), Futa Kera (Rhizomatiks)
- Hardware Engineering: Katsuhiko Harada (Rhizomatiks), Hideaki Tai (Rhizomatiks)
- Fabrication: Toshitaka Mochizuki (Rhizomatiks), Kyohei Mouri (Rhizomatiks), Saki Ishikawa (Rhizomatiks)
- Motion Capture System: Momoko Nishimoto (Rhizomatiks)
- Operation Support: Naoki Ishizuka (Rhizomatiks)
- Technical Support: Muryo Homma (Rhizomatiks), Shintaro Kamijo (Rhizomatiks), Shino Higuchi
- –
- PR Design: Hiroyasu Kimura (Rhizomatiks),Kaori Fuji (Rhizomatiks), Miku Maruno (Rhizomatiks)
- Web Front-End Development: Hirofumi Tsukamoto (Rhizomatiks), Kentaro Mito (armsnox)
- Web Back-End Development: Tatsuya Takemasa (Rhizomatiks)
- Entrance Design: Takahito Hosono (Rhizomatiks)
- –
- PR: Momoko Aoyagi (Rhizomatiks)
- Project Management: Kahori Takemura (Rhizomatiks)
- Producer: Takao Inoue (Rhizomatiks)
- *Only the credits for Rhizomatiks are listed.

———————————

Rhizomatiks 《border installation ver.》
- Creative Director, Technical Director: Daito Manabe (Rhizomatiks Research)
- Technical Director, Hardware Engineer:

Motoi Ishibashi (Rhizomatiks Research)
- AR Engineer: Yuya Hanai (Rhizomatiks Research)
- Visual Programmer: Satoshi Horii (Rhizomatiks Research)
- Composer, Sound Programmer: evala
- Light Designer: Takayuki Fujimoto (Kinsei R&D)
- Software Engineer: Yusuke Tomoto (Rhizomatiks Research)
- Hardware Engineer: Katsuhiko Harada (Rhizomatiks Research)
- Craft: Toshitaka Mochizuki (Rhizomatiks Research), Youichi Sakamoto (Rhizomatiks Research)
- Support received from
- Special Support: WHILL Inc.
- Headphone Provider: Sony Marketing (Japan) Inc.
- Support on 3D Scan and Motion Capture: Crescent inc.
- Support on Lighting Equipment: Color Kinetics Japan Inc., Pi
- supported by YCAM

———————————

Rhizomatiks Research × ELEVENPLAY 《phosphere》
- Visual Direction, Technical Direction: Daito Manabe (Rhizomatiks Research)
- Technical Direction, Hardware Engineering: Motoi Ishibashi (Rhizomatiks Research)
- Visual Programming: Satoshi Horii (Rhizomatiks Research)
- Projection System, Software Engineering: Yuya Hanai (Rhizomatiks Research)
- Space Design: Takahito Hosono (Rhizomatiks Architecture)
- Technical Production Manager: Shintaro Kamijo (Rhizomatiks Research)
- Craft: Toshitaka Mochizuki, Saki Ishikawa (Rhizomatiks Research)
- Technical Support: Muryo Homma, Tomoaki Yanagisawa, Katsuhiko Harada, Momoko Nishimoto (Rhizomatiks Research)
- Art Director: Hiroyasu Kimura (Rhizomatiks Design)
- Designer: Ichiro Kojima, Kaori Fujii (Rhizomatiks Design)
- Web Programming: Hirofumi Tsukamoto (Rhizomatiks Design)
- Producer: Hidenori Chiba (Rhizomatiks)
- Planned and Produced by Spiral, Rhizomatiks co., ltd.
- *Only the credits for Rhizomatiks are listed.

LEXUS DESIGN EVENT 2019 | LEADING WITH LIGHT
- Cast: YU (ELEVENPLAY), SARA (ELEVENPLAY), Greta Cisternimo
- –
- Art Direction, Music, Lighting, Interaction Design, Software Engineering: Daito Manabe (Rhizomatiks)
- Technical Direction Hardware Engineering: Motoi Ishibashi (Rhizomatiks)

- Hardware Engineering, Craft: Youichi Sakamoto (Rhizomatiks), Hideaki Tai (Rhizomatiks), Kyohei Mouri (Rhizomatiks), Yuta Asai (Rhizomatiks)
- Choreographer: MIKIKO
- Motion Performer: ELEVENPLAY
- Music: Daito Manabe (Rhizomatiks), Hopebox
- Lighting Technical Support: Kunio Tamada (TamaTech Lab.)
- Technical Support: Tomoaki Yanagisawa (Rhizomatiks), Tatsuya Ishii (Rhizomatiks), Momoko Nishimoto (Rhizomatiks), Toshitaka Mochizuki (Rhizomatiks), Saki Ishikawa (Rhizomatiks)
- Production Management: Yoko Shiraiwa (ELEVENPLAY)
- Space Design: Takahito Hosono (Rhizomatiks)
- Produce: Keitaro Shimizu (Rhizomatiks)
- Support: Ayumi Ota (Rhizomatiks), Eri Suzuko (Rhizomatiks), Muryo Homma (Rhizomatiks), Shintaro Kamijo (Rhizomatiks)
- –
- Special Support: Mitsui Chemicals, Inc.
- Planning and Production: Rhizomatiks

———————————

Rhizomatiks Research × ELEVENPLAY × Kyle McDonald 《discrete figures》
- Cast: ELEVENPLAY
- Stage Direction, Choreography: MIKIKO
- Artistic Direction, Music: Daito Manabe (Rhizomatiks Research)
- Technical Direction, Hardware Engineering: Motoi Ishibashi (Rhizomatiks Research)
- Machine Learning Direction: Kyle McDonald
- Machine Learning: Yuta Asai (Rhizomatiks Research)
- Projection System, Software Engineering: Yuya Hanai (Rhizomatiks Research)
- Visualization: Satoshi Horii (Rhizomatiks Research)
- Visualization: You Tanaka (Rhizomatiks Research)
- CG Direction: Tetsuka Niiyama (+ Ring / TaiyoKikaku Co., Ltd.)
- CG Produce: Toshihiko Sakata (+ Ring / TaiyoKikaku Co., Ltd.)
- Music: seiho, Setsuya Kurotaki (Rhizomatiks Research), "hanabi" by kotringo
- Videographer: Muryo Homma (Rhizomatiks Research)
- Stage Engineering: Momoko Nishimoto (Rhizomatiks Research)
- Motion Capture: Tatsuya Ishii (Rhizomatiks Research), Saki Ishikawa (Rhizomatiks Research)
- 4D-VIEWS: Crescent, inc.
- Technical Support: Shintaro Kamijo (Rhizomatiks Research)
- Craft: Tomoaki Yanagisawa (Rhizomatiks Research), Toshitaka Mochizuki (Rhizomatiks Research), Kyohei Mouri

- Production Management: Yoko Shiraiwa (ELEVENPLAY), Nozomi Yamaguchi (Rhizomatiks Research), Ayumi Ota (Rhizomatiks Research), Rina Watanabe (Rhizomatiks Research)
- Produce: Takao Inoue (Rhizomatiks Research)
- Production: Rhizomatiks co., ltd.

————————————

ELEVENPLAY × Rhizomatiks 《S．P．A．C．E．》
- Music Main: KAZU - Salty // Nosaj Thing Remix
- Music Intro: Daito Manabe (Rhizomatiks)
- Creative and Technical Director: Daito Manabe (Rhizomatiks)
- Choreographer: MIKIKO (ELEVENPLAY)
- Dancer: SAYA (ELEVENPLAY), KOHMEN (ELEVENPLAY), KAORI (ELEVENPLAY), MARU (ELEVENPLAY), YU (ELEVENPLAY), EMMY (ELEVENPLAY), NANAKO (ELEVENPLAY), SHOKO (ELEVENPLAY), MAI (ELEVENPLAY)
- –
- Machine Learning Engineer: Yuta Asai (Rhizomatiks)
- Visual Programmer: You Tanaka (Rhizomatiks)
- Videographer + Editor: Muryo Homma (Rhizomatiks)
- Stylist: Shinichi Mitter (KiKi inc.), YAEPON, SAQULAI, Inc
- Location Coordinator: Yoko Ishidate (Freelance), Kei Terayama, Satsuki Sato, Zhang Ruijun (THINKR)
- Behind The Scene Videographer + Editor: Tokuhiro Yasukawa, Ubuna Hamasaki (Freelance)
- Sound Operator: Naoki OhnishI (SOUND CREW)
- Project Manager: Kahori Takemura, Naoki Ishizuka (Rhizomatiks)
- Producer: Takao Inoue (Rhizomatiks)

————————————

Perfume 《結成10周年、メジャーデビュー5周年記念！Perfume LIVE @東京ドーム「1 2 3 4 5 6 7 8 9 10 11」》
- Video Programming: Zachary Lieberman (openFrameworks, yesyesno), Daito Manabe (Rhizomatiks, 4nchor5 La6)
- Interactive Crew: Daito Manabe (Rhizomatiks, 4nchor5 La6), Alex Beim (Tangible interaction), Motoi Ishibashi, Tomoaki Yanagisawa, Kanta Horio, Kazuto Wakatsuki (4nchor5 La6), Seiichi Saito, Katsuhiko Harada, Muryo Homma, Hiroyuki Hori, Ichiro Kojima (Rhizomatiks), 2bit, Takashi Suzuki (buffer Renaiss)
- *Only the credits for Rhizomatiks are listed.

————————————

Daito Manabe / MIKIKO / Yasutaka Nakata / Satoshi Horii/ Hiroyasu Kimura 《Perfume global site project #001》
- Planning, Direction, Programming: Daito Manabe (Rhizomatiks)

- Choreography, Supervision: MIKIKO
- Music: Yasutaka Nakata (capsule)
- Website Creative Programming: Satoshi Horii (Rhizomatiks)
- Website Art Direction, Design: Hiroyasu Kimura (Rhizomatiks)
- Website Programming: 2bit (bufferRenaiss)
- Server Engineer: Daisuke Nakahama (Rhizomatiks)
- Markup Engineer: Kentaro Mito (RaD)
- Programming: Satoru Higa (Rhizomatiks), Hiroyuki Hori (Rhizomatiks)
- Planning: AMUSE Inc., UNIVERSAL MUSIC LLC
- Support: Rhizomatiks, 4nchor5 La6, Takahiko Kajima (P.I.C.S.), Yasushi Fukuzawa, Tasuku Mizuno (Creative Commons Japan)
- ©Rhizomatiks co., ltd. + AMUSE Inc. + UNIVERSAL MUSIC LLC

————————————

Perfume 《Perfume 3rd Tour「JPN」"Spring of Life"》
- Software Development: Daito Manabe, Satoru Higa (Rhizomatiks)
- Interaction Design, Visual Programming & Wearable Lighting Design: Daito Manabe (Rhizomatiks, 4nchor5 La6)
- Visual Programming: Satoru Higa (Rhizomatiks, 4nchor5 La6)
- Wearable Device Design & Programming: Tomoaki Yanagisawa (Rhizomatiks, 4nchor5 La6)
- Wearable Device Firmware & Programming: Motoi Ishibashi (Rhizomatiks, 4nchor5 La6)
- Wearable Device Support: Muryo Homma (Rhizomatiks)
- *Only the credits for Rhizomatiks are listed.

————————————

Rhizomatiks 《Physicalizing Data by Rhizomatiks Inspired by Perfume》
- Creative + Technical Director, Producer: Daito Manabe
- Producer: Seiichi Saito
- Production: Rhizomatiks
- Plan: Amuse + Universal Music
- Technical Support: studio TED powered by SPIN Inc., K'S DESIGN LAB
- Modeling Support: Yasojima Proceed Co., Ltd., NTT DATA ENGINEERING SYSTEMS Corporation
- Construction Support: U.C.S Co., Ltd., AMARTERRANCE
- Production Support: P.I.C.S.
- Video Production: McRAY CG, Daihei Shibata + Hiroshi Sato
- Sound Design: Taeji Sawai (Qosmo)
- Equipment Support: Canon Inc.

————————————

Rhizomatiks 《Rhizomatiks inspired by Perfume》
- Organizer: NTT InterCommunication Center [ICC]
- Cooperation: Rhizomatiks co., ltd., AMUSE Inc., UNIVERSAL MUSIC LLC

- –
- Supervisor: MIKIKO (elevenplay)
- Costume Cooperation: MITER Shinichi, TAKEDA Toshio
- 3D Scan, Printing Cooperation: K's Design Lab.
- Holographic Systems Cooperation: Studio TED | Spin Inc.
- Movie Cooperation: P.I.C.S.
- –

————————————

Rhizomatiks 《Perfume WORLD TOUR 2nd "Spending All My Time" Dynamic projection system》
- Interaction Design & Technical Support: Daito Manabe, Motoi Ishibashi, Tomoaki Yanagisawa, Youichi Sakamoto (Rhizomatiks, 4nchor5 La6), Hiroyasu Kimura, Muryo Homma, Satoshi Horii, Satoru Higa, Yusuke Tomoto (Rhizomatiks), Tsubito Ishii (buffer Renaiss), Kentaro Mito (RAD), Kimura (TASCO)
- *Only the credits for Rhizomatiks are listed.

————————————

Perfume 《Perfume Cannes Lions International Festival of Creativity》
- Artist, Programmer: Daito Manabe (Rhizomatiks)
- [Interactive system]
- Programmer: Satoru Higa (Rhizomatiks)
- Hardware Engineer/Designer: Motoi Ishibashi (Rhizomatiks)
- Wearable Device Design/Development: Tomoaki Yanagisawa (Rhizomatiks)
- Installation Support: Yoichi Sakamoto (Rhizomatiks)
- *Only the credits for Rhizomatiks are listed.

————————————

Perfume 《Perfume 4th Tour in DOME「LEVEL3」》
- Technical Support & Interaction Design: Daito Manabe, Motoi Ishibashi, Tomoaki Yanagisawa (Rhizomatiks, 4nchor5 La6), Satoru Higa, Satoshi Horii, Hirock Kimura, Hiroyuki Hori, Muryo Honma, Youichi Sakamoto, Yusuke Tomoto, Tatsuya Takemasa (Rhizomatiks), 2bit (buffer Renaiss)
- *Only credits for Rhizomatiks Research are listed.

————————————

Perfume 《Perfume WORLD》
- Art Director, Designer: Hiroyasu Kimura
- Programmer, Designer: Satoshi Horii
- * Only the credits for Rhizomatiks are listed.

————————————

Perfume 《Perfume 5th Tour 2014「ぐるんぐるん」》
- Technical Support & Interaction Design: Daito Manabe, Motoi Ishibashi, Tomoaki Yanagisawa (Rhizomatiks, 4nchor5 La6), Satoru Higa, Satoshi Horii, Hirock Kimura, Hiroyuki Hori, Muryo Honma, Youichi Sakamoto, Yusuke Tomoto, Tatsuya

Takemasa (Rhizomatiks), 2bit (buffer Renaiss)

- * Only the credits for Rhizomatiks are listed.

————————————

Perfume / MIKIKO / Yasutaka Nakata / Daito Manabe / Yuya　Hanai / Motoi Ishibashi / Satoshi Horii/ Kaoru Sugano 《Perfume live "SXSW 2015"》

- Stage Direction, Movie Direction and Choreograph: MIKIKO (elevenplay)
- Technical Direction and Programming: Daito Manabe (Rhizomatiks)
- Produce, Creative Direction: Kaoru Sugano (dentsu)
- Camera System Development and Programming: Yuya Hanai (Rhizomatiks)
- Technical Direction: Motoi Ishibashi (Rhizomatiks)
- Technical Support: Crescent, Inc. and Ray Corporation

————————————

30周年記念特別番組 MUSIC STATION ウルトラFES 2016 Perfume "Spending all my time" Dynamic VR Display

- Direction + Choreograph: MIKIKO
- Visual + System: Rhizomatiks Research

————————————

【docomo×Perfume】FUTURE-EXPERIMENT VOL. 01 距離をなくせ。

- [WEB SITE]
- Art Director, Designer: Hiroyasu Kimura (Rhizomatiks Design)
- Frontend Engineer: Hirofumi Tsukamoto (Rhizomatiks Design)
- Technical Director: Tatsuya Takemasa (Rhizomatiks Design)
- [LIVE EVENT—Live Performance]
- Planning & Visual Director & Visual System Designer & Lighting Programmer & Visual System Operator: Daito Manabe (Rhizomatiks Research)
- LED Device Designer and Developer & Visual System Operator: Motoi Ishibashi (Rhizomatiks Research)
- Synchronous System Designer & Visual System Developer & Visual System Operator: Yuya Hanai (Rhizomatiks Research)
- LED Device Developer & Visual System Operator: Momoko Nishimoto (Rhizomatiks Research)
- LED Device Developer & Visual System Operator: Kyohei Mouri (Rhizomatiks Research)
- LED Device Developer & Visual System Operator: Rina Yasukouchi (Rhizomatiks Research)
- LED Device Developer & Visual System Operator: Toshitaka Mochizuki (Rhizomatiks Research)
- LED Device Developer & Visual System Operator: Saki Ishikawa (Rhizomatiks Research)
- LED Device Developer & Visual System

Operator: Tatsuya Motoki (Rhizomatiks Research)
- LED Device Developer & Visual System Operator: Tomoaki Yanagisawa (Rhizomatiks Research)
- Visual Programmer & Visual System Operator: Satoshi Horii (Rhizomatiks Research)
- Visual Programmer & Visual System Operator: You Tanaka (Rhizomatiks Research)
- Synchronous System Developer & Visual System Operator: Ryohei Komiyama (Rhizomatiks Research)
- Camera Engineer & Visual System Operator: Muryo Honma (Rhizomatiks Research)
- Visual System Operator: Setsuya Kurotaki (Rhizomatiks Research)
- Producer & Project Manager & Visual System Operator: Takao Inoue (Rhizomatiks Research)
- Technical Support: Shintaro Kamijo (Rhizomatiks Research)
- Technical Support: Tomoyo Obata (Rhizomatiks Research)
- *Only the credits for Rhizomatiks are listed.

————————————

Perfume 《Perfume×TECHNOLOGY presents Reframe》

- Interaction Design: Rhizomatiks (Daito Manabe, Motoi Ishibashi, Yuya Hanai, Satoshi Horii, You Tanaka, Shintaro Kamijo, Katsuhiko Harada, Tomoaki Yanagisawa, Toshitaka Mochizuki, Momoko Nishimoto, Tatsuya Ishii, Yuta Asai, Saki Ishikawa, Kyohei Mouri, Takao Inoue)
- Sound Effect: Setsuya Kurotaki
- Logo Design: Hiroyasu Kimura, Kaori Fujii
- *Only the credits for Rhizomatiks are listed.

————————————

Perfume 《Reframe 2019》

- Technical & Creative Director: Daito Manabe (Rhizomatiks Research), Motoi Ishibashi (Rhizomatiks Research)
- [Sound Effect]
- Recollect (Reframe2019 ver): evala + Daito Manabe (Rhizomatiks Research)
- Record (Daito Manabe Remix): Setsuya Kurotaki
- Koe – Interlude: Daito Manabe (Rhizomatiks Research)
- Pose – Perspective: Daito Manabe (Rhizomatiks Research)
- Body – Analysis: Daito Manabe (Rhizomatiks Research)
- Kiseki – Visualization: Daito Manabe (Rhizomatiks Research) + Kyoko Koyama
- –
- Interactive Design & System Development: Yuya Hanai (Rhizomatiks Research), Tatsuya Ishii (Rhizomatiks Research), Shintaro Kamijo (Rhizomatiks Research), Katsuhiko Harada (Rhizomatiks Research), Yuta Asai (Rhizomatiks Research), 2Bit, Toshitaka Mochizuki (Rhizomatiks Research),

Kyohei Mouri (Rhizomatiks Research), Saki Ishikawa (Rhizomatiks Research), Aya Takamatsu (Rhizomatiks Research), Kahori Takemura (Rhizomatiks Research), Takao Inoue (Rhizomatiks Research)
- Visualization: Satoshi Horii (Rhizomatiks Research), Futa Kera (Rhizomatiks Research)
- Concert Merchandise Designer: Hiroyasu Kimura (Rhizomatiks Design)
- [CG & Visualization]
- Recollect (Reframe2019 ver): Satoshi Horii + Daito Manabe + Yuta Asai (Rhizomatiks Research)
- Record (Daito Manabe Remix): Satoshi Horii (Rhizomatiks Research)
- Pose – Analysis: Yuta Asai (Rhizomatiks Research) + 2Bit, Tetsuka Niiyama + Shingo Horiuchi (Freelance)
- Body – Analysis: Futa Kera (Rhizomatiks Research) + 2Bit
- MUGENMIRAI: Laser Programming by Yuya Hanai + Daito Manabe (Rhizomatiks Research)
- Challenger (Reframe2019 ver): Satoshi Horii (Rhizomatiks Research) + Kenta Hasegawa + Kenta Katsuno + Toshihiko Sakata (+ Ring)
- *Only the credits for Rhizomatiks are listed.

————————————

【docomo×Perfume】FUTURE-EXPERIMENT VOL. 04 その瞬間を共有せよ。

- [TOTAL PLANNING]
- Planning, Creative Direction: Daito Manabe (Rhizomatiks Research)
- Planning, Technical Direction: Motoi Ishibashi (Rhizomatiks Research)
- [LIVE PEFORMANCE（Yokohama Arena)]
- Planning, Creative Direction, Video Direction, Software Engineering, Laser Programming, FreFlow Programming: Daito Manabe (Rhizomatiks Research)
- Technical Direction, Hardware Engineering (Bangle device): Motoi Ishibashi (Rhizomatiks Research)
- Visual Programming: Satoshi Horii (Rhizomatiks Research)
- Software Engineering: Yuya Hanai, Tatsuya Ishii, Tatsuya Motoki (Rhizomatiks Research)
- Technical Support: Muryo Homma, Shintaro Kamijo, Kyohei Mouri, Saki Ishikawa (Rhizomatiks Research)
- Hardware Engineering (Bangle device): Tomoaki Yanagisawa, Toshitaka Mochizuki, Yuta Asai (Rhizomatiks Research)
- Project Management, Produce: Takao Inoue (Rhizomatiks Research)
- [WEB / Special PTA Corner]
- Producer, Director, Designer: Hiroyasu Kimura (Rhizomatiks Design)
- Technical Direction: Tatsuya Takemasa (Rhizomatiks Design)
- Visual Programming: You Tanaka (Rhizomatiks Research)
- Sound Design: Setsuya Kurotaki (Rhizomatiks Research)

- Frontend Programming: Hirofumi Tsukamoto (Rhizomatiks Design)
- Frontend Programming: Takuya Abe (Rhizomatiks Design)
- *Only the credits for Rhizomatiks are listed.

Perfume 《Perfume Live at Coachella Valley Music and Arts Festival 2019》
- [Interaction design]
- Technical Director, Main Software Engineer: Yuya Hanai (Rhizomatiks)
- Video Engineer: Muryo Homma (Rhizomatiks)
- Software Engineer: Shintaro Kamijo (Rhizomatiks)
- Creative Coding: Futa Kera (Rhizomatiks)
- Moving Track Motion Edit: Tatsuya Ishii (Rhizomatiks)
- Technical Director, Main Hardware Designer, Engineer: Motoi Ishibashi (Rhizomatiks)
- Hardware Engineer: Katsuhiko Harada (Rhizomatiks)
- Craft: Toshitaka Mochizuki (Rhizomatiks)
- Circuit Design: Hideaki Tai (Rhizomatiks)
- Producer, Production Management: Takao Inoue (Rhizomatiks)
- Production Assistant: Kahori Takemura (Rhizomatiks)
- *Only the credits for Rhizomatiks are listed.

Rhizomatiks 《Rhizomatiks inspired by Perfume 2020》
- Venue: PARCO MUSEUM TOKYO
- Organizer: PARCO
- Planning and Production: PARCO, Rhizomatiks
- Cooperation: Amuse, Inc.
- Equipment Cooperation: Canon Marketing Japan Inc.
- –
- Direction: Daito Manabe (Rhizomatiks), Motoi Ishibashi (Rhizomatiks)
- Space Design: Takahito Hosono (Rhizomatiks)
- Project Management: Naoki Ishizuka (Rhizomatiks)
- Produce: Takao Inoue (Rhizomatiks)
- [Flash – Virtual Reality]
- Visual Artist: Satoshi Horii (Rhizomatiks)
- [Tiny Baby – Augmented Reality]
- Visual Programming: Kera Futa (Rhizomatiks)
- [Flash – Immersive Projection]
- Projection System Development: Yuya Hanai (Rhizomatiks)
- Visual Artist: Satoshi Horii (Rhizomatiks)
- [Behind The Scene]
- Technical Setup: Tomoaki Yanagisawa (Rhizomatiks), Hideaki Tai (Rhizomatiks), Toshitaka Mochizuki (Rhizomatiks), Yuta Asai (Rhizomatiks)

Perfume 《Perfume 8th Tour 2020 "P Cubed" in Dome》

[Live Crew]
- Creative Director, Technical Director: Daito Manabe (Rhizomatiks)
- Technical Director: Motoi Ishibashi (Rhizomatiks)
- Visual Programmer: Satoshi Horii, You Tanaka, Futa Kera (Rhizomatiks)
- Software Engineer: Yuta Asai (Rhizomatiks)
- Hardware Engineer: Tomoaki Yanagisawa, Toshitaka Mochizuki, Saki Ishikawa (Rhizomatiks)
- System Operator: Shintaro Kamijo (Rhizomatiks)
- Project Manager: Kahori Takemura (Rhizomatiks)
- Producer: Takao Inoue (Rhizomatiks)
- Sound Effect: Daito Manabe (Rhizomatiks), Kyoko Koyama
- –
- Tour Logo Design: Hiroyasu Kimura (Rhizomatiks)
- *Only the credits for Rhizomatiks are listed.

Perfume 《Perfume Online Present Festival》
- [Perfume Imaginary Museum "Time Warp"]
- Creative & Technical Director: Daito Manabe (Rhizomatiks)
- Museum Designer: Satoshi Horii (Rhizomatiks)
- Technical Director: Motoi Ishibashi, Yuya Hanai (Rhizomatiks)
- Producer: Takao Inoue (Rhizomatiks)
- CG & Visual (Opera, Room3 Chrome), GLITTER Teaser Movie: Satoshi Horii (Rhizomatiks)
- Sound Effect Designer: Daito Manabe, Shintaro Kamijo, Kyoko Koyama, Hopebox
- Sound Effect Design Assistant: Naoki Ishizuka (Rhizomatiks), KEKE
- –
- Lightsaber Developer: Motoi Ishibashi, Hideaki Tai, Tomoaki Yanagisawa, Toshitaka Mochizuki (Rhizomatiks)
- Lightsaber Operator: Tomoaki Yanagisawa, Toshitaka Mochizuki, Saki Ishikawa (Rhizomatiks)
- Lightsaber Light Pattern Designer: Daito Manabe (Rhizomatiks)
- [Web Site]
- Creative Director: Daito Manabe (Rhizomatiks)
- Art Director: Hiroyasu Kimura (Rhizomatiks)
- Sound Effect: Daito Manabe (Rhizomatiks), Kyoko Koyama, Hopebox
- Designer: Ichiro Kojima, Kaori Fujii (Rhizomatiks)
- Front-End Engineer: Hirofumi Tsukamoto (Rhizomatiks)
- Back-End Engineer: Tatsuya Takemasa (Rhizomatiks)
- Project Manager: Akinori Kanai (Freelance)
- Producer: Takao Inoue (Rhizomatiks)
- –
- Logo Design: Kaori Fujii, Miku Maruno

(Rhizomatiks)
- PR Movie & End Credits: Kahori Takemura (Rhizomatiks)
- *Only Credits For Rhizomatiks Research Listed.

《Rhizome》
- Visual Design, Programming: Satoshi Horii (Rhizomatiks)
- Technical Cooperation: Panasonic Corporation

《Rhizomatiks Chronicle》
- Visual Design, Programming: Futa Kera (Rhizomatiks)
- Data Creation: Tomoyo Obata (Rhizomatiks)
- Technical Cooperation: Canon Marketing Japan Inc.

《NFTs and CryptoArt-Experiment》
- Visual Design, Programming : Futa Kera (Rhizomatiks)
- System Programming, Server-side Design: 2bit (TSUUBITO ISHII Program Office)
- Server-side Programming: Kosaku Namikura
- Technical Cooperation: Canon Marketing Japan Inc., Kyuzan Inc.
- Special thanks: KIZUNA, BlockchainPROseed

《Rhizomatiks × ELEVENPLAY "multiplex"》
- Visual Design, Programming: Satoshi Horii (Rhizomatiks)
- Choreography: MIKIKO (ELEVENPLAY)
- Dancers: SAYA, KAORI, EMMY, YU, MARU (ELEVENPLAY)
- Projection System/AR System Engineering: Yuya Hanai (Rhizomatiks)
- Video Engineering: Muryo Homma (Rhizomatiks)
- Hardware Engineering, Craft: Toshitaka Mochizuki, Saki Ishikawa, Kyohei Mouri (Rhizomatiks)
- Motion Capture: Momoko Nishimoto (Rhizomatiks), Hajime Kotani, Miyako Toge, Yoshitaka Homma (Crescent, inc.)
- Omni Wheel Motion Editing: Akira Iio, Hiroyuki Mukai (1 inc)
- Sound production support: KEKE
- Technical Cooperation: Panasonic Corporation

R&D (Research & Development)
- 《dissonant imaginary》
- Daito Manabe + Kamitani Lab, Kyoto University and ATR
- –
- 《Trojan Horse》
- Visual Programming: 2bit (TSUUBITO ISHII Program Office)
- Technical Cooperation: DataSign Inc.
- –
- 《morphecore: prototype (2020)》

- Motion Capture Dancer and Choreographer: Shingo Okamoto
- Supervisor: MIKIKO (ELEVENPLAY)
- Music Co-producer: Hopebox
- –
- 《Home Sync Light》
- Planning, Technical Direction: Motoi Ishibashi
- Lighting Design, Programming: Daito Manabe
- Circuit Design: Hideaki Tai
- Product Design: Tomoaki Yanagisawa, Toshitaka Mochizuki
- Technical Support: Saki Ishikawa, Noriko Ishizuka, Nanami Tanaka
- Co-Development: Rhizomatiks & Evixar Inc.
- –
- 《Messaging Mask》
- Creative Direction, Technical Direction, Software Engineering: Yuya Hanai
- Technical Direction, Hardware Engineering: Motoi Ishibashi
- Product Design: Toshitaka Mochizuki
- Visual Effect: Futa Kera
- Project Management: Kahori Takemura
- Project Management, Produce: Takao Inoue
- Supervise: Daito Manabe
- (Behind the scene) Video Shooting&Editor: Takashi Ninomiya
- –
- 《RTK Robotics Experiment》
- Hardware Engineering: Katsuhiko Harada, Kyohei Mouri (Rhizomatiks)
- Software Engineering: Yuta Asai (Rhizomatiks)

《Rhizomatiks Archive & Behind the scene》
- Video Editing: Kahori Takemura, Muryo Homma (Rhizomatiks), Kenzo Hazama

---

《particles 2021》
- Rail Design: Youichi Sakamoto (Rhizomatiks)
- Circuit Design and Firmware: Hideaki Tai (Rhizomatiks)
- Ball Design and Development: Tomoaki Yanagisawa (Rhizomatiks)
- Laser Tracking System Development: Yuya Hanai (Rhizomatiks)
- Motion Capture: Momoko Nishimoto (Rhizomatiks), Hajime Kotani, Miyako Toge, Yoshitaka Homma (Crescent, inc.)
- Lifter and Hopper Design and Production: Yukio Akiba (Gagit)
- Rail Production: ARRK
- Rail Setup Assistance: TASKO
- Ball production support: Momoko Nishimoto, Saki Ishikawa, Noriko Ishizuka, Nanami Tanaka, Toshitaka Mochizuki, Kyohei Mouri (Rhizomatiks)

《Epilogue》
- Surveillance Camera System Development: Yuta Asai, Kyohei Mouri (Rhizomatiks), 2bit

(TSUUBITO ISHII Program Oce)

《Device Counter》
- Software Engineering: Sumito Kamoi (Flowplateaux)
- Technical Cooperation: Sony Music Entertainment Inc.

《rhizomatiks_multiplex online》
- Front-end Engineering: Yo Tanaka (Rhizomatiks)
- Interface Design: Hiroyasu Kimura, Kaori Fujii (Flowplateaux)
- Back-end Engineering: Tatsuya Takemasa (Flowplateaux)
- Venue Modeling: Takahito Hosono (Rhizomatiks)

写真クレジット
Photo Credits

particles
[pp.4-5, 29 right middle]
Courtesy of Yamaguchi Center for
Arts and Media [YCAM],
photo by Ryuichi Maruo (YCAM)
[pp.28-29]
Daito Manabe (Rhizomatiks)

Takao Kawaguchi "TABLEMIND"
[p.20 top]
Photo by Hiroki Taguchi

LED in my mouth
[p.23 bottom]
LAFORET GRAND BAZAR "Geee" CM
(Laforet HARAJUKU),
CD/AD: Keiichi Uemura,
photo by Nicci Keller

chains
[pp.34-35]
Exhibition view: "GLOBALE:
New Sensorium—Exiting from Failures of
Modernization," curated by Yuko Hasegawa,
© ZKM | Center for Art and Media,
photo by Tobias Wootton, Jonas Zilius.

Deleted Reality
[p.36]
Installation view of the exhibition Fertile
Landscapes at Maison de la culture du Japon
à Paris

oscillation
[p.37]
NSK 100th Exhibition
"SENSE OF MOTION" (2016),
venue: Spiral Garden (Spiral 1F),
photo by Muryo Homma

dissonant imaginary
[p.38 middle]
Photo by Hanayuki Higashi

Tokyo Tokyo FESTIVAL Special 13
Light and Sound Installation
"Coded Field"
[p.41]
Courtesy of Rhizomatiks

Lucid Motion
[pp.42-43]
Produced in collaboration with
ARTECHOUSE, Washington, DC,
Fall 2019

Yakushimaru Etsuko Metro Orchestra
"Nornir" Music Video
[p.50 right top]
Photo by MIRAI seisaku

Website "SYMPHONY"
for the NHK Special
"NEXT WORLD: Our Future"
[p.65 bottom]
©NHK

FORM
[pp.68-69]
J-CULTURE FEST2017
@the Tokyo International Forum,
photo by Hiroyuki Takahashi / NEP

Dolce&Gabbana Fall Winter 2018/19
Women's Fashion Show
[p.73 top]
Courtesy of Albertone
[p.73 bottom]
Courtesy of Dolce&Gabbana

Arca "Mutant; Faith"
[p.78]
Photo by ANNIE FORREST

KAZU "Come Behind Me, So Good!
(Official video by Daito Manabe +
Kenichiro Shimizu)"
[p.79]
© 2019 Ponderosa Music Records

border 2021
[p.92, p.93 top]
Photo by hiroko hirota

phosphere
[p.94]
Photo by Albert Muñoz,
©Sónar Festival ©Advanced Music

discrete figures
[p.96 left middle, left bottom]
Photo by Tomoya Takeshita
[pp.96-97]
Photo by Suguru Saito

discrete figures Special Edition
[p.96 left top]
Sapporo Cultural Art Theater hitaru,
©kenzo kosuge

Perfume Cannes Lions International
Festival of Creativity
[p.109 top]
©Cannes Lions,Dentsu.inc

Perfume live @SXSW 2015
[p.113]
©Amuse, Inc. +
UNIVERSAL MUSIC LLC +
Rhizomatiks co.,ltd. + DENTSU INC.

[docomo × Perfume]
FUTURE-EXPERIMENT VOL.01
Eliminate the Distance
[p.115]
©NTT DOCOMO, INC.

Perfume×TECHNOLOGY
presents Reframe
[pp.116-117]
Courtesy of NHK

Reframe 2019
[pp.118-119]
Photo by Yosuke Kamiyama

[docomo×Perfume]
FUTURE-EXPERIMENT VOL.04
Share that moment
[pp.120-121]
©NTT DOCOMO, INC.

Installation view of rhizomatiks_multiplex
[pp.129-139, 142-145, 146 bottom,
147-157]
Photo by Muryo Homma

From Ars Electronica website
[pp.204, 205 top, 206]
©Ars Electronica Linz GmbH

本書は、下記の展覧会にあわせて刊行されました。

ライゾマティクス_マルティプレックス

会期 ｜ 2021年3月20日（土）ー6月22日（火）
会場 ｜ 東京都現代美術館 企画展示室 地下2階
主催 ｜ 公益財団法人東京都歴史文化財団 東京都現代美術館
助成 ｜ 令和2年度文化庁優れた現代美術の国際発信促進事業
協賛 ｜ ブルームバーグL.P.／株式会社ミクシィ
技術協力 ｜ パナソニック株式会社／キヤノンマーケティングジャパン株式会社／株式会社DataSign／株式会社ソニー・ミュージックエンタテインメント／株式会社Kyuzan
協力 ｜ 株式会社アミューズ／ユニバーサル ミュージック合同会社／一般財団法人カルチャー・ヴィジョン・ジャパン／株式会社アブストラクトエンジン

企画 ｜ 長谷川祐子
担当学芸員 ｜ 森山朋絵（東京都現代美術館）
展覧会アシスタント ｜ 井波吉太郎（東京都現代美術館）／岸本遼太郎（本展アシスタント）
広報 ｜ 中島三保子、工藤千愛子、岡本真理子（東京都現代美術館）

コンセプト・テクニカルディレクション・ビジュアルデザイン・サウンドデザイン ｜ 真鍋大度（ライゾマティクス）
コンセプト・テクニカルディレクション・ハードウェアエンジニアリング ｜ 石橋素（ライゾマティクス）
プロデュース・プロダクションマネジメント ｜ 井上貴生（ライゾマティクス）
プロダクションマネジメント ｜ 竹村佳保里、小幡倫世、石塚直樹（ライゾマティクス）
スペースデザイン ｜ 細野隆仁（ライゾマティクス）
ポスターグラフィックス ｜ 堀井哲史（ライゾマティクス）
グラフィック・デザイン ｜ 木村浩康、藤井かおり（フロウプラトウ）
翻訳 ｜ 石塚直樹（ライゾマティクス）
広報 ｜ 四元朝子、青柳桃子（ライゾマティクス）

会場施工 ｜ スーパー・ファクトリー株式会社：佐野 誠

This book was published in conjunction with the following exhibition.

rhizomatiks_multiplex

Exhibition Period ｜ Saturday, 20 March–Tuesday, 22 June, 2021
Venue ｜ Museum of Contemporary Art Tokyo (MOT)
Special Exhibition: Exhibition Gallery B2F
Organized by ｜ Museum of Contemporary Art Tokyo operated by Tokyo Metropolitan Foundation for History and Culture
Supported by ｜ The Agency for Cultural Affairs Government of Japan in the fiscal 2020
Sponsored by ｜ Bloomberg L.P. / mixi, Inc.
Technical Cooperation by ｜ Panasonic Corporation / Canon Marketing Japan Inc. / DataSign Inc. / Sony Music Entertainment (Japan) Inc. / Kyuzan Inc.
In Cooperation with ｜ AMUSE INC. / UNIVERSAL MUSIC LLC / Culture Vision Japan Foundation Inc. / Abstract Engine Co., Ltd.

Curator ｜ Yuko Hasegawa
Curator in charge ｜ Tomoe Moriyama (Museum of Contemporary Art Tokyo)
Exhibition Assistants ｜ Yoshitaro Inami (Museum of Contemporary Art Tokyo) / Ryotaro Kishimoto (exhibition assistant)
Public Relations ｜ Mihoko Nakajima, Chiako Kudo and Mariko Okamoto (Museum of Contemporary Art Tokyo)

Concept, Technical Direction, Visual Design, Sound Design ｜ Daito Manaba (Rhizomatiks)
Concept, Technical Direction, Hardware Engineering ｜ Motoi Ishibashi (Rhizomatiks)
Produce, Production Management ｜ Takao Inoue (Rhizomatiks)
Production Management ｜ Kahori Takemura, Tomoyo Obata, Naoki Ishizuka (Rhizomatiks)
Space Design ｜ Takahito Hosono (Rhizomatiks)
Poster Graphics : Satoshi Horii (Rhizomatiks)
Graphic Design ｜ Hiroyasu Kimura, Kaori Fujii (Flowplateaux)
Translation ｜ Naoki Ishizuka (Rhizomatiks)
Public Relations ｜ Tomoko Yotsumoto, Momoko Aoyagi (Rhizomatiks)

Exhibition Technician ｜ SUPER-FACTORY Inc.: Makoto Sano

謝辞

「ライゾマティクス_マルティプレックス」展の開催ならびに本書の出版にあたり、
多数の協力機関・関係各位に多大なるご協力を賜りました。
ここに記して深謝の意を表明いたします。

文化庁
ブルームバーグ L.P.
株式会社ミクシィ
パナソニック株式会社
キヤノンマーケティングジャパン株式会社
株式会社DataSign
株式会社ソニー・ミュージックエンタテインメント
株式会社Kyuzan
イレブンプレイ
KIZUNA
BlockchainPROseed
株式会社クレッセント
株式会社アミューズ
ユニバーサル ミュージック合同会社
一般財団法人カルチャー・ヴィジョン・ジャパン
株式会社アブストラクトエンジン
Ars Electronica Linz GmbH
国際オリンピック委員会

Acknowledgement

For realize the exhibition and publication of "rhizomatiks_multiplex,"
we would like to express our sincerest gratitude to all of those organization and individual contributor below.

Agency for Cultural Affairs
Bloomberg L.P
mixi, Inc.
Panasonic Corporation
Canon Marketing Japan Inc.
DataSign Inc.
Sony Music Entertainment (Japan) Inc.
Kyuzan Inc.
ELEVENPLAY
KIZUNA
BlockchainPROseed
Crescent,inc.
AMUSE INC.
UNIVERSAL MUSIC LLC
Culture Vision Japan Foundation Inc.
Abstract Engine Co., Ltd
Ars Electronica Linz GmbH
Olympic Foundation for Culture and Heritage

ライゾマティクス_マルティプレックス

2021年6月18日 初版発行

執筆｜ライゾマティクス（真鍋大度、石橋素）／長谷川祐子／森山朋絵
監修｜東京都現代美術館
編集｜薮崎今日子、臼田桃子（フィルムアート社）／森山朋絵（東京都現代美術館）／小幡倫世、青柳桃子、四元朝子（ライゾマティクス）
編集補｜井波吉太郎（東京都現代美術館）／岸本遼太郎（本展アシスタント）／阿部七海、呂青（本展インターン）

翻訳｜ダリル・ウィー／ダニエル・ゴンザレス

ブックデザイン｜刈谷悠三＋角田奈央（neucitora）

発行者｜上原哲郎
発行所｜株式会社フィルムアート社
〒150-0022東京都渋谷区恵比寿南1-20-6 第21荒井ビル
Tel: 03-5775-2001
Fax: 03-5725-2626
http://www.filmart.co.jp

印刷・製本｜株式会社アイワード

本書の無断転写、転載、複製を禁じます。

rhizomatiks_multiplex

First Edition June 18, 2021

Texts｜Rhizomatiks (Daito Manabe, Motoi Ishibashi) / Yuko Hasegawa / Tomoe Moriyama
Supervised by｜Museum of Contemporary Art Tokyo
Editors｜Kyoko Yabusaki, Momoko Usuda (Film Art Inc.) / Tomoe Moriyama (Museum of Contemporary Art Tokyo) /
Tomoyo Obata, Momoko Aoyagi, Tomoko Yotsumoto (Rhizomatiks)
Editorial Assistants｜Yoshitaro Inami (Museum of Contemporary Art Tokyo) / Ryotaro Kishimoto (Exhibition Assistant) /
Nanami Abe, Lyu Qing (Interns at the exhibition)

Translators｜Darryl Wee / Daniel González

Design｜Yuzo Kariya, Nao Kakuta (neucitora)

Publisher｜Tetsuro Uehara
Published by｜Film Art Inc.
21 Arai Building, 1-20-6, Ebisu-minami, Shibuya-ku, Tokyo 150-0022
Tel: +81-(0)3-5775-2001
Fax: +81-(0)3-5725-2626
http://www.filmart.co.jp

Printing and Binding｜iword Co., Ltd.

ISBN978-4-8459-2036-5 C0070

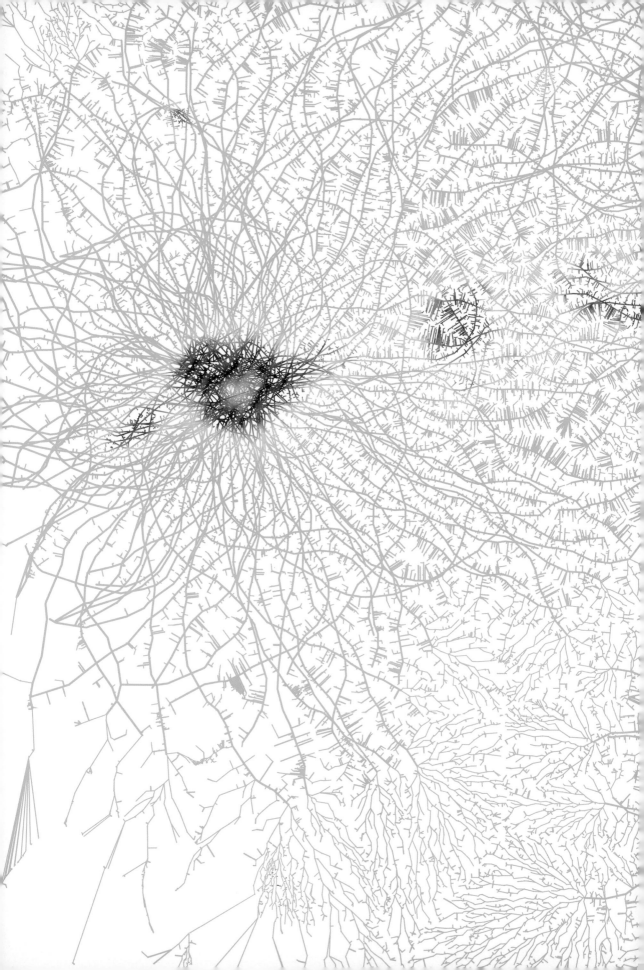

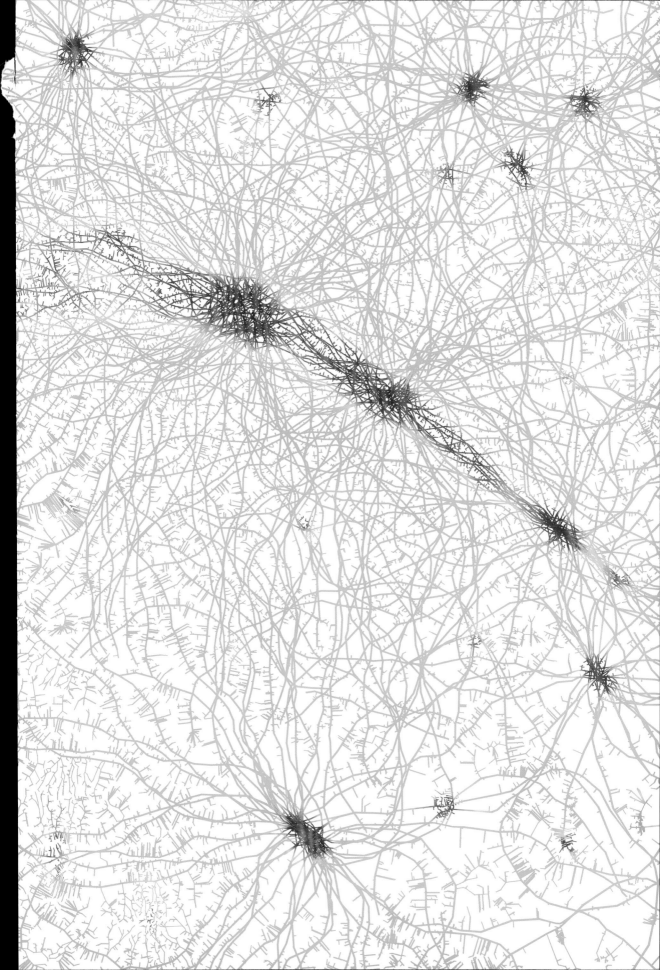

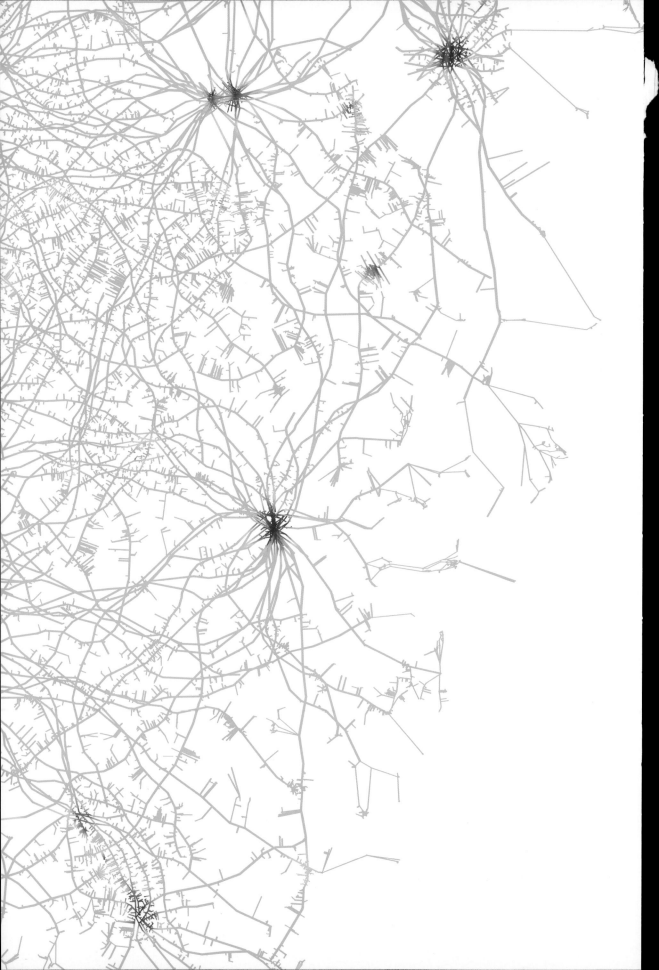